# 2004-2005
# Edition

# Ten-Tronck's™

# CELEBRITY DIRECTORY

# 2004-2005
# Edition

# Ten-Tronck's™

# CELEBRITY DIRECTORY

**AIR** Axiom Information Resources

ISSN 1083-1614

ISBN 0-943213-48-7

Printed in the United States of America

---

**SPECIAL SALES**

The Celebrity Directory™ is available at special quantity discounts. For information, write:

Axiom Information Resources, Inc., P.O. Box 8015-XIX, Ann Arbor, Michigan 48107 U.S.A.

# Introduction

Welcome to the new and updated 2004-2005 Celebrity Directory™. This new edition incorporates many changes suggested by our readers' enthusiastic response to previous editions. As always, our aim is to provide the reference librarian, speaking engagement coordinator, general researcher or fan with the easiest-to-use, most accurate and comprehensive collection of celebrity names and addresses available anywhere.

The editors have researched and arranged data on thousands of prominent persons engaged in all fields of human accomplishment throughout the world. If a person is famous and worth locating, it's almost certain that his or her name and address is listed in the convenient, alphabetically-arranged Celebrity Directory™.

Most of the celebrities listed in this directory welcome correspondence concerning their lives and work. Please remember when writing to a celebrity, as well as writing to Axiom Information Resources Inc., it is always best to enclose a stamped, self-addressed envelope. Of course, the editorial staff and publisher cannot guarantee that listed celebrities will respond to correspondence.

Also note that this directory is not a mailing list and shall not be considered as such, due the length of time it takes to gather and publish this book inaccuracies are inevitable. Nevertheless we have made every effort possible to ensure that the information contained in the Celebrity Directory™ is up-to-date and accurate as possible. We also cannot accept responsibility for inaccuracies created by a celebrity's moving or changing his or her mail arrangements after the directory went to press.

We welcome any suggestions or inquiries concerning the Celebrity Directory™, and we sincerely hope this new edition will provide our readers with even more entertainment and information. All inquiries concerning this book should be sent to Axiom Information Resources, Inc., P.O. Box 8015-XIX, Ann Arbor, Michigan 48107 U.S.A.

## A

**Willie Aames**
10209 S.E. Division Street
Portland, OR 97266
"Actor"

**Caroline Aaron**
9067-C Nemo Street
West Hollywood, CA 90069
"Actress"

**Henry Aaron**
4171 Jonesboro Road
Union City, GA 30291
"Ex-Baseball Player"

**Tommy Aaron**
440 East Lake Drive
Gainesville, GA 30504
"Golfer"

**ABBA**
Postbus 3079
NL-4700 GB Roosendaal HOL-
LAND
"Rock & Roll Group"

**Bruce Abbott**
4526 Wilshire Blvd.
Los Angeles, CA 90010
"Actor"

**Dihanne Abbott**
460 West Avenue #46
Los Angeles, CA 90065
"Actress"

**Gregory Abbott**
P.O. Box 68
Bergenfield, NY 07621
"Singer"

**Paula Abdul**
21650 Oxnard Street #1925
Woodland Hills, CA 91367
"Singer"

**Kareem Abdul-Jabbar**
5458 Wilshire Blvd.
Los Angeles, CA 90036
"Basketball Player"

**Abdullah The Butcher**
1000 S. Industrial Blvd.
Dallas, TX 75207
"Wrestler"

**Akeem Abdul Olajuwon**
10 Greenway Plaza E.
Houston, TX 77046
"Basketball Player"

**Ian Abercrombie**
1040 North Gardner
Los Angeles, CA 90046
"Actor"

**F. Murray Abraham**
c/o WMA
1325 Avenue of Americas
New York, NY 10019
"Actor"

**Jim Abrahams**
501 - 10 Street
Santa Monica, CA 90402
"Director, Producer"

**Joe Abrahams**
9460 Wilshire Blvd. #700
Beverly Hills, CA 90212
"Basketball Player"

**Norm Abram**
P.O. Box 2284
South Berrington, VT 05407
"Home Repair TV Host"

**Dan Abrams**
c/o NBC News
30 Rockefeller Plaza #300
New York, NY 10019
"Legal Correspondent"

**Leslie Abramson**
4929 Wilshire Blvd.
Los Angeles, CA 90010
"Attorney"

**Ray Abruzzo**
20334 Pacific Coast Hwy.
Malibu, CA 90265
"Actor"

**AC/DC**
675 Third Avenue #300
New York, NY 10017
"Rock & Roll Group"

**Joss Ackland**
76 Oxford Street
London W1N 9FD ENGLAND
"Actor"

**Jensen Ackles**
1122 South Robertson Blvd. #15
Los Angeles, CA 90035
"Actor"

**Gayle Ackroyd**
499 Main Street South
Brompton, Ont. L6Y 4V8
CANADA
"Songwriter, Guitarist"

**Timothy Ackroyd**
33 Chepstone Road
London W2 5BP ENGLAND
"Actor"

**Jay Acovone**
P.O. Box 12493
Philadelphia, PA 19151
"Actor"

**Amy Acuff**
1 RCA Dome, #140
P.O. Box 120
Indianapolis, IN 46206
"Olympic High Jumper"

**Red Adair**
P.O. Box 747
Bellville, TX 77418
"Fire Extinguishing Expert"

**Theo Adam**
Schillerstr. 14
01326 Dresden GERMANY
"Basso-Baritone"

**Salvatore Adamo**
522 Avenue Louise
Brussels BELGIUM
"Singer"

**Brooke Adams**
121 North San Vicente Blvd.
Beverly Hills, CA 90211
"Actress"

**Bryan Adams**
425 Carrall Street #500
Vancouver, BC V6B 6E3
CANADA
"Singer"

**Cindy Adams**
475 Park Avenue, PH-B
New York, NY 10022
"Actress"

**Don Adams**
2160 Century Park East #110
Los Angeles, CA 90067
"Actor, Writer, Director"

**Edie Adams**
8040 Okean Terrace
Los Angeles, CA 90046
"Singer, Actor"

**Gerry Adams**
51/55 Falls Road
Belfast BT 12
NORTHERN IRELAND
"Political Leader

**Jane Adams**
72 Dartmouth Drive
Rancho Mirage, CA 92270
"Author"

**Jeb Adams**
28301 Foothill Drive
Agoura Hills, CA 91301
"Actor"

**Joey Lauren Adams**
8942 Wilshire Blvd.
Beverly Hills, CA 90211
"Actor"

**Julie Adams**
5915 Corbin Avenue
Tarzana, CA 91356
"Actress"

**Maria Adams**
151 El Camino Drive
Beverly Hills, CA 90212
"Actress"

**Mason Adams**
570 Park Avenue #9B
New York, NY 10021
Actor"

**Maud Adams**
P.O. Box 10838
Beverly Hills, CA 90213
"Actress, Model"

**Oleta Adams**
4840 Peninsula Pointe Drive
Hermitage, TN 37076
R&B Singer"

**Richard Adams**
26 Church Street
Whitechurch, Hants. ENGLAND
"Author"

**Tom Adams**
29-31 Kings Road
London SW3 ENGLAND
"Actor"

**ADC Band**
17397 Santa Barbara
Detroit, MI 48221
"Rock & Roll Group"

**Herb Adderly**
P.O. Box 219
Mantua, NJ 08051
"Musician"

**Isabelle Adjani**
20 av. Rapp
F-75007 Paris FRANCE
"Actress"

**Tracee Adkins**
2100 West End Avenue #1000
Nashville, TN 37203
"Singer"

**Lou Adler**
3969 Villa Costera
Malibu, CA 90265
"Director, Producer"

**King Bhumibol Adulyadey**
Villa Chiralada
Bangkok, THAILAND
"King Of Thailand"

**Aerosmith**
9200 Sunset Blvd. #1000
Los Angeles, CA 90069
"Rock & Roll Group"

**Ben Affleck**
8500 Wilshire Blvd. #700
Beverly Hills, CA 90211
"Actor"

**Casey Affleck**
9830 Wilshire Blvd.
Beverly Hills, CA 90212
"Actor"

**Andre Agassi**
3960 Howard Hughes Parkway #750
Las Vegas, NV 89109
"Tennis Player"

**Christina Aguilera**
1100 Alta Loma Road #2000
West Hollywood, CA 90069
"Singer"

**Mark Aguier**
3265 Circle Center
Fresno, CA 93703
"Ex-Basketball Player"

**Jenny Agutter**
302-308 Regent Street
London W1R 5AL ENGLAND
"Actress"

**Danny Aiello**
30 Chestnut Ridge Road
Saddle River, NJ 07458
"Actor"

**Troy Aikman**
P.O. Box 8051
Colleyville, TX 76034
"ex-Football Player"

**Anouk Aimee**
201 rue du Faubourg St. Honore
F-75008 Paris, FRANCE
"Actress"

**Karen Akers**
c/o Origlio PR
333 West 39th Street
New York, NY 10018
Actress & Singer"

**Emperor Akihoto**
The Imperial Palace
1-1 Chiyoda - Chiyoda-Ku
Tokyo, JAPAN
"Emperor of Japan"

**Alabama**
P.O. Box 685029
Ft. Payne, AL 35968
"C&W Group"

**Steve Alaimo**
13385 West Dixie Highway
North Miami, FL 33161
"Singer"

**Brick Alan**
976 Murfreesboro Road #93
Nashville, TN 37217
"Singer"

**Buddy Alan**
600 East Gilbert
Tempe, AZ 85281
"Singer"

**Captain Lou Albano**
16 Mechanic Street
Carmel, NY 10512
"Wrestler"

**Edward Albee**
14 Harrison Street
New York, NY 10013
"Writer, Producer"

**Anna Marie Alberghetti**
11906 Wilshire Blvd. #24
Los Angeles, CA 90025
"Actress, Singer"

**Edward Albert**
27320 Winding Way
Malibu, CA 90265
"Actor"

**Prince Albert**
Palais De Monaco
Boite Postal 518
Monte Carlo Monaco
"Prince of Monaco"

**Dolores Albin**
23388 Mulholland Drive
Woodland Hills, CA 91364
"Actress"

**Medeleine Albright**
1318 - 34th Street NW
Washington, DC 20007
"Secretary of State"

**Dr. Tenley Albright**
20 First Street
Colorado Springs, CO 80906
"Skater"

**Amy Alcott**
1301 Montana Avenue
Santa Monica, CA 90403
"Golfer"

**Alan Alda**
1122 South Robertson Blvd. #15
Los Angeles, CA 90035
"Actor"

**Ginger Alden**
79 Shelley Renee Lane
Cordova, TN 38018
"Model"

**Norman Alden**
106 North Croft Avenue
Los Angeles, CA 90048
"Actor"

**Nadia Aldridge**
1875 Century Park East #2250
Los Angeles, CA 90067
"Model"

**Dr. Buzz Aldrin**
10380 Wilshire Blvd. #703
Los Angeles, CA 90024
"Astronaut"

**Edwin "Buzz" Aldrin, Jr.**
838 N. Doheny Drive #1407
W. Hollywood, CA 90069
"Astronaut"

**Frank Aletter**
5430 Corbin Avenue
Tarzana, CA 91356
"Actor"

**Kyle Aletter**
5430 Corbin Avenue
Tarzana, CA 91356
"Actress"

**Denise Alexander**
270 N. Canon Drive #1199
Beverly Hills, CA 90210
"Actress"

**Doyle Alexander**
5416 Hunter Park Court
Arlington Park, TX 76017
"Ex-Baseball Player"

**Flex Alexander**
c/o Greenblat
9346 Civic Center Drive
Beverly Hills, CA 90210
"Actor"

**Gary Alexander**
1133 Hayworth Avenue
Los Angeles, CA 90035
"Singer"

**Jane Alexander**
1100 Pennsylvania Ave. NW #202
Washington, DC 20506
"Actress"

**Jason Alexander**
6230-A Wilshire Blvd. #103
Los Angeles, CA 90048
"Actor"

**Sasha Alexander**
9465 Wilshire Blvd. #600
Beverly Hills, CA 90212
"Actress"

**Shana Alexander**
P.O. Box 429
Wainscott, NY 11975
"News Correspondent"

**Van Alexander**
7920 Sunset Blvd. #300
Los Angeles, CA 90046
"Concert Pianist"

**Kim Alexis**
2219 West Olive Ave., PMB 10038
Burbank, CA 91506
"Supermodel"

**Kristian Alfonso**
10061 Riverside Drive #798
Toluca Lake, CA 91602
"Actress"

**Laila Ali**
P.O. Box 491246
Los Angeles, CA 90049
"Boxer & Daughter of Muhammad
Ali

**Muhammad Ali**
P.O. Box 187
Berrien Springs, MI 49103
"Former Boxing Champion"

**Tatyana Ali**
c/o Evolution
1776 Broadway, 15th Floor
New York, NY 10019
"Actress"

**Gary Allan**
2100 West End Avenue #1000
Nashville, TN 37203
"Singer"

**Jed Allan**
13576 Cheltenham Drive
Sherman Oaks, CA 91423
"Actor"

**Betty Allen**
645 St. Nicholas Avenue
New York, NY 10030
"Mezzo-Soprano"

**Chad Allen**
6926 Pacific View Drive
Los Angeles, CA 90068
"Actor"

**Debbie Allen**
P.O. Box 120849
Nashville, TN 37212
"Actress"

**Elizabeth Allen**
P.O. Box 243
Lake Peekskill, NY 10537
"Actress"

**Joan Allen**
8942 Wilshire Blvd. #219
Beverly Hills, CA 90211
"Actress"

**Jonelle Allen**
8730 Sunset Blvd. #480
Los Angeles, CA 90069
"Actress, Singer"

**Karen Allen**
171 West 79th Street #21
New York, NY 10024
"Actress"

**Marcus Allen**
111 South St. Joseph Street
South Bend, IN 46601
"ex-Football Player"

**Marty Allen**
5750 Wilshire Blvd. #580
Los Angeles, CA 90036
"Actor, Comedian"

**Nancy Allen**
9830 Wilshire Blvd.
Beverly Hills, CA 90212
"Actress"

**Rex Allen, Jr.**
2825 Blue Brick Drive
Nashville, TN 37214
"Singer"

**Sean Barbara Allen**
732 South Plymouth Blvd. #E
Los Angeles, CA 90005
"Actress, Writer"

**Tim Allen**
1122 South Robertson Blvd. #15
Los Angeles, CA 90035
"Actor"

**Woody Allen**
48 East 92nd Street
New York, NY 10128
"Actor, Director, Comedian"

**Kirstie Alley**
1100 North Osceola Avenue
Clearwater, FL 33755
"Actress"

**Michael Allinson**
112 Knollwood Drive
Larchmont, NY 10538
"Actor"

**Donnie Allison**
355 Quaid Drive
Salisbury, NC 28147
"Race Car Driver"

**Mose Allison**
34 Dogwood Street
Smithtown, NY 11787
"Pianist, Composer"

**Greg Allman**
1776 Broadway #1500
New York, NY 10019
"Musician"

**Christopher Allport**
1342 Pine Street
Santa Monica, CA 90405
"Actor"

**Gloria Allred**
6300 Wilshire Blvd. #1500
Los Angeles, CA 90048
"Attorney, Feminist"

**June Allyson**
P.O. Box 666
Ojai, CA 93024
"Actress"

**Maria Conchita Alonso**
121 South Almont Drive
Los Angeles, CA 90048
"Actress"

**Felipe Alou**
7263 Davit Circle
Lake Worth, FL 33467
"Ex-Baseball Player"

**Hollis Alpert**
P.O. Box 142
Shelter Island, NY 11964
"Writer"

**Carol Alt**
4526 Wilshire Blvd.
Los Angeles, CA 90010
"Actress"

**Jeff Altman**
4628 Halbrent Avenue
Sherman Oaks, CA 91403
"Comedian, Actor"

**Robert Altman**
9200 Harrington Drive
Potomac, MD 20854
"Financier"

**Luigi Alva**
via Moscova 46/3
20121 Mailand ITALY
"Tenor"

**Lance Alworth**
990 Highland Drive #300
Solana Beach, CA 92075
"Ex-Football Player"

**Christiane Amanpour**
2 Stephen Street #100
London W1P 1PL ENGLAND
"Broadcast Journalist"

**Rodney Amateau**
133 1/2 South Linden Drive
Beverly Hills, CA 90212
"Film Writer, Producer"

**Lauren Ambrose**
9560 Wilshire Blvd. #516
Beverly Hills, CA 90212
"Actress"

**John Patrick Amedori**
301 West 53rd Street #4K
New York, NY 11504
"Actor"

**Nicolas Amer**
14 Great Russell Street
London WC1B ENGLAND
"Actor"

**America**
9255 Sunset Blvd. #600
Los Angeles, CA 90069
"Rock & Roll Group"

**Aldrich Ames**
P.O. Box 3000
White Deer, PA 17887
"Alledged Spy"

**Ed Ames**
1457 Claridge
Beverly Hills, CA 90210
"Singer"

**Rachel Ames**
1736 Marisol Drive
Ventura, CA 93001
"Author"

**Madchen Amick**
7700 Balboa Blvd.
Van Nuys, CA 91406
"Actress"

**Idi Amin**
Box 8948
Jidda 21492 SAUDI ARABIA
"Deposed Ruler"

**Martin Amis**
34-43 Russell Street
London WC2B 5HA ENGLAND
"Author"

**Deborah Amos**
c/o National Public Radio
2025 "M" Street N.W.
Washington, DC 20036
"News Correspondent"

**John Amos**
1505 10th Street
Santa Monica, CA 90401
"Actor"

**Tori Amos**
11845 West Olympic Blvd #1125
Los Angeles, CA 90064
"Singer"

**Wally (Famous) Amos**
P.O. Box 897
Kallua, HI 96734
"Founder of Famous Amos Cookies"

**Ana-Alicia**
1801 Avenue of the Stars #902
Los Angeles, CA 90067
"Actress"

**Anastacia**
The Plaza
535 Kings Road
London SW10 OSZ ENGLAND
"Songwriter, Producer, Dancer"

**Anthony Anderson**
1619 Broadway #900
New York, NY 10019
"Actor"

**Bill Anderson**
P.O. Box 6721
San Bernardino, CA 92412
"Singer"

**Brad Anderson**
13022 Wood Harbour Drive
Montgomery, TX 77356
"Cartoonist"

**Daryl Anderson**
24136 Friar Street
Woodland Hills, CA 91367
"Actor"

**Gillian Anderson**
1122 S. Robertson Blvd. #15
Los Angeles, CA 90035
"Actress"

**Harry Anderson**
422 - 292nd Avenue NE
Fall City, WA 98024
"Magician, Actor"

**Jack Anderson**
P.O. Box TT
McLean, VA 22101
"News Correspondent"

**Loni Anderson**
20652 Lassen Street #98
Chatsworth, CA 91311
"Actress"

**Louie Anderson**
2756 North Green Valley Parkway
#449
Las Vegas, NV 89014
"Comedian"

**Lynn Anderson**
P.O. Box EE
Taos, NM 87571
"Singer"

**Mary Anderson**
1127 Norman Place
Los Angeles, CA 90049
"Actress"

**Melody Anderson**
P.O. Box 350
New York, NY 10028
"Actress"

**Pamela Anderson-Lee**
8370 Wilshire Blvd, #210
Beverly Hills, CA 90212
"Actress"

**Paul Anderson**
1603 McIntosh Street
Vidalia, GA 30474
"Weightlifter"

**Rebecca Moesta Anderson**
P.O. Box 767
Monument, CO 80132
"Author"

**Richard Anderson**
10120 Cielo Drive
Beverly Hills, CA 90210
"Actor"

**Richard Dean Anderson**
1122 South Robertson Blvd. #15
Los Angeles, CA 90035
"Actor"

**George "Sparky" Anderson**
P.O. Box 6415
Thousand Oaks, CA 91359
"Ex-Baseball Manager"

**Terry Anderson**
50 Rockefeller Plaza
New York, NY 10020
"News Correspondent"

**John Andretti**
P.O. Box 2104
Davidson, NC 28036
"Race Car Driver"

**Mario Andretti**
457 Rose Inn Avenue
Nazareth, PA 18064
"Race Car Driver"

**Michael Andretti**
3310 Airport Road
Allentown, PA 18103
"Race Car Driver"

**Prince Andrew**
Sunninghill Park
Windsor, ENGLAND
"England Royalty"

**Anthony Andrews**
Langham House
302 - 308 Regent Street
London W1B 3AT ENGLAND
"Actor"

**Julie Andrews**
P.O. Box 491668
Los Angeles, CA 90049
"Singer"

**Patti Andrews**
9823 Aldea Avenue
Northridge, CA 91354
"Singer"

**Tige Andrews**
4914 Encino Terrace
Encino, CA 91316
"Actor, Writer"

**Maya Angelou**
3240 Valley Road
Winston-Salem, NC 28106
"Writer, Poet"

**The Angels**
P.O. Box 2553
Westminster, MD 21158
"Rock & Roll Group"

**Jean-Hughes Anglade**
151 El Camino Drive
Beverly Hills, CA 90212
"Actress"

**Philip Anglim**
2404 Grand Canal
Venice, CA 90291
"Actor"

**Edward Anhalt**
500 Amalfi Drive
Pacific Palisades, CA 90272
"Writer, Producer"

**Jennifer Aniston**
1122 South Robertson Blvd. #15
Los Angeles, CA 90035
"Actress"

**John Aniston**
4872 Topanga Canyon Blvd. #311
Woodland Hills, CA 91364
"Actor"

**Paul Anka**
10573 West Pico Blvd., PMB 159
Los Angeles, CA 90064
"Singer"

**Ann-Margaret**
5664 Cahuenga Blvd. #336
North Hollywood, CA 91601
"Actress"

**Kofi Annan**
799 United Nations Plaza
New York, NY 10017
"United Nations Secretary"

**Princess Anne**
Gatcombe Park
Glouchestershire, ENGLAND
"England Royalty"

**Wallis Annenberg**
10273 Century Woods Place
Los Angeles, CA 90067
"Magazine Executive"

**Francesca Annis**
2 Vicarage Court, Flat #2
London W8 ENGLAND
"Actress"

**Michael Ansara**
4624 Park Mirasol
Calabasas, CA 91302
"Actor"

**Susan Anspach**
P.O. Box 5605
Santa Monica, CA 90409
"Actress"

**Adam Ant**
19 S. Molton, Mayfair
London W1K 5LE ENGLAND
"Singer"

**Lysette Anthony**
47 Brewer Street
London W1F 9UF ENGLAND
"Actress"

**Ray Anthony**
9288 Kinglet Drive
Los Angeles, CA 90069
"Orchestra Leader"

**Susan Anton**
16830 Ventura Blvd. #300
Encino, CA 91436
"Actress"

**Lou Antonio**
530 Gaylord Drive
Burbank, CA 91505
"Actor, Writer, Director"

**Michelangelo Antonioni**
Via Vincenzo Tiberio 18
I-00191 Rome, ITALY
"Film Director"

**Gabrielle Anwar**
9560 Wilshire Blvd. #516
Beverly Hills, CA 90212
"Actress"

**Rocky Aoki**
8685 N.W. 53rd Terrace
Miami, FL 33155
"Food Entrepreneur"

**Luis Aparicio**
Calle 67 #26-82
Maracalbo VENEZUELA
"Ex-Baseball Player"

**Katrin Apel**
WSV Oberhof 05 eV
Box 1343
D-98559 Oberhof GERMANY
"Olympic Skier"

**Fiona Apple**
9200 Sunset Blvd. #530
Los Angeles, CA 90069
"Singer"

**Christina Applegate**
20411 Chapter Drive
Woodland Hills, CA 91364
"Actress"

**John Aprea**
401 South Detroit Street #113
Los Angeles, CA 90036
"Actor"

**Michael Apted**
13176 Boca de Canon Lane
Los Angeles, CA 90049
Film Director"

**Amy Aquino**
9615 Brighton Way #300
Beverly Hills, CA 90210
"Actress"

**Yassir Arafat**
P.O. Box 115
Jericho PALESTINE
"Politician"

**Alan Arbus**
6767 Forest Lawn Drive #101
Los Angeles, CA 90068
"Actor"

**Loreen Arbus**
8841 Appian Way
Los Angeles, CA 90046
"Writer"

**Anne Archer**
13201 Old Oak Lane
Los Angeles, CA 90049
"Actress"

**Bernard Archer**
Holt Barton
Witham Frairy
Somerset ENGLAND
"Actor"

**Jeffrey Archer**
Peninsulta Heights
93 Albert Emankment
London SE1 7TY ENGLAND
"Author"

**Army Archerd**
442 Hilgard Avenue
Los Angeles, CA 90024
"Columnist"

**Fanny Ardant**
20 Av Rapp
F-75007 Paris FRANCE
"Actress"

**Bruce Arena**
1801 S. Prairie Avenue
Chicago, IL 60616
"Soccer Coach"

**Moshe Arens**
49 Hagderat
Savyon, ISRAEL
"Politician"

**Asia Argento**
Via Pisanelli 2
00196 Rome ITALY
"Actor"

**Alexis Arguello**
1 Hall of Fame Drive
Canastota, NY 13032
"Boxer"

**Oscar Arias**
Apdo 8-6410-1000
San Jose, COSTA RICA
"Politician"

**Ben Aris**
47 West Square
London SE11 4SP ENGLAND
"Actor"

**Adam Arkin**
1964 Westwood Blvd. #400
Los Angeles, CA 90025
"Actor, Director"

**Alan Arkin**
21 E. 40th Street #1705
New York, NY 10016-0501
"Actor"

**Giorgio Armani**
Palazzo Durini 24
1-20122 Milan ITALY
"Fashion Designer"

**Joan Armatrading**
2 Ramillies Street
London W11 4SQ ENGLAND
"Singer, Guitarist"

**Jillian Armenante**
121 North San Vicente Blvd.
Beverly Hills, CA 90211
"Actress"

**Gene Armour**
843 N Sycamore Avenue
Los Angeles, CA 90038
"Politician"

**Russell Arms**
2918 Davis Way
Palm Springs, CA 92262
"Actor, Singer"

**Anne Armstrong**
Armstrong Ranch
Armstrong, TX 78338
"Politician"

**Bess Armstrong**
151 El Camino Drive
Beverly Hills, CA 90212
"Actress"

**Curtis Armstrong**
3867 Shannon Road
Los Angeles, CA 90027
"Actor"

**Debbie Armstrong**
Taos Sky Valley, Box 710
Taos, NM 87525
"Skier"

**Garner Ted Armstrong**
P.O. Box 2525
Tyler, TX 75710
"Evangelist, Author"

**Lance Armstrong**
98 San Jacinto Blvd. #430
Austin, TX 78701
"Bicyclist"

**Neil Armstrong**
P.O. Box 436
Lebanon, OH 45036
"Astronaut"

**R.G. Armstrong**
3856 Reklaw Drive
North Hollywood, CA 91604
"Actor"

**Desi Arnaz, Jr.**
P.O. Box 69684
Boulder City, NV 89006
"Actor"

**Lucie Arnaz**
P.O. Box 636
Cross River, NY 10518
"Actress"

**Liv Arnesen**
119 North 4th Street #206
Minneapolis, MN 55401
"Explorer"

**James Arness**
P.O. Box 5267
Culver City, CA 90231
"Actor"

**Jon Arnett**
6603 Beachview Drive
Rancho Palos Verdes, CA 90275
"Ex-Football Player"

**Jeanetta Arnette**
9229 Sunset Blvd. #311
Los Angeles, CA 90069
"Actress"

**Alison Arngrim**
13774-A Mono Way #220
Sonora, CA 95370
"Actress"

**Eddy Arnold**
P.O. Box 97
Brentwood, TN 37027
"Singer"

**Tom Arnold**
1122 S. Robertson Blvd. #15
Los Angeles, CA 90035
"Actor"

**Francois Arnoul**
53 rue Censier
F-75005 Paris FRANCE
"Actress"

**Stefan Arnsten**
1017 Laurel Way
Beverly Hills, CA 90210
"Actor"

**Alexis Arquette**
1505 - 10th Street
Santa Monica, CA 90401
"Actor"

**David Arquette**
1122 South Robertson Blvd #15
Los Angeles, CA 90035
"Actor"

**Patricia Arquette**
1122 South Robertson Blvd. #15
Los Angeles, CA 90035
"Actress"

**Rosanna Arquette**
c/o Evolution
7720 Sunset Blvd.
Los Angeles, CA 90046
"Actress"

**Rod Arrants**
5757 Wilshire Blvd. #510
Beverly Hills, CA 90036
"Actor"

**Rosa Arredondo**
3500 West Olive Avenue #1400
Burbank, CA 91505
"Actress"

**Arrested Development**
2409 Hillsboro Road #100
Nashville, TN 37212
"Rock & Roll Band"

**Gus Arriola**
P.O. Box 3275
Carmel, CA 93921
"Cartoonist"

**Gloria Arroyo-Macapagal**
Malacanang Palace
Manila PHILIPPINES
"Politician"

**Beatrice Arthur**
2000 Old Ranch Road
Los Angeles, CA 90049
"Actress"

**Maureen Arthur**
9171 Wilshire Blvd. #530
Beverly Hills, CA 90210
"Actress"

**Ashanti**
c/o Pyramid
89 Fifth Avenue, 7th Floor
New York, NY 10003
"R&B Singer"

**Dana Ashbrook**
1180 South Beverly Drive #608
Los Angeles, CA 90035
"Actress"

**Daphne Ashbrook**
1505 10th Street
Santa Monica, CA 90401
"Actress"

**Jane Asher**
24 Cale Street
London SSW3 3QU ENGLAND
"Actress"

**William Asher**
54-337 Oak Hill Blvd.
La Quinta, CA 92253
"Writer, Producer"

**Renee Asherson**
28 Elsworth Road
London NW3 ENGLAND
"Actress"

**David Ashford**
53 Moat Drive
Harrow, Middlesex ENGLAND
"Actor"

**Evelyn Ashford**
818 Plantation Lane
Walnut, CA 91789
"Athlete"

**Ashford & Simpson**
254 West 72nd Street #1-A
New York, NY 10023
"Vocal Duo"

**Jennifer Ashley**
1640 S. Sepulveda Blvd. #350
Los Angeles, CA 90025
"Actress"

**John Ashton**
P.O. Box 49698
Los Angeles, CA 90049
"Actor"

**Luke Askew**
1431 SW Park Avenue #405
Portland, OR 97201
"Actor"

**Asleep At The Wheel**
P.O. Box 463
Austin, TX 78767
"Rock & Roll Group"

**Edward Asner**
3556 Mound View Avenue
Studio City, CA 91604
"Actor"

**Jules Asner**
E! Network
5750 Wilshire Blvd.
Los Angeles, CA 90036
"TV Show Host"

**Jennifer Aspen**
1640 South Sepulveda Blvd. #530
Los Angeles, CA 90025
"Actress"

**Armand Assante**
367 Windsor Highway
New Windsor, NY 12553
"Actor"

**Thalia Assuras**
524 West 57th Street
New York, NY 10019
"News Anchor"

**Robyn Astaire**
1155 San Ysidro Drive
Beverly Hills, CA 90210
"Widower of Fred Astaire"

**John Astin**
P.O. Box 49698
Los Angeles, CA 90049
"Actor, Director, Writer"

**Mackenzie Astin**
4526 Wilshire Blvd.
Los Angeles, CA 90010
"Actor"

**Sean Astin**
P.O. Box 57858
Sherman Oaks, CA 91413
"Actor"

**William Atherton**
5102 San Feliciano Drive
Woodland Hills, CA 91364
"Actor"

**Christopher Atkins**
6934 Bevis Avenue
Van Nuys, CA 91405
"Actor"

**Sharif Atkins**
8436 West 3rd Street, #740
Los Angeles, CA 90048
"Actor"

**Tom Atkins**
10100 Santa Monica Blvd. #2500
Los Angeles, CA 90067
"Actor"

**Rowan Atkinson**
5 Soho Square
London W1V 5DE ENGLAND
"Actor, Comedian"

**Atlantic Rhythm Section**
1257 Arcade Street
St. Paul, MN 55106
"R&B Band"

**David Attenborough**
5 Park Road
Richmond Green
Surrey ENGLAND
"TV Producer"

**Sir Richard Attenborough**
Beaver Lodge
The Green Richmond TW9 1NQ
England
"Writer, Producer"

**Margaret Atwood**
481 University Avenue #900
Ontario M3G 2E9 CANADA
"Authoress"

**Rene Auberjonois**
8271 Melrose Avenue #208
Los Angeles, CA 90046
"Actor"

**Jacques Aubuchon**
20978 Rios Street
Woodland Hills, CA 91364
"Actor"

**Louis Auchincloss**
1111 Park Avenue
New York, NY 10028
"Author, Critic"

**Stephanie Audran**
20 rue av. Rapp
F-75007 Paris FRANCE
"Actor"

**Red Auerbach**
1150 W. Columbus Avenue
Springfield, MA 01105
"Basketball Executive"

**Nadja Auermann**
Via San Vittore 40
I-20123 Milan ITALY
"Actress"

**Claudine Auger**
20 rue av. Rapp
F-75007 Paris FRANCE
"Actress"

**Ira Augustain**
3900 Ramboz Drive
Los Angeles, CA 90063
"Actor"

**Hubert "Geese" Ausbie**
400 East Van Buren #300
Phoenix, AZ 85004
"Harlem Globetrotter"

**Karen Austin**
8436 West Third Street #740
Los Angeles, CA 90048
"Actress"

**Sherrie Austin**
1908 Wedgewood Avenue
Nashville, TN 37212
"Singer"

**Teri Austin**
4245 Laurel Grove
Studio City, CA 91604
"Actress"

**Tracy Austin**
5 Williamsburg Lane
Rolling Hills Estates, CA 90274
"Tennis Player"

**Alan Autry**
P.O. Box 989
Clovis, CA 93613
"Actor"

**Frankie Avalon**
4303 Spring Forest Lane
Westlake Village, CA 91362
"Singer"

**Richard Avedon**
407 East 75th Street
New York, NY 10021
"Photographer"

**James Avery**
195 S. Beverly Drive #400
Beverly Hills, CA 90212
"Actor"

**Margaret Avery**
P.O. Box 3493
Los Angeles, CA 90078
"Actress"

**Val Avery**
84 Grove Street #19
New York, NY 10014
"Actor"

**Charlotte Ayanna**
955 South Carrillo Drive #300
Los Angeles, CA 90048
"Actress"

**Dan Aykroyd**
8383 Wilshire Blvd. #550
Beverly Hills, CA 90211
"Actor"

**John Aylward**
1450 South Robertson Blvd.
Los Angeles, CA 90035
"Actor"

**Leah Ayres**
15718 Milbank
Encino, CA 91436
"Actress"

**Rosalind Ayres**
37 Berwick Street
London W1V 3RF ENGLAND
"Actress"

**Hank Azaria**
9701 Wilshire Blvd., 10th Floor
Beverly Hills, CA 90212
"Actor"

**Paul Azinger**
1101 N. Kentucky Avenue #100
Winter Park, FL 32789
"Golfer"

**Charles Aznavour**
76-78 ave. des Champs Elysses
F-75008 Paris FRANCE
"Singer"

**Candice Azzara**
9255 Sunset Blvd. #620
Los Angeles, CA 90069
"Actress"

# B

**B-52**
947 N. La Cienega Blvd. #G
Los Angeles, CA 90069
"Rock & Roll Group"

**Shirley Babashoff**
17254 Santa Clara Street
Santa Ana, CA 92708
"Swimmer"

**Bruce Babbitt**
5169 Watson Street, NW
Washington, DC 20016
"ex-Secretary of Interior"

**Harry Babbitt**
7 Rue St. Cloud
Newport Beach, CA 91660
"Conductor"

**Tai Babilonia**
13889 Valley Vista Blvd.
Sherman Oaks, CA 91423
"Ice Skater"

**Baby's**
1545 Archer Road
Bronx, NY 10462
"Music Group"

**Babyface**
10231 Charing Cross Road
Los Angeles, CA 90064
"Singer"

**Baby Peggy (Diana Serra Carey)**
2219 Canyon Brook Lane
Newman, CA 95360
"Former Child Star

**Lauren Bacall**
1 West 72nd Street #43
New York, NY 10023
"Actress"

**Catherine Bach**
15930 Woodvale Road
Encino, CA 91436
"Actress"

**Emmanuella Bach**
20 Avenue, Rapp
F-75007 Paris FRANCE
"Actress"

**Burt Bacharach**
681 Amalfi Drive
Pacific Palisades, CA 90272
"Composer, Pianist"

**Don Bachardy**
145 Adelaide Drive
Santa Monica, CA 90402
"Writer"

**Bachman-Turner-Overdrive**
1505 West 2nd Avenue, #200
Vancouver BC V6H 3Y4  Canada
"Rock and Roll Group"

**Wally Backman**
421 North Main Street
Prineville, OR 97554
"Baseball Player"

**Henny Backus**
10914 Bellagio Road
Los Angeles, CA 90077
"Actress"

**James Bacon**
10982 Topeka Drive
Northridge, CA 91324
"Actor"

**Kevin Bacon**
P.O. Box 668
Sharon, CT 06069
"Actor"

**Sarah Badel**
4 Ovington Gardens
London SW3 1LS ENGLAND
"Actress"

**Penn Badgley**
151 El Camino Drive
Beverly Hills, CA 90212
"Actror"

**John Badham**
3344 Clarendon Road
Beverly, HIlls, CA 90210
"Film Director"

**Jane Badler**
21 Cardigan Place
Albert Park
Victoria 3206 AUSTRALIA
"Singer"

**Erykah Badu**
151 El Camino Drive
Beverly Hills, CA 90212
"Singer"

**Max Baer, Jr.**
P.O. Box 1831
Zephyr Cove, NV 89448
"Film Director"

**Joan Baez**
P.O. Box 1026
Menlo Park, CA 94025
"Singer"

**Vince Bagetta**
3928 Madelia Avenue
Sherman Oak, CA 91403
"Actor"

**Vernel Bagneris**
220 West 48th Street
New York, NY 10036
"Actor, Screenwriter"

**Donovan Bailey**
606 - 1185 Edington Ave. East
Toronto, Ont. M3C 3C6 CANADA
"Sprinter"

**G.W. Bailey**
22934 Frisca Drive
Valencia, CA 91354
"Actor"

**Jim Bailey**
5909 West Colgate Avenue
Los Angeles, CA 90036
"Actor"

**Joel Bailey**
6550 Murietta Road
Van Nuys, CA 91401
"Actor"

**Razzy Bailey**
P.O. Box 62
Geneva, NE 68361
"Singer"

**Barbara Bain**
1501 Skylark Lane West
West Hollywood, CA 90069
"Actress"

**Conrad Bain**
1230 Chickory Lane
Los Angeles, CA 90049
"Actress"

**Beryl Bainbridge**
42 Albert Street
London NW1 7NU ENGLAND
"Author"

**Jimmy Baio**
11662 Duque Drive
Studio City, CA 91604
"Actor"

**Scott Baio**
4333 Forman Avenue
Toluca Lake, CA 91602
"Actor"

**Scott Bairstow**
P.O. Box 57593
Sherman Oaks, CA 91403
"Actor"

**Oksana Baiul**
P.O. Box 577
Simsbury, CT 06070
"Ice Skater"

**Anita Baker**
8216 Tivoli Cove Drive
Las Vegas, NV 89128
"Singer"

**Carroll Baker**
P.O. Box 480589
Los Angeles, CA 90048
"Actress"

**Diane Baker**
P.O. Box 480492
Los Angeles, CA 90048
"Actress, Director"

**Dusty Baker**
40 Livingston Terrace Drive
San Bruno, CA 94066
"Ex-Baseball Player"

**Graham Baker**
232 North Canon Drive
Beverly Hills, CA 90210
"Film Director"

**Howard Baker**
P.O. Box 8
Huntsville, TN 37756
"Former Senator"

**James Baker III**
910 Louisiana Street
Houston, TX 77002
"Ex-Government Official"

**Joe Don Baker**
23339 Hatteras
Woodland Hills, CA 91364
"Actor"

**Raymond Baker**
254-A 26th Street #312
Santa Monica, CA 90402
"Actor"

**Roy Ward Baker**
125 Gloucester Road
London SW7 4TE ENGLAND
"Film Director"

**Simon Baker**
Norman House, Cambridge Place
Cambridge CB2 1NS ENGLAND
"Opera Singer"

**Tyler Baker**
4731 Laurel Canyon Blvd. #200
North Hollywood, CA 91607
"Actor"

**Brenda Bakker**
5835 Lemp Avenue
North Hollywood, CA 91601
"Actress"

**James (Jim) Bakker**
P.O. Box 567
Vernon, FL 32462
"ex-TV Evangelist"

**Tammy Faye Bakker-Messner**
1527 Woody Creek Road
Matthews, NC 28105
"Ex-TV Evangelist"

**Scott Bakula**
15300 Ventura Blvd. #315
Sherman Oaks, CA 91403
"Actor"

**Bob Balaban**
390 West End Avenue
New York, NY 10024
"Actor"

**Belinda Balaski**
P.O. Box 461011
Los Angeles, CA 90046
"Actress"

**Adam Baldwin**
1301 Carlyle Avenue
Santa Monica, CA 90402
"Actor"

**Alec Baldwin**
725 Arizona Avenue #100
Santa Monica, CA 90212
"Actor"

**Daniel Baldwin**
151 El Camino Drive
Bevelry Hills, CA 90212
"Actor"

**Judith Baldwin**
P.O. Box 4723
Valley Village, CA 91617
"Actress"

**Margaret Baldwin**
P.O. Box 1106
Williams Bay, WI 53191
"Author"

**Stephen Baldwin**
550 South Barrington Avenue #1214
Los Angeles, CA 90049
"Actor"

**William Baldwin**
8500 Wilshire Blvd. #700
Beverly Hills, CA 90211
"Actor"

**Christian Bale**
9800 S. Pacific Coast Hwy. #8-206
Redondo Beach, CA 90277
"Actor"

**Carla Balenda**
15848 Woodvale
Encino, CA 91316
"Actress"

**Marty Balin**
436 Belvedere Street
San Francisco, CA 94117
"Singer, Songwriter"

**Fairuza Balk**
1180 South Beverly Drive #608
Los Angeles, CA 90035
"Actress"

**Alan Ball**
9560 Wilshire Blvd. #516
Beverly Hills, CA 90212
"Actor"

**Carl Ballantine**
2575 N. Beachwood Drive
Los Angeles, CA 90068
"Actor, Comedian"

**Christine Ballard**
11501 Chandler Blvd.
North Hollywood, CA 91601
"TV Writer, Director"

**Hank Ballard**
P.O. Box 8406
Santa Cruz, CA 95061
"Singer"

**Kaye Ballard**
P.O. Box 922
Rancho Mirage, CA 92270
"Actress, Singer"

**Lucinda Ballard**
180 East End Avenue
New York, NY 10028
"Costume Designer"

**Mark Ballou**
9300 Wilshire Blvd. #555
Beverly Hills, CA 90212
"Actor"

**Talia Balsam**
1505 10th Street
Santa Monica, CA 90401
"Actress"

**Jamie Bamber**
10100 Santa monica Blvd. #2500
Los Angeles, CA 90067
"Actor"

**Eric Bana**
8-2 Sandilands Street #2
South Melbourne
Victoria 3205 AUSTRALIA
"Actor and Comedian"

**Anne Bancroft**
2301 La Mesa Drive
Santa Monica, CA 90405
"Actress, Writer, Director"

**Prince Bandar al-Saud**
601 New Hampshire Avenue N.W.
Washington, DC 20037
"Royalty"

**Antonio Banderas**
3110 Main Street #205
Santa Monica, CA 90405
"Actor"

**Sal Bando**
104 West Juniper Lane
Mequon, WI 52092
"Ex-Baseball Player"

**Moe Bandy**
P.O. Box 5331
Sevierville, TN 37864
"Singer"

**Victor Banerjee**
10 East Harrington
Calcutta 700071 INDIA
"Actor"

**Bever-Leigh Banfield**
9460 Wilshire Blvd. #300
Beverly Hills, CA 90212
"Actress"

**Abolhassan Bani Sadr**
Auvers-Sur-Oise
FRANCE
"Politician"

**Ernie Banks**
1060 W. Addison Street
Chicago, IL 60613
"Ex-Baseball Player"

**Jonathan Banks**
1505 10th Street
Santa Monica, CA 90401
"Actor"

**Tony Banks**
507 Tirstan Lane
Pikesville, MD 21208
"Keyboard Player"

**Tyra Banks**
c/o IMG Models
304 Park Avenue S. PH N.
New York, NY 10010
"Model"

**Floyd Bannister**
6701 East Caballo Drive
Paradise Valley, AZ 85253
ex-Baseball Player"

**Sir Roger Bannister**
21 Bardwell Road
Oxford OX2 6SV ENGLAND
"Actor"

**Jack Bannon**
5923 Wilbur Avenue
Tarzana, CA 91356
"Actor"

**Ehud Barak**
Box 3263
Tel-Aviv ISRAEL
"Prime Minister"

**Christine Baranski**
Woodcreek Road
Bethlehem, CT 06751
"Actress"

**Angela Baraquio**
4321 Likini Street
Honolulu, HI 96818
"Miss America 2001"

**Adrienne Barbeau**
14724 Ventura Blvd. #505
Sherman Oaks, CA 91403
"Actress"

**Glynis Barber**
1 Leicester Place
London NC2H 7BP ENGLAND
"Actress"

**Joseph Barbera**
15301 Ventura Blvd., Bldg. East
Sherman Oaks, CA 91403
"Film Producer"

**Paula Barbieri**
P.O. Box 20483
Panama City, FL 32411
"Actress"

**John Barbour**
4254 Forman Avenue
Toluca Lake, CA 91602
"Writer, Comedian"

**Javier Bardem**
9560 Wilshire Blvd., 5th Floor
Beverly Hills, CA 90212
"Actor"

**Brigitte Bardot**
La Madrigue F-83990
St. Tropez, FRANCE
"Actress"

**Bobby Bare**
P.O. Box 2422
Hendersonville, TN 37077
"Singer, Songwriter"

**Bob Barker**
5757 Wilshire Blvd. #206
Los Angeles, CA 90036
"TV Show Host"

**Clive Barker**
P.O. Box 691885
Los Angeles, CA 90069
"Author"

**Jennifer Barker**
9255 Sunset Blvd. #920
West Hollywood, CA 90069
"Actress"

**Ellen Barkin**
9830 Wilshire Blvd.
Beverly Hills, CA 90212
"Actress"

**Charles Barkley**
7615 East Vaquero Drive
Scottsdale, AZ 85258
"Basketball Player"

**Peter Barkworth**
47 Flask Walk
London NW3 ENGLAND
"Actor, Comedian"

**Randy Barlow**
5514 Kelly Road
Brentwood, TN 37027
"Singer"

**Joanna Barnes**
267 Middle Road
Santa Barbara, CA 93108
"TV Writer"

**Priscilla Barnes**
3393 Barham Blvd.
Los Angeles, CA 90068
"Actress"

**Barney**
300 E. Bethany Road # 8000
Allen, TX 75002
"Cartoon Personality"

**Doug Barr**
P.O. Box 63
Rutherford, CA 94573
"Actor"

**Julia Barr**
275 - 7th Avenue #2600
New York, NY 10001
"Actress"

**Steve Barr**
P.O. Box 395
Mt. Laurel, NJ 08054
"Cartoonist"

**Majel Barrett**
P.O. Box 691370
W. Hollywood, CA 90069
"Actress"

**Rona Barrett**
P.O. Box 1620
Santa Ynez, CA 93460
"Gossip Columnist"

**Barbara Barrie**
15 W. 72nd Street #2A
New York, NY 10023
"Actress"

**Maurice Barrier**
201 rue du Fg. St. Honore
F-75008 Paris FRANCE
"Actor"

**Dana Barron**
280 S. Beverly Drive #400
Beverly Hills, CA 90212
"Actress"

**Sydney Biddle Barrows**
210 West 70th Street
New York, NY 10023
"Alleged Madam, Socialite"

**Dave Barry**
1 Herald Plaza
Miami, FL 33101
"Comedian"

**Gene Barry**
12178 Ventura Blvd. #205
Studio City, CA 91604
"Entertainer & Actor"

**John Barry**
540 Centre Island Road
Oyster Bay, NY 11771
"Composer"

**Len Barry**
3096 Janice Circle
Chamblee, GA 30341
"Singer"

**ex-Mayor Marion Barry**
161 Raleigh Street SE
Washington, DC 20032
"Ex-Mayor"

**Patricia Barry**
P.O. Box 49895
Los Angeles, CA 90049
"Actress"

**Raymond Barry**
4526 Wilshire Blvd.
Los Angeles, CA 90010
"Actor"

**Sy Barry**
34 Saratoga Drive
Jericho, NY 11753
"Cartoonist"

**Drew Barrymore**
1122 South Robertson Blvd. #15
Los Angles, CA 90035
"Actress"

**John Blyth Barrymore**
144 South Peck Drive
Beverly Hills, CA 90212
"Actor"

**John Barrymore III**
1479 Lloyd Way
Mountain View, CA 94040
"Actor"

**Jean Bartel**
229 Bronwood Avenue
Los Angeles, CA 90049
"Actress"

**Steve Bartkowski**
10745 Bell Road
Duluth, GA 30136
"Ex-Football Player"

**Bonnie Bartlett**
12805 Hortense Street
Studio City, CA 91604
"Actress"

**Peter Barton**
10417 Eastbourne #3
Los Angeles, CA 90025
"Actor"

**Skye McCole Bartusiak**
P.O. Box 580486
Houston, TX 77258
"Actress"

**Mikhail Baryshnikov**
9830 Wilshire Blvd.
Beverly Hills, CA 90212
"Ballet Dancer"

**Harry Basch**
920 1/2 So. Serrano Avenue
Los Angeles, CA 90006
"Actor"

**David Alan Basche**
1316 North Hayworth Avenue #1
Los Angeles, CA 90046
"Actor"

**Blake Bashoff**
1345 N. Maple Drive #300
Beverly Hills, CA 90210
"Actor"

**Basia**
9830 Wilshire Blvd.
Beverly Hills, CA 90212
"Rock & Roll Group"

**Carmen Basilio**
67 Boxwood Drive
Rochester, NY 14617
"Boxer"

**Kim Basinger**
1123 Pacific Street #G
Santa Monica, CA 90405
"Actress"

**Lance Bass**
c/o Owen
119 - 17th Avenue South
Nashville, TN 37203
"Singer"

**Angela Bassett**
9465 Wilshire Blvd. #430
Beverly Hills, CA 90212
"Actress"

**Shirley Bassey**
24 Avenue Princess Grace #1200
Monte Carlo MONACO
"Singer"

**William Bast**
6691 Whitley Terrace
Los Angeles, CA 90068
"Screenwriter"

**Amelia Batchelor**
14811 Mulholland Drive
Los Angeles, CA 90024
"Actress"

**Jason Bateman**
3127 Barbara Court
Los Angeles, CA 90068
"Actor"

**Justine Bateman**
11288 Ventura Blvd #190
Studio City, CA 91604
"Actress"

**Alan Bates**
122 Hamilton Terrace
London NW8 94T ENGLAND
"Actor"

**Kathy Bates**
6220 Del Valle
Los Angeles, CA 90048
"Actress"

**Randall Batinkoff**
1330 - 4th Street
Santa Monica, CA 90401
"Actor"

**Bobbie Battista**
1 CNN Center
Box 105366
Atlanta, GA 30349
"News Anchor"

**Kathleen Battle**
Lonedale Chambers
27 Chancery Lane
London WC2A 1PF ENGLAND
"Opera Singer"

**Sen. Max Baucus**
225 Cruse #3
Helena, MT 59601
"Politician"

**Belinda Bauder**
6401 West 6th Street
Los Angeles, CA 90048
"Actress"

**Bruce Bauer**
12456 Ventura Blvd. #1
Studio City, CA 91604
"Actor"

**Hank Bauer**
11284 Pflumm Road
Shawnee Mission, KS 67215
"Ex-Baseball Player"

**Jamie Lyn Bauer**
9460 Wilshire Blvd. #300
Beverly Hills, CA 90212
"Actress"

**Steven Bauer**
1505 10th Street
Santa Monica, CA 90401
"Actor"

**Sammy Baugh**
c/o General Delivery
Rotan, TX 79546
"Ex-Football Player"

**Jon "Bowzer" Bauman**
3168 Oakshire Drive
Los Angeles, CA 90068
"Actor, Singer"

**Meredith Baxter**
2049 Century Park E. #2500
Los Angeles, CA 90067
"Actress"

**Stanley Baxter**
2 Ormond Road, Richmond
Surrey TW10 6TH ENGLAND
"Actor, Comedian"

**Michael Bay**
9830 Wilshire Blvd.
Beverly Hills, CA 90212
"Actor"

**Bay City Rollers**
294-296 Nether Street
Finchley #3
London N# 1RJ ENGLAND
"Rock & Roll Group"

**Birch Bayh**
1350 "I" Street NW
Washington, DC 20005
"Ex-Senator"

**Don Baylor**
56325 Riviera
La Quinta, CA 92253
"Manager & Baseball Player"

**Elgin Baylor**
1150 West Columbus Avenue
Springfield, MA 01105
"Ex-Basketball Player"

**Beach Boys**
8942 Wilshire Blvd.
Beverly Hills, CA 90211
"Rock & Roll Group"

**Michael Beach**
1823 Virgina Road
Los Angeles, CA 90019
"Actor"

**Stephanie Beacham**
1131 Alta Loma Road #517
West Hollywood, CA 90069
"Actress"

**Jennifer Beals**
8383 Wilshire Blvd., #550
Beverly Hills, CA 90211
"Actress"

**Alan Bean**
9173 Briar Forest Drive
Houston, TX 77024
"Astronaut, Painter"

**Orsen Bean**
444 Carol Canal
Venice, CA 90291
"Actor, Comedian"

**Sean Bean**
52/53 Poland Street
London S1F 7LX ENGLAND
"Actor"

**Amanda Bearse**
15332 Antioch Street #143
Pacific Palisades, CA 90272
"Actress"

**Emmanuelle Beart**
20 Avenue Rapp
F-75007 Paris FRANCE
"Actress"

**Allyce Beasley**
147 North Windsor Blvd.
Los Angeles, CA 90004
"Actress"

**Beastie Boys**
15 Maiden Lane #8
New York, NY 10104
"Rap Group"

**Queen Beatrix**
Kasteel Drakesteijn
Lage Vuursche 3744 BA
HOLLAND
"Royalty"

**Ned Beatty**
2706 North Beachwood Drive
Los Angeles, CA 90068
"Actor"

**Warren Beatty**
13671 Mulholland Drive
Beverly Hills, CA 90210
"Actor, Director, Writer"

**Joe Beaver**
101 Pro Rodeo Drive
Colorado Springs, CO 80919
"Rodeo Champion"

**Beavis & Butt-Head**
1515 Broadway #400
New York, NY 10036
"Music Group"

**Michael Bechloss**
c/o Simon & Schuster
1230 Avenue of the Americas
New York, NY 10020
"Author"

**Beck**
31652 Second Avenue
Laguna Beach, CA 92677
"Singer"

**Jeff Beck**
1 Water Lane
London NW1 8NZ England
"Singer, Guitarist"

**Marilyn Beck**
P.O. Box 11079
Beverly Hills, CA 90213
"Columnist, Critic"

**Michael Beck**
9300 Wilshire Blvd. #410
Beverly Hills, CA 90212
"Actor"

**Boris Becker**
Lub Modia GmbH, Engelhardstr. 12
D-81369 Munich GERMANY
"Tennis Player"

**Tyson Beckford**
c/o Bethann Management
36 Moore Street
New York, NY 10013
"Male Super Model"

**David Beckham**
SFX Sports Group
1624 High Street, Knowle
Solihull B93 OJU ENGLAND
"Soccer Player"

**Victoria Beckham** (Posh Spice)
15-22 St. Christopher's Place
London W1M 5HE ENGLAND
"Singer"

**Bonnie Bedelia**
309 West 49th Street #1700
New York, NY 10019
"Actress"

**Brian Bedford**
10100 Santa Monica Blvd. #2500
Los Angeles, CA 90067
"Actor"

**Kabir Bedi**
8271 Melrose Avenue #202
Los Angeles, CA 90046
"Actor"

**The Bee Gees**
20505 US 19 N. #12-290
Clearwater, FL 34624
"Rock & Roll Group"

**David Beecroft**
4558 Longridge Avenue
Sherman Oaks, CA 91423
"Actor"

**Dirk Been**
819 N. Inglewood Avenue #2
Inglewood, CA 90302
"TV Survivor Contestant"

**Leslie Bega**
9460 Wilshire Blvd. #300
Beverly Hills, CA 90212
"Actress"

**Jason Beghe**
400 South Beverly Drive #216
Beverly Hills, CA 90212
"Actor"

**Ed Begley, Jr.**
151 El Camino Drive
Beverly Hills, CA 90212
"Actor"

**Joy Behar**
c/o WMA
1325 Avenue of the Americas
New York, NY 10019
"Female Comedian"

**Sam Behrens**
c/o CBS Y&R
7800 Beverly Blvd. #3305
Los Angeles, CA 90036
"Actor"

**Nina Beilina**
400 West 43rd Street #7D
New York, NY 10036
"Violinist"

**David Belafonte**
829 South Bundy Drive
Los Angeles, CA 90049
"Actor"

**Harry Belafonte**
300 West End Avenue #5A
New York, NY 10023
"Singer, Actor"

**Shari Belafonte**
10345 W. Olympic Blvd. #200
Los Angeles, CA 90064
"Actress, Model"

**Christine Belford**
1801 Avenue of the Stars #902
Los Angeles, CA 90067
"Actress"

**Belita**
Rose Cottage
44 Crabtree Lane
London SW6 6LW ENGLAND
"Actress, Ballerina"

**Archie Bell**
P.O. 46912
Atlanta, GA 30559
"Singer"

**Bell Biv Devoe**
8942 Wilshire Blvd.
Beverly Hills, CA 90211
"R&B Group"

**Catherine Bell**
23843 Avenue Crocker #1
Valencia, CA 91355
"Actress"

**E.E. Bell**
11365 Ventura Blvd. #100
P.O. Box 7403
Studio City, CA 91604
"Actor"

**Felicia Bell**
12360 Riverside Drive, #317
North Hollywood, CA 91607
"Actress"

**George Bell**
324 West 35th Street
Chicago, IL 60616
"Baseball Player"

**Griffin Bell**
206 Townsend Place NW
Atlanta, GA 30327
"Ex-Government Official"

**Laura Lee Bell-Bundy**
7800 Beverly Blvd. #3305
Los Angeles, CA 90036
"Actress"

**Tom Bell**
108 Torriano Avenue
London NW5 ENGLAND
"Actor"

**Bellamy Brothers**
3017 Poston Avenue
Nashville, TN 37203
"Vocal Duo"

**Bruce Belland**
6226 Elisa Place
Encino, CA 91436
"TV Writer"

**Kathleen Beller**
P.O. Box 806
Half Moon Bay, CA 94019
"Actress"

**Maria Bello**
9830 Wilshire Blvd.
Beverly Hills, CA 90212
"Actress"

**Saul Bellow**
Boston University
745 Commonwealth Avenue
Boston, MA 02215
"Writer"

**Louie Bellson**
901 Winding River Road
Vero Beach, FL 32963
"Drummer"

**Pamela Bellwood**
7444 Woodrow Wilson Drive
Los Angeles, CA 90046
"Actress, Photographer"

**Jean-Paul Belmondo**
9 rue des St. Peres
F-75007 Paris FRANCE
"Actor"

**Olivier Belmondo**
20 Avenue Rapp
F-75007 Paris FRANCE
"Actress"

**Robert Beltran**
2210 Talmadge Street
Los Angeles, CA 90027
"Actor"

**James Belushi**
12250 Addison Street
Valley Village, CA 91607
"Actor"

**Richard Belzer**
Chelsea Pier 62
West 23rd & 12th Avenue
New York, NY 10011
"Actor"

**Pat Benatar**
4611 Deerwatch Drive
Chantilly, VA 20151
"Singer"

**Brian Benben**
1990 South Bundy Drive #200
Los Angeles, CA 90025
"Actor"

**Johnny Bench**
324 Bishopsbridge Drive
Cincinnati, OH 45255
"Ex-Baseball Player"

**Peter Benchley**
35 Boudinot Street
Princeton, NJ 08540
"Author"

**Paulo Benedeti**
11364 Ventura Blvd. #100
Box 7403
Studio City, CA 91604
"Actor"

**Dirk Benedict**
P.O. Box 634
Bigfork, MT 59911
"Actor"

**Nick Benedict**
10637 Burbank Blvd.
No. Hollywood, CA 91601
"Actor"

**Paul Benedict**
84 Rockland Place
Newton, MA 02164
"Actor"

**Lourdes Benedicto**
211 South Poinsettia Place #3
Los Angeles, CA 90036
"Actress"

**Roberto Benigni**
via Traverse dio Vergaio
44 Prato ITALY
"Actor"

**Annette Bening**
13671 Mulholland Drive
Beverly Hills, CA 90210
"Actress"

**Lucy Benjamin**
19 Denmark Street
London WC2H 8NA ENGLAND
"Actress"

**Richard Benjamin**
P.O. Box 57593
Sherman Oaks, CA 91403
"Actor, Director"

**Brooke Bennett**
2566 Bedford News Drive
West Palm Beach, FL 33414
"Swimmer"

**Bruce Bennett**
2702 Forester Road
Los Angeles, CA 90064
"Actor"

**Hywell Bennett**
2D Wimpole Street
London W1G OEB ENGLAND
"Actor"

**Tony Bennett**
130 West 57th Street #9D
New York, NY 10019
"Singer"

**Joan Benny**
1131 Coldwater Canyon
Beverly Hills, CA 90210
"Wife of Jack Benny"

**George Benson**
519 Next Day Hill Drive
Englewood, NJ 07631
"Singer, Guitarist"

**Robby Benson**
1505 - 10th Street
Santa Monica, CA 90401
"Actor"

**John Bentley**
Wedgewood House
Peterworth
Sussex ENGLAND
"Actor"

**Barbi Benton**
40 North 4th Street
Carbondale, CO 81623
"Actress, Model"

**Robert Benton**
950 Third Avenue #26
New York, NY 10022
"Film Director"

**A.J. Benza**
5750 Wilshire Blvd.
Los Angeles, CA 90036
"TV Show Host"

**Daniel Benzali**
1875 Century Park East #2250
Los Angeles, CA 90067
"Actor"

**Trevor Berbeck**
903 - 8th Street
New Westmininster BC CANADA
"Boxer"

**Tom Berenger**
9830 Wilshire Blvd.
Beverly Hills, CA 90212
"Actor"

**Marisa Berenson**
c/o Zelig
57 rue de Tubigo
F-75003 Paris FRANCE
"Actress"

**Elena Berezhanaya**
Russian Skating Assn.
Luznetskaya Naberenhnya 8
118871 Moscow RUSSIA
"Skater"

**Matrica Berg**
2100 West End Avenue #1000
Nashville, TN 37203
"C & W Singer & Songwriter"

**Patty Berg**
P.O. Box 1607
Ft. Meyers, FL 33902
"Golfer"

**Peter Berg**
433 North Camden Drive #500
Beverly Hills, CA 90210
"Actor"

**Candice Bergen**
1122 S. Robertson Blvd. #15
Los Angeles, CA 90035
"Actress"

**Mrs. Edgar Bergen**
1485 Carla Ridge Drive
Beverly Hills, CA 90210
"Actress"

**Polly Bergen**
101 West 55th Street #7K
New York, NY 10019
"Actress"

**Senta Berger**
Robert-Koch-Stasse 10
D-82031 Grunwald, GERMANY
"Actress"

**Lee Bergere**
32 Beach Plum Way
Hampton, NH 03842
"Actor"

**Alan Bergman**
714 North Maple Drive
Beverly Hills, CA 90210
"Lyricist"

**Ingmar Bergman**
P.O. Box 27127
S-10252 Stockholm SWEDEN
"Film Director"

**Marilyn Bergman**
714 North Maple Drive
Beverly Hills, CA 90210
"Lyricist"

**Peter Bergman**
4799 White Oak Avenue
Encino, CA 91316
"Actor"

**Luciano Berio**
11 Colombaig Radiocobdoli
53100 Siena, ITALY
"Composer, Conductor"

**Elizabeth Berkeley**
1100 Glendon Avenue #1000
Los Angeles, CA 90024
"Actress"

**David Berkowitz #78A1976**
Sullivan Corr. Fac., Box AG
Fallsburg, NY 12733
"Prisoner"

**Warren Berlinger**
10642 Arnel Place
Chatsworth, CA 91311
"Actor"

**Shelley Berman**
268 Bell Canyon Road
Bell Canyon, CA 91307
"Comedian"

**Crystal Bernard**
8436 West Third Street #650
Los Angeles, CA 90048
"Actress"

**Ed Bernard**
P.O. Box 7965
Northridge, CA 91326
"Actor"

**Edward L. Bernds**
6455 Woodman Avenue
Van Nuys, CA 91401
"Writer"

**Sandra Bernhard**
9465 Wilshire Blvd. #4308
Beverly Hills, CA 90212
"Comedianne, Actress"

**Kevin Bernhardt**
9300 Wilshire Blvd. #410
Beverly Hills, CA 90212
"Actor"

**Collin Bernsen**
8281 Melrose Avenue #200
Los Angeles, CA 90046
"Actor"

**Corbin Bernsen**
13535 Hatteras Street
Van Nuys, CA 91401
"Actor"

**Elmer Bernstein**
2715 Pearl Street
Santa Monica, CA 90405
"Composer, Conductor"

**Jay Bernstein**
9360 Beverly Crest Drive
Beverly Hills, CA 90210
"Talent Agent"

**Kenny Bernstein**
1105 Seminole
Richardson, TX 75080
"Race Car Driver"

**Yogi Berra**
8 Quarry Road
Little Falls, NJ 07424
"Ex-Baseball Player & Manager"

**Claude Berri**
10 rue Lincoln
75008 Paris FRANCE
"Actor"

**Bertice Berry**
4619 Mission Gorge #B
San Diego, CA 92120
"Inspirational Speaker"

**Chuck Berry**
Berry Park, Buckner Road
Wentzville, MO 63385
"Singer, Songwriter"

**Halle Berry**
1368 North Doheny Place
Los Angeles, CA 90069
"Actress"

**John Berry**
3310 West End Avenue #550
Nashville, TN 37203
"Singer"

**Ken Berry**
13911 Fenton Avenue
Sylmar, CA 91342
"Actor, Dancer"

**Michael Berryman**
P.O. Box 1482
Sonoma, CA 95476
"Actor"

**Valerie Bertinelli**
9255 Sunset Blvd., PMB 1010
West Hollywood, CA 90069
"Actress"

**Luc Besson**
53 rue Anpere
F-75017 Paris FRANCE
"Actor"

**Ahmed Best**
P.O. Box 707
Renton, WA 98057
"Actor"

**James Best**
P.O. Box 621027
Oviedo, FL 32762
"Actor"

**Kevin Best**
P.O. Box 1164
Hesperia, CA 92345
"Actor"

**Pete Best**
#8 Hyman's Green, West Derby
Liverpool 12 ENGLAND
"Ex-Beatle"

**Martine Bestwicke**
1810 Santa Monica Road
Carpinteria, CA 93013
"Actress"

**Ivy Bethune**
8033 Sunset Blvd. #221
Los Angeles, CA 90046
"Actress"

**Zina Bethune**
8033 Sunset Blvd. #221
Los Angeles, CA 90046
"Actress"

**Gary Bettenhausen**
2550 Tree Farm Road
Martinsville, IN 46151
"Race Car Driver"

**Lyle Bettger**
P.O. Box 791867
Pai, HI 96779
"Actor"

**Turhan Bey**
1443 North Doheny Drive
Los Angeles, CA 90069
"Actor"

**Richard Beymer**
8383 Wilshire Blvd. #550
Beverly Hills, CA 90211
"Actor"

**Jeff Bezos**
1516 - 2nd Avenue, 2nd Floor
Seattle, WA 98101
"Amazon.com Founder"

**Benazir Bhutto**
70 Clifton Road
Karachi, PAKISTAN
"Politician"

**Sen. Joseph Biden, Jr.**
1105 Market Street #2000
Wilmington, DE 19801
"Politician"

**Michael Biehn**
11220 Valley Spring Lane
No. Hollywood, CA 91602
"Actor"

**Thom Bierdz**
1888 N. Crescent Heights Blvd.
Los Angeles, CA 90069
"Actor"

**Ramon Bieri**
19963 Arce Street
Northridge, CA 91324
"Actor"

**Theodore Bikel**
1131 Alta Loma Road #523
Los Angeles, CA 90069
"Actor, Singer"

**Dr. Carl Bilancione**
2828 Casa Aloma Way
Winter Park, FL 32792
"Survivor Contestant"

**Tony Bill**
73 Market Street
Venice, CA 90291
"Actor, Director"

**Peter Billingsley**
9028 Sunset Blvd., PH #1
Los Angeles, CA 90069
"Child Actor"

**Roger Bingham**
255 Eads Road
Crittenden, KY 41030
"Survivor Contestant"

**Traci Bingham**
8721 Sunset Blvd. #205
Los Angeles, CA 90069
"Actress"

**Juliette Binoche**
5 Rue Clemont Marot
F-75008 Paris FRANCE
"Actress"

**Matt Biondi**
1404 Rimer Drive
Moraga, CA 94556
"Swimmer"

**Thora Birch**
P.O. Box 69156
West Hollywood, CA 90069
"Actress"

**Larry Bird**
310 Neopolitan Way
Naples, FL 34103
"ex-Basketball Player"

**Jane Birkin**
20 av Rapp
F-75007 Paris FRANCE
"Actress"

**David Birney**
20 Ocean Park Blvd. #11
Sanata Monica, CA 90405
"Actor"

**Joey Bishop**
534 Via Lido Nord
Newport Beach, CA 92660
"Actor, Comedian"

**Kelly Bishop**
147 Brentwood Drive
South Orange, NJ 07079
"Actress"

**Stephen Bishop**
P.O. Box 1821
Ojai, CA 93024
"Singer, Composer"

**Jacqueline Bisset**
1122 S. Robertson Blvd. #15
Los Angeles, CA 90035
"Actress"

**Josie Bissett**
1122 S. Robertson Blvd. #15
Los Angeles, CA 90035
"Actress"

**Yannick Bisson**
55A Sumuch Street
Toronto, Ontario
M5A 3J6  Canada
"Actor"

**Cilla Black**
10 Abbey Orchard Street
London SW1P 2JP ENGLAND
"Singer"

**Clint Black**
9255 Sunset Blvd. #600
Los Angeles, CA 90069
"Singer"

**Jack Black**
9560 Wilshire Blvd. #516
Beverly Hills, CA 90212
"Actor"

**Michael Ian Black**
9560 Wilshire Blvd. #516
Beverly Hills, CA 90212
"Actor"

**Black Oak Arkansas**
6400 Pleasant Park Drive
Chanhassen, MN 55317
"C&W Group"

**Honor Blackman**
1 Duchess Street #1
London W1W 6AN ENGLAND
"Actress"

**Joan Blackman**
P.O. Box 273
Guerneville, CA 95446
"Actess"

**Mr. Blackwell**
531 South Windsor Blvd.
Los Angeles, CA 90005
"Designer, Publisher"

**Nina Blackwood**
23705 Vanowen Street #111
West Hills, CA 91307
"Music Correspondent"

**Taurean Blacque**
5049 Rock Springs Road
Lithonia, GA 30038
"Actor"

**Ruben Blades**
1187 Coast Village Road #1
Montecito, CA 93108
"Singer, Actor, Songwriter"

**David Blaine**
1776 Broadway #1500
New York, NY 10019
"Magician"

**Nell Walden Blaine**
3 Ledge Road
Gloucester, MA 01930
"Painter"

**Betsy Blair**
11 Chalcot Gardens
England's Lane
London NW3 4YB ENGLAND
"Actress"

**Bonnie Blair**
1223 Aspen Court
Delafield, WI 53018
"Skater"

**Janet Blair**
3661 1/2 Glendon Avenue
Los Angeles, CA 90034
"Actress"

**Linda Blair**
4727 Wilshire Blvd. #333
Beverly Hills, CA 90210
"Actress"

**Lionel Blair**
68 Old Brompton Road #200
London SW7 3LQ ENGLAND
"TV Personality, Dancer"

**Selma Blair**
9100 Wilshire Blvd.
6th Floor, West Tower
Beverly Hills, CA 90212
"Actress

**Prime Minister Tony Blair**
10 Downing Street
London, SWI, ENGLAND
"Politician"

**Bud Blake**
P.O. Box 146
Darariscotta, ME 04543
"Cartoonist"

**James Blake**
70 West Red Oak Lane
White Plains, NY 10604
"Tennis Player"

**Robert Blake** #7253166
LA Central Jail
7100 High Power Unit, Box 86164
Los Angeles, CA 90086
"Actor"

**Susan Blakely**
8436 West Third Street #740
Los Angeles, CA 90048
"Actress"

**Michael Blakemore**
11A St. Martin's Almhousees
Bayham
London NW1 ENGLAND
"Film Director"

**Ronee Blakley**
8033 Sunset Blvd. #693
Los Angeles, CA 90046
"Singer, Actress"

**Tammy Blanchard**
8942 Wilshire Blvd.
Beverly Hills, CA 90211
"Actress"

**Cate Blanchette**
P.O. Box 128
Surrey Hills NSW 2010 AUSTRA-
LIA
"Actress"

**George Blanda**
79001 Lago Drive
La Quinta, CA 92253
"Ex-Football Player"

**Mark Blankfield**
141 South El Camino Drive #205
Beverly Hills, CA 90212
"Actor"

**Rosa Blasi**
8060 Melrose Avenue
Los Angeles, CA 90046
"Actress"

**Freddie Blassie**
215 W. Hartdale Avenue
Hartdale, NY 10530
"Wrestler, Manager"

**The Blasters**
1924 Spring Street
Paso Robles, CA 93446
"Rock & Roll Group"

**Richard Blasucci**
353 1/2 North Gardner
Los Angeles, CA 90036
"Actor, Writer"

**Jeff Blatnick**
848 Whitney Drive
Schenectady, NY 12309
"Wrestler"

**Drew Bledsoe**
1 Bills Drive
Orchard Park, NY 14127
"Football Player"

**Yasmine Bleeth**
104-60 Queens Blvd. #10C
Forest Hills, NY 11375
"Actress"

**Rocky Bleier**
701 Filbert Street
Pittsburg, PA 15232
"Ex-Football Player"

**Brian Blessed**
7 Great Russell Street
London W2 3RA ENGLAND
"Actor"

**Brenda Blethyn**
61-63 Portobello Road
London W1N OAX ENGLAND
"Actress"

**Mary J. Blige**
c/o The Firm
9100 Wilshire Blvd. #100W
Beverly Hills, CA 90210
"Singer"

**Blink 182**
P.O. Box 232247
Encinitas, CA 92023
"Music Group"

**Stacey Blitsch**
296 Church Street
San Francisco, CA 94114
"Roller Derby Player"

**Wolf Blitzer**
8929 Holly Leaf Lane
Bethesda, MD 20817
"News Correspondent"

**Hunt Block**
P.O. Box 462
Green's Farms, CT 06436
"Actor"

**Dirk Blocker**
5063 La Ramada Drive
Santa Barbara, CA 93111
"Actor"

**Michael Blodgett**
10485 National Blvd. #22
Los Angeles, CA 90034
"Actor"

**Linda Bloodworth-Thomason**
4024 Radford Avenue, Bldg. 5 #104
Studio City, CA 91604
"Film Producer"

**Brian Bloom**
11 Croydon Court
Dix Hills, NY 11746
"Actor"

**Claire Bloom**
18-21 Jermyn Street, #300
London SW1Y 6HP ENGLAND
"Actress"

**Lindsay Bloom**
P.O. Box 412
Weldon, CA 93263
"Actress"

**Verna Bloom**
327 East 82nd Street
New York, NY 10028
"Actress"

**Mayor Michael Bloomberg**
499 Park Avenue
New York, NY 10022
"Politician"

**Betsy Bloomingdale**
131 Delfern Drive
Los Angeles, CA 90077
"Business Executive"

**Lisa Blount**
5750 Wilshire Blvd. #580
Los Angeles, CA 90036
"Actress"

**Mel Blount**
6 Mel Blount Drive
Claysville, PA 15323
"Ex-Football Player"

**Kurtis Blow**
1800 Argyle Avenue #408
Hollywood, CA 90028
"Singer"

**Vida Blue**
P.O. Box 1449
Pleasanton, CA 94566
"Ex-Baseball Player"

**Blues Brothers Band**
173 Brighton Avenue
Boston, MA 02134
"Music Group"

**Judy Blume**
244 Fifth Avenue, 11th Floor
New York, NY 10021
"Writer"

**Ann Blyth**
P.O. Box 9754
Rancho Santa Fe, CA 92067
"Actress"

**True Boardman**
2951 Paisano Road
Pebble Beach, CA 93593
"Actor"

**Michael Boatman**
1432 Sunnycrest Drive
Fullerton, CA 92835
"Actor"

**Lorena Bobbitt**
709 Gray Avenue
Durham, NC 27701
"Cut off Husband's Penis"

**Nicole Bobek**
P.O. Box 4534
Tequesta, FL 33469
"Figure Skater"

**Andrea Bocelli**
c/o MT Opera & Blues
Via Emerlo 16
I-40126 Bologna ITALY
"Opera Singer"

**Steven Bochco**
10201 West Pico Blvd.
Bldg. #1, Room #112
Los Angeles, CA 90035
"Writer, Producer"

**Hart Bochner**
P.O. Box 5617
Beverly Hills, CA 90210
"Actor"

**Lloyd Bochner**
42 Haldeman Road
Santa Monica, CA 90402
"Actor"

**Tom Bodett**
P.O. Box 3249
Homer, Alaska 99603
"Motel 6 Spokesman"

**Rudy Boesch**
1413 Franklin Drive
Virginia Beach, VA 23454
"TV Show Survivor"

**Peter Bogdanovich**
151 El Camino Drive
Beverly Hills, CA 90212
"Film Writer, Director"

**Suzy Bogguss**
124 - 12th Avenue #410
Nashville, TN 37203
"Singer"

**Eric Bogosian**
c/o WMA
1325 Avenue of the Americas
New York, NY 10019
"Actor"

**Heidi Bohay**
48 Main Street
South Bound Brook, NJ 08880
"Actress"

**Richard Bohringer**
14 Avenue Duquesne
95160 Dewil-la-Barre FRANCE
"Actor"

**David Boies**
80 Business Park Drive #110
Armonk, NY 10504
"Attorney"

**Brian Boitano**
c/o Keith Sherman
1500 Broadway #505
New York, NY 10036
"Ice Skater"

**Tiffany Bolling**
12483 Braddock Drive
Los Angeles, CA 90066
"Actress"

**Joseph Bologna**
16830 Ventura Blvd. #326
Encino, CA 91436
"Actor, Writer, Director"

**Henry Boltinoff**
7518A English Ct.
Lake Worth, FL 33467
"Cartoonist"

**Michael Bolton**
P.O. Box 679
Branford, CT 06516
"Singer"

**Danny Bonaduce**
2651 La Cuesta Drive
Los Angeles, CA 90046
"Actor"

**Julian Bond**
c/o NAACP
4805 Mt Hope Drive
Baltimore, MD 21215
"Politician"

**Philip Bond**
50 High Street
Abergwynfi
W. Gamorgan SA13 3YW
ENGLAND
"Actor"

**Steve Bond**
3500 West Olive Avenue #920
Burbank, CA 91505
"Actor"

**Tommy "Butch" Bond**
993 Delaware Street
Imperial Beach, CA 91932
"Actor"

**Barry Bonds**
9595 Wilshire Blvd. #711
Beverly Hills, CA 90212
"Baseball Player"

**Gary U.S. Bonds**
875 Avenue of the Americas #1908
New York, NY 10001
"Singer"

**Peter Bonerz**
3637 Lowry Road
Los Angeles, CA 90027
"Actor, Director"

**Lisa Bonet**
1551 Will Geer Road
Topanga, CA 90290
"Actress"

**Jon Bon Jovi**
248 West 17th Street #501
New York, NY 10011
"Rock & Roll Group"

**Helena Bonham-Carter**
7 West Heath Avenue
London SW14 6HP ENGLAND
"Actress"

**Bobby Bonilla**
390 Round Hill Road
Greenwich, CT 06831
"Baseball Player"

**Elayna Bonner**
Uliza Tschakalowa 48
Moscow, RUSSIA
"Politician"

**Frank Bonner**
8436 West 3rd Street #740
Los Angeles, CA 90048
"Actor, Director"

**Chastity Bono**
8968 Vista Granda
West Hollywood, CA 90069
"Cher's Daughter"

**Booker T & the MGs**
Huetteldorferstr. 259
1140 Vienna AUSTRIA
"R&B Group"

**Debby Boone**
4334 Kester Avenue
Sherman Oaks, CA 91403
"Singer"

**Pat Boone**
9200 Sunset Blvd. #1007
Los Angeles, CA 90069
"Actor, Singer"

**Randy Boone**
1429 Pine Valley Loop
Fayetteville, NC 28305
"Actor"

**Charley Boorman**
"The Glebe"
Annanoe County Wicklow
IRELAND
"Film Director"

**John Boorman**
21 Thurloe Square
London SW7-2SD ENGLAND
"Film Director"

**Elayne Boosler**
1122 South Roberston Blvd. #15
Los Angeles, CA 90035
"Comedienne"

**Debra Boostrum**
269 S. Beverly Drive #440
Beverly Hills, CA 90212
"Model"

**Adrian Booth**
3922 Glenridge Drive
Sherman Oaks, CA 91423
"Actor"

**Connie Booth**
10 Primrose Hill, Fitroy Hill
London WW1 8TR ENGLAND
"Actress"

**Powers Boothe**
23629 Long Valley Road
Hidden Hills, CA 91302
"Actor"

**Cornell Borchers**
Elchelgarten 2
D-82335 Berg GERMANY
"Actress"

**Amanda Borden**
3536 Woodbridge Blvd.
Fairfield, OH 45014
"Gymnast"

**Lynn Borden**
16161 Ventura Blvd. #675
Encino, CA 91436
"Actress"

**David Boreanaz**
1122 S. Robertson Blvd. #15
Los Angeles, CA 90035
"Actor"

**Bjorn Borg**
1787 Century Park Way
West Bldg. 18, #430
Blue Bell, PA 19402
"Tennis Player"

**Jim Borgman**
617 Vine Street
Cincinnati, OH 45201
"Cartoonist"

**Ernest Borgnine**
3055 Lake Glen Drive
Beverly Hills, CA 90210
"Actor"

**Tova Borgnine**
3055 Lake Glen Drive
Beverly Hills, CA 90210
"Actress"

**Denise Borino**
28 Conduit Court
Roseland, NJ 07068
"Actress"

**Robert Bork**
6520 Ridge Street
McLean, VA 22101
"Judge"

**Matt Borlenghi**
8721 Sunset Blvd. #210
Los Angeles, CA 90069
"Actor"

**Col. Frank Borman**
P.O. Box 1139
Fairacres, NM 88033
"Astronaut"

**Philip Bosco**
55 Sunset Court
Haworth, NJ 07641
"Actor"

**Tom Bosley**
2822 Royston Place
Beverly Hills, CA 90210
"Actor"

**Barbara Bosson**
694 Amalfi Drive
Pacific Palisades, CA 90272
"Actress"

**Boston**
9200 Sunset Blvd. #900
Los Angeles, CA 90069
"Rock & Roll Group"

**Ralph Boston**
3301 Woodbine Avenue
Knoxville, TN 37914
"Track Athlete"

**Barry Bostwick**
170 South Mountain Road
New City, NY 11956
"Actor"

**Brian Bosworth**
170 S. Mountain Road
New City, NY 11956
"Actor, Football Player"

**Kate Bosworth**
9560 Wilshire blvd. #500
Beverly Hills, CA 90212
"Actress"

**Joe Bottoms**
1015 Gayley Avenue #300
Los Angeles, CA 90024
"Actor"

**Sam Bottoms**
4719 Willowcrest Avenue
Toluca Lake, CA 91602
"Actor"

**Timothy Bottoms**
532 Hot Springs Road
Santa Barbara, CA 93108
"Actor"

**Pierre Boulez**
1 Pl. Igor Stravinsky
F-75004 Paris FRANCE
"Composer, Conductor"

**Jim Bouton**
P.O. Box 188
North Edremont, MA 01252
"Ex-Baseball Player"

**John Bowab**
2598 Green Valley
Los Angeles, CA 90046
"TV Director"

**Riddick Bowe**
714 Ahmer Drive
Fort Washington, MD 20022
"Boxer"

**Julie Bowen**
252 North Larchmont Blvd. #200
Los Angeles, CA 90004
"Actress"

**Antoinette Bower**
1529 North Beverly Glen
Los Angeles, CA 90077
"Actress"

**David Bowie**
180-182 Tottenham Court Road
London W1P 9LE ENGLAND
"Singer, Actor"

**Lauren Bowles**
9701 Wilshire Blvd., 10th Floor
Beverly Hills, CA 90212
"Actress"

**Peter Bowles**
125 Gloucester Road
London SW7 ENGLAND
"Actor"

**Christopher Bowman**
5653 Kester Avenue
Van Nuys, CA 91411
"Skater"

**Sen. Barbara Boxer (CA)**
112 Hart Office Bldg.
Washington, DC 20510
"Politician"

**Bruce Boxleitner**
P.O. Box 5513
Sherman Oaks, CA 91403
"Actor"

**Lara Flynn Boyle**
9777 Wilshire Blvd. #504
Beverly Hills, CA 90212
"Actress"

**Peter Boyle**
130 East End Avenue
New York, NY 10024
"Actor"

**Boyz II Men**
10675 Santa Monica Blvd.
Los Angeles, CA 90025
"R&B Group"

**Sir Jack Brabham**
Box 654
Miranda NSW 2228 AUSTRALIA
"Race Car Driver"

**Lorraine Bracco**
1505 10th Street
Santa Monica, CA 90401
"Actress"

**Ray Bradbury**
10265 Cheviot Drive
Los Angeles, CA 90064
"Author"

**Barbara Taylor Bradford**
450 Park Avenue #1903
New York, NY 10022
"Writer"

**Richard Bradford**
8675 West Washington Blvd. #203
Culver City, CA 90232
"Actor"

**Benjamin Bradlee**
3014 "N" Street NW
Washington, DC 20007
"Journalist"

**Bill Bradley**
711 Fifth Avenue #900
New York, NY 10022
"Ex-Senator"

**Ed Bradley**
285 Central Park West
New York, NY 10024
"Newscaster"

**James Bradley**
32 Lynden Street
New York, NY 1058
"Author"

**Kathleen Bradley**
11365 Venura Blvd. #100
Studio City, CA 91604
"Actress"

**Terry Bradshaw**
8911 Shadey Lane Drive
Shreveport, LA 7118
"Ex-Football Player"

**James Brady**
1255 "I" Street #1100
Washington, DC 20005
"Ex-White House Press Sec."

**Orla Brady**
1729 N. Sycamore Avenue
Hollywood, CA 90028
"Actress"

**Tom Brady**
Foxboro Stadium
Route 1
Foxbore, MA 02035
"Football Player"

**Wayne Brady**
14622 Venture Blvd. #1012
Sherman Oaks, CA 91403
"Actor"

**Eric Braeden**
13723 Romany Drive
Pacific Palisades, CA 90272
"Actor"

**Zach Braff**
955 S. Carrillo Drive #300
Los Angeles, CA 90048
"Actor"

**Sonia Braga**
41 River Terrance #1104
New York, NY 10282
"Actress"

**Billy Bragg**
27a Floral Street 3rd Floor
London WC2E 9DQ ENGLAND
"Singer"

**Don Bragg**
90 State Street
Penns Grove, NJ 08069
"Track Athlete"

**Delaney Bramlett**
10723 Johanna Avenue
Sunland, CA 91040
"Guitarist"

**Kenneth Branagh**
Studios Road
Shepperton
Middlesex TW17 0QD ENGLAND
"Actor, Director"

**Ralph Branca**
c/o Westchester Country Club
Rye, NY 10580
"Baseball Player"

**Klaus Maria Brandauer**
Bartensteingasse 8/9
A-1010 Vienna AUSTRIA
"Actor, Director"

**Jonathan Brandis**
13828 Weddington
Van Nuys, CA 91401
"Actor"

**Marlon Brando**
13828 Weddington
Van Nuys, CA 91401
"Actor"

**Michael Brandon**
280 South Beverly Drive #400
Beverly Hills, CA 90212
"Actor"

**Brandy**
22817 Ventura Blvd. #432
Woodland Hills, CA 91364
"Singer"

**Laura Branigan**
8942 Wilshire Blvd. #219
Beverly Hills, CA 90211
"Singer, Songwriter"

**Richard Branson**
Manor Royal, Crasley
W. Sussex RH10 2ND ENGLAND
"Business Executive"

**Zeke Bratkowski**
224 N. Anchors Lake Drive
Santa Rosa Beach, FL 32459
"Football Player"

**Benjamin Bratt**
11777 San Vicente Blvd. #600
Los Angeles, CA 90049
"Actor"

**Andre Braugher**
361 Charlton Avenue
South Orange, NJ 07079
"Actor"

**Toni Braxton**
6545 Old Riverside Drive NW
Atlanta, GA 30328
"Singer"

**Sen. John Breaux (LA)**
Senate Hart Building #516
Washington, DC 20510
"Politicain"

**Julian Bream**
122 Wigmore Street
London W1 ENGLAND
"Guitarist"

**Peter Breck**
6310 San Vicente Blvd. #520
Los Angeles, CA 90048
"Actor"

**Craig Breedlove**
200 North Front Street
Rio Vista, CA 94571
"Land Speed Holder"

**Buddy Bregman**
11288 Ventura Blvd. #700
Studio City, CA 91604
"Director, Producer"

**Tracey E. Bregman**
7800 Beverly Blvd. #3371
Los Angeles, CA 90036
"Actress"

**Eileen Brennan**
974 Mission Terrace
Camarillo, CA 93010
"Actress"

**Melissa Brennan**
6520 Platt Avenue #634
West Hills, CA 91307
"Actress"

**Amy Brenneman**
17145 Rancho Street
Encino, CA 91316
"Actress"

**David Brenner**
3748 Amber Lantern Circle
Las Vegas, NV 89147
"Comedian, Talk Show Host"

**Dori Brenner**
2106 Canyon Drive
Los Angeles, CA 90068
"Actress"

**Bobbie Bresee**
P.O. Box 1222
Hollywood, CA 90078
"Actress, Model"

**Martin Brest**
831 Paseo Miramar
Pacific Palisades, CA 90272
"Film Writer, Director"

**George Brett**
P.O. Box 419969
Kansas City, MO 64141
"ex-Baseball Player"

**Teresa Brewer**
584 Prospect Street
New Haven, CT 06511
"Singer"

**Jordana Brewster**
9830 Wilshire Blvd.
Beverly Hills, CA 90212
"Actress"

**Justice Stephen Breyer**
1 - 1st Street NE
Washington, DC 20543
"Supreme Court Justice"

**Richard Briars**
24, Hanway Street
London W1T 1UH ENGLAND
"Actor"

**Beth Brickell**
P.O. Box 26
Paron, AR 72122
"Writer, Director"

**Edie Brickell**
88 Central Park West
New York, NY 10023
"Singer"

**Beau Bridges**
5525 North Jed Smith Road
Hidden Hills, CA 91302
"Actor, Director"

**Brooke Marie Bridges**
7800 Beverly Blvd. #3305
Los Angeles, CA 90035
"Actress"

**Jeff Bridges**
985 Hot Springs Road
Montecito, CA 93108
"Actor"

**Todd Bridges**
2621 Oakwood Avenue
Venice, CA 90291
"Actor"

**Richard Briers**
24 Hanway Street
London W1T 1UH ENGLAND
"Actor"

**Charlie Brill**
3635 Wrightwood Drive
Studio City, CA 91604
"Actor"

**Bernie Brillstein**
9150 Wilshire Blvd. #350
Beverly Hills, CA 90212
"Talent Agent"

**Wilfred Brimley**
B-7 Ranch
Lehi, UT 84043
"Actor"

**Christie Brinkley**
1122 South Robertson Blvd. #15
Los Angeles, CA 90035
"Model"

**Valerie Brisco-Hooks**
1 Hoosier Dome
Indianapolis, IN 46225
"Actress"

**Mai Britt**
1520 S. Beverly Glen Blvd. #403
Los Angeles, CA 90024
"Actress"

**Morgan Brittany**
3434 Cornell Road
Agoura Hills, CA 91301
"Actress, Model"

**Connie Britton**
1100 Glendon Avenue #1000
Los Angeles, CA 90024
"Actress"

**Tony Britton**
76 Oxford Street
London W1N 0AX ENGLAND
"Actor"

**Amber Brkich**
104 - 1st Street
Beaver, PA 15009
"Survivor Contestant"

**Bill Brochtrup**
1801 Avenue of the Stars #902
Los Angeles, CA 90067
"Actor"

**Lou Brock**
61 Berkley Plaza
Saint Charles, MO 63301
"Ex-Baseball Player"

**Peter Brock**
Box 3297
North Burnley, Victoria 3121
AUSTRALIA
"Race Car Driver"

**Erin Brockovich-Ellis**
5707 Corsa Avenue
Westlake Village, CA 91361
"Environmental Researcher"

**Beth Broderick**
1505 - 10th Street
Santa Monica, CA 90401
"Actress"

**Matthew Broderick**
P.O. Box 69646
Los Angeles, CA 90069
"Actor"

**Kevin Brodie**
4292 Elmer Avenue
North Hollywood, CA 91602
"Actor"

**Lane Brody**
P.O. Box 24775
Nashville, TN 37202
"Singer"

**Ronnie Brody**
21 Bartle Road
London W11 ENGLAND
"Actor"

**Tom Brokaw**
941 Park Avenue #14C
New York, NY 10025
"Newscaster"

**James Brolin**
P.O. Box 56927
Sherman Oaks, CA 91413
"Actor"

**Josh Brolin**
450 North Rossmore Avenue #704
Los Angeles, CA 90004
"Actor"

**Edgar M. Bronfman**
31122 Broad Beach Road
Malibu, CA 90265
"Distillery Executive"

**Charles Bronson**
P.O. Box 2644
Malibu, CA 90265
"Actor"

**Faith Brook**
109 Jermyn Street
London SW1Y 6A5 ENGLAND
"Actress"

**Jayne Brook**
9150 Wilshire Blvd. #350
Beverly Hills, CA 90212
"Actress"

**Gary Brooker**
5 Cranley Gardens
London SW7 ENGLAND
"Singer, Composer"

**Brooklyn Bridge**
P.O. Box 309M
Bayshore, NY 11706
"Rock & Roll Group"

**Brooks & Dunn**
300 Tenth Avenue South
Nashville, TN 37203
"Country Music Duo"

**Albert Brooks**
14955 Ventura Blvd. #228
Sherman Oaks, CA 91403
"Actor, Writer, Director"

**Avery Brooks**
P.O. Box 93-1198
Los Angeles, CA 90093
"Actor"

**Donnie Brooks**
1817 West Verdugo Avenue
Burbank, CA 91506
"Comedian"

**Garth Brooks**
1111 17th Avenue South
Nashville, TN 37212
"Singer"

**James L. Brooks**
8942 Wilshire Blvd.
Beverly Hills, CA 90211
"TV Writer, Producer"

**Mel Brooks**
2301 La Mesa Drive
Santa Monica, CA 90405
"Actor, Writer, Director"

**Kevin Brophy**
15010 Hamlin Street
Van Nuys, CA 91411
"Actor"

**Pierce Brosnan**
24955 Pacific Coast Hwy. #C-205
Malibu, CA 90265
"Actor, Model"

**Dr. Joyce Brothers**
1530 Palisades Avenue
Fort Lee, NJ 07024
"Psychologist & TV Personality

**Louise Brough**
1808 Voluntary Road
Vista, CA 92083
"Tennis Player"

**Aaron Brown**
c/o CNN
5 Penn Plaza
New York, NY 10001
"TV News Anchor "

**Bobby Brown**
1324 Thomas Place
Ft. Worth, TX 76107
"Singer"

**Bryan Brown**
110 Queen Street
Woollahra NSW 2025
AUSTRALIA
"Actor"

**Clarence "Gatemouth" Brown**
P.O. Box 958
Bogalusa, LA 70429
"Singer, Guitarist"

**Denise Brown**
P.O. Box 3777
Monarch Bay, CA 92629
"Nicole Brown-Simpson's Sister"

**Dwier Brown**
749 1/2 N. Lafayette Park Pl.
Los Angeles, CA 90026
"Actor"

**Errol Brown**
P.O. Box 106
Rochdale OL16 4HW ENGLAND
"Singer"

**Georg Stanford Brown**
2565 Greenvalley Road
Los Angeles, CA 90046
"Actor, Director"

**Helen Gurley Brown**
1 West 81st Street #220
New York, NY 10024
"Author, Editor"

**James Brown**
P.O. Box 1051
Augusta, GA 30903
"Singer

**Mayor Jerry Brown**
200 Harrison Street
Oakland, CA 94607
"Politician"

**Jim Brown**
1851 Sunset Plaza Drive
Los Angeles, CA 90069
"Ex-Football Player, Actor"

**Jim Ed Brown**
1300 Division Street #102
Nashville, TN 37203
"Singer"

**Johnny Brown**
2732 Woodhaven Drive
Los Angeles, CA 90068
"Performer"

**Julie Brown**
11288 Ventura Blvd. #728
Studio City, CA 91604
"Comedienne"

**Lisa Brown**
448 West 44th Street
New York, NY 10036
"Actress"

**Nacio Herb Brown, Jr.**
1739 DeCamp Drive
Beverly Hills, CA 90210
"Actor"

**Peter Brown**
854 Cypress Avenue
Hermosa Beach, CA 90254
"Actor"

**Roger Aaron Brown**
400 South Beverly Drive #216
Beverly Hills, CA 90212
"Actor"

**Ruth Brown**
P.O. Box 170429
San Francisco, CA 94117
"Singer"

**Shay Brown**
499 Erin Drive
Knoxville, TN 37919
Roller Skater"

**Susan Brown**
11931 Addison Street
North Hollywood, CA 91607
"Actress"

**T. Graham Brown**
P.O. Box 1547
Goodlesville, TN 37070
"C & W Singer"

**Thomas Wilson Brown**
3033 Vista Crest
Los Angeles, CA 90068
"Actor"

**Mayor Willie L. Brown, Jr.**
401 Van Ness Avenue #336
San Francisco, CA 94102
"Politician"

**Woody Brown**
6548 Colbath Avenue
Van Nuys, CA 91401
"Actor"

**Jackson Browne**
2746 Kling Street
Studio City, CA 91604
"Singer, Composer"

**Kathy Browne**
P.O. Box 2939
Beverly Hills, CA 90213
"Actress"

**Roscoe Lee Browne**
3531 Wonderview Drive
Los Angeles, CA 90068
"Actor, Writer, Director

**Kurt Browning**
175 Bloor Street E. #400
South Tower
Toronto, Ont. M4W 3R8 CANADA
"Ice Skater"

**Ricou Browning**
5221 SW 196th Lane
Ft. Lauderdale, FL 33332
"Writer, Producer"

**Dave Brubeck**
221 Millstone Road
Wilton, CT 06807
"Pianist"

**Carol Bruce**
1055 N. Kingsley Avenue #104
Los Angeles, CA 90029
"Actress"

**Jerry Bruckheimer**
1631 Tenth Street
Santa Monica, CA 90404
"Film Producer"

**Chelsea Brummet**
P.O. Box 450802
Kissimmee, FL 34745
"Actress"

**Bo Brundin**
1716 Clybourn Avenue
Burbank, CA 91505
"Actor"

**Carla Bruni**
4, rue De La Paix
75002 Paris FRANCE
"Model"

**Frank Bruno**
c/o Centurion House
Railway Street
Hertford SG14 1AP ENGLAND
"Boxer"

**Ellen Bry**
2401 Main Street
Santa Monica, CA 90405
"Actress"

**Dora Bryan**
11 Marine Parade
Brighton Sussex ENGLAND
"Actress"

**Zachary Ty Bryan**
2222 Foothill Blvd. #E-285
La Canada, CA 91011
"Actor"

**Anita Bryant**
P.O. Box 5331
Sevierville, TN 37864
"Singer"

**Kobe Bryant**
P.O. Box 491787
Los Angeles, CA 90049
"Basketball Player"

**Michael Bryant**
19 Deanhill Court
Upper Richmond
London SW14 7DJ ENGLAND
"Actor"

**Scott Bryce**
6500 Wilshire Blvd. #2200
Los Angeles, CA 90048
"Actor"

**Zbigniew Brzezinski**
1800 "K" St. NW #400
Washington, DC 20006
"Politician"

**Sergei Bubka**
Kuibisheva St. 42
252023 Kiev UKRAINE
"Pole-Vaulter"

**Angela "Bay" Buchanan**
909 11th Street NE
Washington, D.C. 20002
"Pat Buchanan's Sister"

**Patrick J. Buchanan**
1017 Savile Lane North
McLean, VA 22101
"Politician, Columnist"

**Horst Buchholz**
Clavadoiras
CH-7078 Lenzerheide
SWITZERLAND
"Actor"

**Art Buchwald**
4327 Hawthorne Street NW
Washington, DC 20016
"Columnist"

**Betty Buckner**
10643 Riverside Drive
Toluca Lake, CA 91602
"Actress"

**Bill Buckner**
2425 W. Victory Road
Meridian, ID 83642
"Ex-Baseball Player"

**Lindsay Buckingham**
900 Airole Way
Los Angeles, CA 90077
"Singer, Songwriter"

**The Buckinghams**
P.O. Box 1821
Ojai, CA 93024
"Rock & Roll Group"

**Betty Buckley**
404 Park Avenue South, 10th Floor
New York, NY 10016
"Actress"

**William F. Buckley, Jr.**
215 Lexington Avenue
New York, NY 10016
"Author, Editor"

**Julie Budd**
163 Amsterdam Avenue #224
New York, NY 10023
"Actress"

**Terence Budd**
29 Rylette Road
London W12 ENGLANG
"Actor"

**Zola Budd**
1 Church Row
Wandsworth Plain
London SW18 ENGLAND
"Runner"

**Maria Bueno**
Rua Consolagao 3414 #10
1001 Edificio Augustus
Sao Paulo, BRAZIL
"Tennis Player"

**Jimmy Buffet**
540 South Ocean Blvd.
Palm Beach, FL 33480
"Singer, Songwriter"

**Warren Buffett**
3555 Farnam Street
Omana, NE 68131
"Business Executive"

**The Buggles**
c/o Island Recordss Ltd.
22 St. Peters Square
London W69 NW ENGLAND
"Rock & Roll Group"

**Vincent T. Bugliosi**
3699 Wilshire Blvd. #350
Los Angeles, CA 90010
"Attorney, Author"

**Genevieve Bujold**
21642 Rambla Vista
Malibu, CA 90265
"Actress"

**Donald Buka**
1501 Beacon Street #1802
Brookline, MA 02146
"Actor"

**Ray Buktenica**
2057 N. Beverly Glen Blvd.
Los Angeles, CA 90077
"Actor"

**Joyce Bulifant**
3500 West Olive Avenue #920
Burbank, CA 91505
"Actress"

**Richard Bull**
200 East Delware Place #20F
Chicago, IL 60611
"Actor"

**Sandra Bullock**
9830 Wilshire Blvd.
Beverly Hills, CA 90212
"Actress"

**Grace Bumbry**
165 West 57th Street
New York, NY 10019
"Opera Singer"

**Brooke Bundy**
833 N. Martel Avenue
Los Angeles, CA 90046
"Actress"

**Jim Bunning**
4 Fairway Drive
Southgate, KY 41071
"Politician, Ex-Baseball Player"

**Lou Burdette**
17709 Deer Isle Circle
Winter Garden, FL 34787
"Ex-Baseball Player"

**Eric Burdon**
1924 Spring Street
Paso Robles, CA 93446
"Singer"

**Gregg Burge**
420 Madison Avenue #1400
New York, NY 10017
"Singer"

**Gary Burghoff**
13701 Riverside Drive #201
Sherman Oaks, CA 91423
"Actor"

**Richard Burgi**
30872 Coast Hwy. #166
Laguna Beach, CA 92651
"Actor"

**Delta Burke**
1407 Broadway #1615
New York, NY 10018
"Actress"

**Paul Burke**
2217 Avenida Caballeros
Palm Springs, CA 92262
"Actor"

**Soloman Burke**
751 Bridgeway #300
Sausalito, CA 94965
"Singer"

**Dennis Burkley**
5145 Costello Avenue
Sherman Oaks, CA 91423
"Actor"

**Tom Burleson**
c/o General Delivery
Newland, NC 28657
"Actor"

**Carol Burnett**
8383 Wilshire Blvd. #1034
Beverly Hills, CA 90211
"Actress, Comedienne"

**Nancy Burnett**
7800 Beverity Blvd. #3305
Los Angeles, CA 90036
"Actress"

**Edward Burns**
588 Broadway #210
New York, NY 10012
"Actor, Screenwriter"

**Eileen Burns**
4000 West 43rd Street
New York, NY 10036
"Actress"

**Eric Burns**
448 1/2 N. Stanley Avenue
Los Angeles, CA 90046
"News Correspondent"

**James MacGregor Burns**
Bee Hill Road
Williamstown, MA 01267
"Political Scientist, Historian"

**Jere Burns**
1465 Lindacrest Drive
Beverly Hills, CA 90210
"Actor"

**Ken Burns**
Maple Grove Road
Walpole, NH 03608
"Documentary Producer"

**Kenny Burrell**
163 Third Avenue #206
New York, NY 10003
"Jazz Musician"

**Leroy Burrell**
1801 Ocean Park Blvd. #112
Santa Monica, CA 90405
"Track & Field"

**Darren E. Burrows**
8436 West Third Street#704
Los Angeles, CA 90048
"Actor"

**James Burrows**
9242 Beverly Blvd. #200
Beverly Hills, CA 90210
"Writer, Producer"

**Ellen Burstyn**
P.O. Box 217
Palisades, NY 10964
"Actress"

**Ed Burton**
660 West Hile Road
North Shores, MI 49441
"Film Director"

**Kate Burton**
P.O. Box 5617
Beverly Hills, CA 90210
"Actress"

**Lance Burton**
3770 S. Las Vegas Blvd.
Las Vegas, NV 89109
"Magician"

**Levar Burton**
102 South Almont Drive
Los Angeles, CA 90048
"Actor"

**Tim Burton**
1010 East 2nd Street #1
Long Beach, CA 90802
"Actor, Director, Producer"

**Tony Burton**
3500 W. Olive Avenue #1400
Burbank, CA 91505
"Actor"

**Warren Burton**
280 S. Beverly Drive #400
Beverly Hills, CA 90212
"Actor"

**Gary Busey**
18424 Coastline Drive
Malibu, CA 90265
"Actor"

**Timothy Busfield**
151 El Camino Drive
Beverly Hills, CA 90212
"Actor"

**Bush**
3500 West Olive #600
Burbank, CA 91505
"Rock & Roll Band"

**Barbara Bush**
9 West Oak Drive
Houston, TX 77056
"Ex-First Lady"

**Dick Bush**
8 Grande Parade, #16
Plymouth
Devon PL1 3DF ENGLAND
"Cinematographer"

**George Bush, Sr.**
9 West Oak Drive
Houston, TX 77056
"Ex-President of United States"

**George W. Bush, Jr.**
1600 Pennslyvania Avenue
Washington, DC 20500
"President"

**Gov. Jeb Bush (FL)**
The Capitol
402 South Monroe Street
Tallahassee, FL 32399
"Politician"

**Kate Bush**
P.O. Box 120, Welling
Kent DA16 3DS ENGLAND
"Singer, Songwriter"

**Laura Bush**
1600 Pennslyvania Avenue
Washington, DC 20500
"First Lady

**Joe Bushkin**
435 East 52nd Street
New York, NY 10022
"Pianist, Composer"

**Dr. Jerry Buss**
P.O. Box 10
Inglewood, CA 90306
"Basketball Team Owner"

**Mangosutho Buthelezi**
Union Bldg.
Pretoria 0001
South Africa
"Zulu Chief"

**Dick Butkus**
2121 George Halsa Drive NW
Canton, OH 44708
"Ex-Football Player"

**Brett Butler**
315 Longvue Court
Duluth, GA 30155
"Baseball Player"

**Dean Butler**
1310 Westholme Avenue
Los Angeles, CA 90024
"Actor"

**Jerry Butler**
164 Woodstone Drive
Buffalo Grove, IL 60089
"Singer"

**Yancy Butler**
8383 Wilshire Blvd. #550
Beverly Hills, CA 90211
"Actress"

**Mary Jo Buttafuoco**
P.O. Box 335
Agoura Hills, CA 91376
"Joey's wife"

**Butthole Surfers**
315 South Coast Highway #100
Encinitas, CA 92024
"Rock & Roll Band"

**Dick Button**
250 West 57th Street #818
New York, NY 10107
"TV Producer"

**Red Buttons**
778 Tortuoso Way
Los Angeles, CA 90077
"Actor"

**Sarah Buxton**
9220 Sunset Blvd. #305
Los Angeles, CA 90069
"Actress"

**Ruth Buzzi**
2309 Malaga Road
Los Angeles, CA 90068
"Actress"

**Gabriel Byrne**
955 S. Carrillo Drive #300
Los Angeles, CA 90048
"Actor"

**Martha Byrne**
40 West 57th Street
New York, NY 10019
"Actress"

**Sen. Robert Byrd (WV)**
Senate Hart Building #311
Washington, DC 20510
"Politicain"

**Tom Byrd**
14011 Ventura Blvd. #213
Sherman Oaks, CA 91403
"Actor"

**Tracy Byrd**
P.O. Box 128195
Nashville, TN 37212
"Singer"

**David Byrne**
195 Chrystie Street #901-F
New York, NY 10002
"Singer, Songwriter"

**Edd Byrnes**
P.O. Box 1623
Beverly Hills, CA 90213
"Actor"

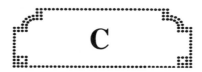

**James Caan**
P.O. Box 6646
Denver, CO 80206
"Actor"

**Montserrat Caballe**
Avenieda de los Madrones 27
E-28043 Madrid SPAIN
"Opera Singer"

**Lorenzo Caccialanza**
9150 Wilshire Blvd. #175
Beverly Hills, CA 90212
"Actor"

**Ava Cadell**
8484 Wilshire Blvd. #745
Bevelry Hills, CA 90211
"Actress, Model"

**Frank Cady**
110 East 9th Street #C-1005
Los Angeles, CA 90079
"Actor"

**Sid Caesar**
1910 Loma Vista
Beverly Hills, CA 90210
"Actor, Comedian"

**Charlotte Caffery**
4800 Bryn Mawr Road
Los Angeles, CA 90027
"Guitarist"

**Stephen Caffrey**
8430 Santa Monica Blvd. #200
West Hollywood, CA 90069
"Actor"

**Nicholas Cage**
1122 Robertson Blvd. #15
Los Angeles, CA 90035
"Actor"

**Dean Cain**
3224 Malibu Canyon Road
Malibu, CA 90265
"Actor"

**Sir Michael Caine**
Rectory Farm House
North Stoke
Wallingford OX10 6BQ ENGLAND
"Actor"

**Bobby Caldwell**
1800 Argyle Avenue #408
Hollywood, CA 90028
"Singer"

**Joseph Cali**
247 South Beverly Drive #102
Beverly Hills, CA 90212
"Actor"

**Anthony Call**
134 East 70th Street
New York, NY 10021
"Actor"

**Brandon Call**
1801 Avenue of the Stars #902
Los Angeles, CA 90067
"Actor"

**James Callahan**
1159 Via Estrellada
Fallbrook, CA 92028
"Actor"

**K. Callan**
14724 Ventura Blvd. #505
Sherman Oaks, CA 91403
"Actress"

**Michael (Mickey) Callan**
1651 Camden Avenue #3
Los Angeles, CA 90025
"Actor"

**Charlie Callas**
2180 Center Avenue
Fort Lee, NJ 07024
"Comedian, Actor"

**Thomas Callaway**
400 South Beverly Drive #101
Beverly Hills, CA 90212
"Actor"

**Lt. William Calley**
V.V. Vicks Jewelry
Cross Country Plaza
Columbus, GA 31906
"Ex-Military"

**Simon Callow**
12-13 Poland Street
London WIV 3DE ENGLAND
"Actor"

**John Calvin**
3639 Regel Place
Los Angeles, CA 90068
"Actor"

**Hector Camacho**
14 Fulton Street
Weehawken, NJ 07086
"Boxer"

**Candace Cameron-Bure**
8369-A Sausalito Avenue
West Hills, CA 91304
"Actress"

**Dean Cameron**
3500 W. Olive Ave. #1400
Burbank, CA 91505
"Actor"

**James Cameron**
919 Santa Monica Blvd.
Santa Monica, CA 90401
"Director"

**John Cameron**
35 Ragged Hall Lane
St. Albans
Herts. AL2 3LB ENGLAND
"Composer, Conductor"

**Kirk Cameron**
P.O. Box 8665
Calabasas, CA 91372
"Actor"

**Colleen Camp**
473 North Tigertail Road
Los Angeles, CA 90049
"Actress"

**Bert Campaneria**
P.O. Box 5096
Scottsdale, AZ 85261
"Ex-Baseball Player"

**Alan Campbell**
130 West 42nd Street #2400
New York, NY 10036
"Actor"

**Sen. Ben Campbell (CO)**
Senate Russell Building #380
Washington, DC 20510
"Politicain"

**Billy Campbell**
1122 South Roxbury Drive
Los Angeles, CA 90035
"Actor"

**Bruce Campbell**
8205 Santa Monica Blvd. #1-827
Los Angeles, CA 90046
"Actor"

**Cheryl Campbell**
5 Milner Place
London N1 ENGLAND
"Actress"

**Christian Campbell**
12533 Woodgreen
Los Angeles, CA 90066
"Actor"

**Earl Campbell**
2937 Thousand Oaks Drive
Austin, TX 78746
"ex-Football Player"

**Glen Campbell**
28 Biltmore Estate
Phoenix, AZ 85016
"Singer, Actor, Composer"

**Julia Campbell**
1505 10th Street
Santa Monica, CA 90401
"Actress"

**Ken Campbell**
74 Watermint Quay
London N16 ENGLAND
"Actor"

**Luther Campbell**
8400 N.E. 2nd Avenue
Miami, FL 33138
"Rap Singer"

**Naomi Campbell**
199 Layfayette Street #700
New York, NY 10012
"Model"

**Neve Campbell**
12533 Woodgreen Street
Los Angeles, CA 90066
"Actress"

**Nicholas Campbell**
1206 N. Orange Grove
Los Angeles, CA 90046
"Actor"

**Tevin Campbell**
27A Floral Street #300
London WC2E 9DQ ENGLAND
"Singer"

**Tisha Campbell**
5750 Wilshire Blvd. #640
Los Angeles, CA 90036
"Actress"

**William Campbell**
21502 Velicata Street
Woodland Hills, CA 91364
"Actor"

**Jane Campion**
87 Pitt Street
Redfern NSW 2016 AUSTRALIA
"Actress"

**David Canary**
903 South Mansfield Avenue
Los Angeles, CA 90036
"Actor"

**John Candelaria**
606 Wingspread
Peachtree City, GA 30269
"Ex-Baseball Player"

**Philippe Candeloro**
35 rue Felicien David
F-75016 Paris FRANCE
"Figure Skater"

**Jack Canfield**
P.O. Box 30880
Santa Barbara, CA 93130
"Author, Professional Speaker"

**Bobby Cannavale**
251 West 95th Street #65
New York, NY 10025
"Actor"

**Stephen J. Cannell**
1220 Hillcrest
Pasadena, CA 91106
"TV Writer, Producer"

**Billy Cannon**
176 Shirley Circle
Monterey, LA 71354
"ex-Football Player"

**Dyan Cannon**
10551 Wilshire Blvd. #405
Beverly Hills, CA 90211
"Actress, Writer"

**Freddie Cannon**
18641 Cassandra Street
Tarzana, CA 91356
"Singer, Songwriter"

**J. D. Cannon**
c/o ICM
40 West 57th Street, 18th Floor
New York, NY 10019
"Actor"

**Katherine Cannon**
1310 Westholme Avenue
Los Angeles, CA 90024
"Actress"

**Jose Canseco**
5601 LeRoy Collins Avenue
Miami Beach, FL 33140
"Baseball Player"

**Joanna Canton**
5312 Kester Avenue #8
Sherman Oaks, CA 91411
"Actress"

**Lana Cantrell**
300 East 71st Street
New York, NY 10021
"Singer, Actress"

**John Cappelletti**
28791 Brant Lane
Laguna Niguel, CA 92677
"Ex-Football Player"

**Frank Capra, Jr.**
1447 South Jameson Lake
Santa Barbara, CA 93108
"Actor"

**Ahna Capri**
8227 Fountain Avenue #2
Los Angeles, CA 90046
"Actress"

**Jennifer Capriatti**
525 Plymouth Road #317
Plymouth Meeting, PA 19462
"Tennis Player"

**Kate Capshaw**
P.O. Box 869
Pacific Palisades, CA 90272
"Actress"

**Captain & Tennille**
(Toni & Daryl Dragon)
7123 Franktown Road
Carson City, NV 89704
"Music Duo"

**Irene Cara**
110 West 26th Street, 3rd Floor
South
New York, NY 10001
"Actress, Singer"

**Pierre Cardin**
59 rue du Faubourg
St-Honore
F-75008 Paris, FRANCE
"Fashion Designer"

**Claudia Cardinale**
Via Flaminia KW77
Prima Porta
00188 Rome, ITALY
"Actress"

**Rod Carew**
5144 East Crescent Drive
Anaheim, CA 92807
"Ex-Baseball Player"

**Clare Carey**
9200 Sunset Blvd. #1130
Los Angeles, CA 90069
"Actress"

**Drew Carey**
955 S. Carrillo Drive, #100
Los Angeles, CA 90048
"Actor"

**Harry Carey, Jr.**
P.O. Box 3256
Durango, CO 81302
"Actor"

**Jim Carey**
47 Kingman Street
Weymouth, MA 02188
"Hockey Player"

**Mariah Carey**
151 El Camino Drive
Beverly Hills, CA 90212
"Singer"

**Rick Carey**
119 Rockland Avenue
Larchmont, NY 10538
"Swimmer"

**Ron Carey**
419 N. Larchmont Blvd.
Los Angeles, CA 90004
"Actor"

**Len Cariou**
10100 Santa Monica Blvd. #2500
Los Angeles, CA 90067
"Actor"

**George Carlin**
11911 San Vicente Blvd. #348
Los Angeles, CA 90049
"Comedian"

**Belinda Carlisle**
14724 Ventura Blvd., PH
Sherman Oaks, CA 91403
"Singer, Songwriter"

**Kitty Carlisle-Hart**
32 East 64th Street
New York, NY 10021
"Actress"

**Mary Carlisle**
517 North Rodeo Drive
Beverly Hills, CA 90210
"Actress"

**King Juan Carlos**
Palacio de La Carcuela
Madrid, SPAIN
"Royalty"

**Tucker Carlson**
P.O. Box 105466
Atlanta, GA 30348
News Anchor, Reporter"

**Larry Carlton**
34 North Palm Street #100
Ventura, CA 93001
"Guitarist"

**Rebekah Carlton-Luff**
9300 Wilshire Blvd.#410
Beverly Hills, CA 90212
"Actress"

**Steve Carlton**
555 S. Camino Del Rio #B2
Durango, CO 81301
"Ex-Baseball Player"

**Robert Carlyle**
76 Oxford Street
London W1N OAX ENGLAND
"Actor"

**Eric Carmen**
1679 S. Belvoir Blvd.
South Euclid, OH 44121
"Singer, Songwriter"

**Julie Carmen**
4526 Wilshire Blvd.
Los Angeles, CA 90010
"Actress"

**Ian Carmichael**
The Priory, Grosmont
Whitby, Yorks. YO22 SQT
ENGLAND
"Actor, Producer"

**Jean Carn**
P.O. Box 27641
Philadelphia, PA 19150
"Singer"

**Judy Carne**
2 Horatio Street #10N
New York, NY 10014
"Actress"

**Princess Caroline**
Villa Le Clos St. Pierre
Avenue Saint Martin
Monte Carlo MONACO
"Royalty"

**Leslie Caron**
10 av. George V
F-75116 Paris FRANCE
"Actress"

**A.J. Carothers**
2110 The Terrace
Los Angeles, CA 90049
"Screenwriter"

**Carleton Carpenter**
R.D. #2 Chardavoyne Road
Warwick, NY 10990
"Actor"

**Charisma Carpenter**
1122 South Robertson Blvd. #15
Los Angeles, CA 90035
"Actress"

**John Carpenter**
8532 Hollywood Blvd.
Los Angeles, CA 90046
"Actor, Director"

**Mary-Chapin Carpenter**
15030 Ventura Blvd. #1-710
Sherman Oaks, CA 91403
"Singer"

**Richard Capenter**
P.O. Box 3787
Thousand Oaks, CA 91359
"Pianist, Composer"

**Scott Carpenter**
P.O. Box 3161
Vail, CO 81658
"Astronaut"

**Caleb Carr**
8899 Beverly Blvd. #102
Los Angeles, CA 90048
"Author"

**Darlene Carr**
9200 Sunset Blvd. #1130
Los Angeles, CA 90069
"Actress"

**Jane Carr**
121 N. San Vicente Blvd.
Beverly Hills, CA 90211
"Actress"

**Vikki Carr**
P.O. Box 780968
San Antonio, TX 78278
"Singer, Songwriter"

**David Carradine**
628C S. San Fernando Blvd.
Burbank, CA 91502
"Actor"

**Keith Carradine**
P.O. Box 460
Placeville, CO 81430
"Actor, Singer"

**Robert Carradine**
355 So. Grand Ave. #4150
Los Angeles, CA 90071
"Actor"

**Tia Carrere**
836 N. LaCienega Blvd., PMB 204
West Hollywood, CA 90069
"Actress"

**Jim Carrey**
P.O. Box 57593
Sherman Oaks, CA 91403
"Comedian, Actor"

**Mathieu Carriere**
Ottenser Markplatz 11
22765 Hamburg GERMANY
"Actor"

**Debbie Lee Carrington**
8428-D Melrose Avenue
West Hollywood, CA 90069
"Actress"

**Lord Carrington**
Manor House
Bledlow, Aylesbury
Buckinghamshire HP17 9PE
ENGLAND
"Politician"

**Diahann Carroll**
151 El Camino Drive
Beverly Hills, CA 90212
"Actress, Singer"

**Pat Carroll**
14 Old Tavern Lane
Harwich Port, MA 02646
"Actress"

**Kitty Carruthers**
22 East 71st Street
New York, NY 10021
"Ice Skater"

**Peter Carruthers**
22 East 71st Street
New York, NY 10021
"Ice Skater"

**Julius Carry**
4091 Farmdale Avenue
Studio City, CA 91604
"Actor"

**Marcey Carsey**
4024 Radford Ave. #3
Studio City, CA 91604
"TV Producer"

**Joanna Carson**
400 St. Cloud Road
Los Angeles, CA 90024
"Ex-Wife of Johnny Carson"

**Johnny Carson**
6962 Wildlife
Malibu, CA 90265
"Ex- TV Show Host, Comedian"

**Amy Carter**
1 Woodland Drive
Plains, GA 31780
"Ex-President's Daughter"

**Benny Carter**
2200 Hercules Drive
Los Angeles, CA 90046
"Saxophonist"

**Chris Carter**
9242 Beverly Blvd. #200
Beverly Hills, CA 90210
"Writer, Producer"

**Deana Carter**
9255 Sunset Blvd. #200
Los Angeles, CA 90069
"Singer"

**Dixie Carter**
P.O. Box 1980
Studio City, CA 91614
"Actress"

**Jack Carter**
1023 Chevy Chase Drive
Beverly Hills, CA 90210
"Comedian, Actor"

**Jimmy Carter**
One Copenhill Avenue, #105515
Atlanta, GA 30348
"Former President of USA"

**John Carter**
13563 Ventura Blvd. #200
Sherman Oaks, CA 91403
"Actor"

**Lynda Carter**
9200 Harrington Drive
Potomac, MD 20854
"Actress, Singer"

**Mel Carter**
1161 NW 76th Avenue
Ft. Lauderdale, FL 33322
"Singer, Actor"

**Ralph Carter**
21 St. James Place
Brooklyn, NY 11205
"Actor"

**Rosalyn Carter**
One Copenhill Avenue, #105515
Atlanta, GA 30348
"Former First Lady"

**Rubin "Hurricane" Carter**
85 King Street #318
Toronto, Ont. MBC 7G3 CANADA
"Boxer, Ex-Convict"

**Terry Carter**
244 Madison Avenue #332
New York, NY 10016
"Actor"

**Thomas Carter**
140 North Tigertail Road
Los Angeles, CA 90049
"Actor, Director"

**Gabrielle Carteris**
13775-A Mono Way #220
Sonora, CA 95370
"Actress"

**Veronica Cartwright**
12754 Sarah Street
Studio City, CA 91604
"Actress"

**Anthony Caruso**
1706 Mandeville Lane
Los Angeles, CA 90049
"Actor"

**David Caruso**
270 N. Canon Drive #1058
Beverly Hills, CA 90210
"Actor"

**Dana Carvey**
775 E. Blythdale Avenue
Mill Valley, CA 94941
"Comedian, Actor"

**Rosie Casals**
P.O. Box 537
Sausalito, CA 94966
"Tennis Player"

**Harold Case**
34 Cunningham Park
Harrow, Middlesex
HA1 4AL ENGLAND
"Cinematographer"

**Steve Case**
22000 AOL Way
Dulles, DC 20166
"AOL Founder"

**Bernie Casey**
6145 Flight Avenue
Los Angeles, CA 90056
"Actor, Ex-Football Player"

**Lawrence Casey**
4139 Vanette Place
North Hollywood, CA 91604
"Actor"

**Johnny Cash**
700 Johnny Cash Parkway
Hendersonville, TN 37075
"Singer"

**June Carter Cash**
700 Johnny Cash Parkway
Hendersonville, TN 37075
"Singer"

**Pat Cash**
281 Clarence Street
Sydney NSW 2000 AUSTRALIA
"Tennis Player"

**Rosanne Cash**
45 West 11th Street #7B
New York, NY 10011
"Singer, Songwriter"

**Tommy Cash**
P.O. Box 1230
Hendersonville, TN 37077
"World Performer, Entertainer"

**Philip Casnoff**
216 S. Plymouth Blvd.
Los Angeles, CA 90004
"Actor"

**Tina Caspary**
11350 Ventura Blvd. #206
Studio City, CA 91604
"Actress"

**Billy Casper**
P.O. Box 210010
Chula Vista, CA 91921
"Golfer"

**Nick Cassavetes**
22223 Buena Ventura Street
Woodland Hills, CA 91364
"Actor"

**Jean-Pierre Cassel**
48 rue de Chevallier de la Barre
F-75018 Paris FRANCE
"Actor"

**Seymour Cassell**
1505 10th Street
Santa Monica, CA 90401
"Actor"

**Joanna Cassidy**
P.O. Box 74123
Los Angeles, CA 90004
"Actress"

**Patrick Cassidy**
1505 10th Street
Santa Monica, CA 90401
"Actor"

**Ryan Cassidy**
4949 Strohm Avenue
North Hollywood, CA 91601
"Actor"

**Shaun Cassidy**
8484 Wilshire Blvd. #500
Beverly Hills, CA 90212
"Actor, Singer"

**Oleg Cassini**
15 East 63rd Street
New York, NY 10021
"Fashion Designer"

**John Castle**
126 Kennington Park Road
London W1 ENGLAND
"Mezzo-Soprano"

**Fidel Castro**
Palacio del Gobierno
Havana, CUBA
"Politician"

**Darlene Cates**
P.O. Box 39
Forney, TX 75126
"Actress"

**Gilbert Cates**
936 Hilts Avenue
Los Angeles, CA 90024
"Film Director"

**Phoebe Cates**
1636 3rd Avenue #309
New York, NY 10128
"Actress"

**Mary Jo Catlett**
4375 Farmdale Avenue
Studio City, CA 91604
"Actress"

**Kim Cattrall**
1 River Place
New York, NY 10036
"Actress"

**Emma Caulfield**
3500 West Olive Avenue, #920
Burbank, CA 91505
"Actress"

**Maxwell Caufield**
5252 Lennox Avenue
Sherman Oaks, CA 91401
"Actor"

**Steve Cauthen**
167 South Main Street
Walton, KY 41094
"Horse Racer"

**Carrie Cavalier**
3200 Wyoming Avenue
Burbank, CA 91505
"Actress"

**Michael Cavanaugh**
1936 Golden Hills Drive
St. Peters, MO 63376
"Actor"

**Dick Cavett**
697 Middle Neck Road
Great Neck, NY 11023
"TV Show Host, Comedian"

**James Caviezel**
8929 Clifton Way #103
Beverly Hills, CA 91211
"Actor"

**Evonne Goolagong Cawley**
Private bag 6060
Richmond S. Vic. 3121 AUSTRA-
LIA
"Tennis Player"

**Christopher Cazenove**
9300 Wilshire Blvd. #555
Beverly Hills, CA 90212
"Actor"

**Matt Cedeno**
11365 Ventura Blvd. #100
Box 7403
Studio City, CA 91604
"Actor"

**Orlando Cepeda**
P.O. Box 1212
Suison City, CA 94585
"Ex-Baseball Player"

**Michael Cera**
9 Sultan Street #200
Toronto, Ont. M5S 1L6 CANADA
"Actor"

**Eugene Cernan**
P.O. Box 19809
Houston, TX 77224
"Astronaut"

**Rick Cerrone**
63 Eisenhower
Cresskill, NJ 07626
"Ex-Baseball Player"

**Peter Cetara**
8900 Wilshire Blvd. #300
Beverly Hills, CA 90211
"Singer, Musician"

**Ron Cey**
22714 Creole Road
Woodland Hills, CA 91364
"Ex-Baseball Player"

**Alex Chadwick**
c/o National Public Radio
2025 "M" Street N.W.
Washington, DC 20036
"News Correspondent"

**Sen. Lincoln Chafee (RI)**
141A Senate Russell Bldg.
Washington, DC 20510
"Politicain"

**Mme. Chaing Kai-Shek**
Waldrof Tower, 100 East 50th Street
New York, NY 10022
"Politician"

**Chairmen of the Board**
11320 Pine Valley Club Drive
Charlotte, NC 28277
"Music Group"

**George Chakiris**
13701 Riverside Drive #201
Sherman Oaks, CA 91423
"Actor"

**Sarah Chalke**
8391 Beverly Blvd. #372
Los Angeles, CA 90048
"Actress"

**Richard Chamberlain**
P.O. Box 2861
Honolulu, HI 96792
"Actor, Producer"

**Marilyn Chambers**
1122 White Rock
Dixon, IL 60121
"Actress"

**Tom Chambers**
P.O. Box 1369
Phoenix, AZ 85001
"Basketball Player"

**Marge Champion**
484 West 43rd Street
New York, NY 10036
"Actress, Dancer"

**Charles Champlin**
2169 Linda Flora Drive
Los Angeles, CA 90024
"Film Critic"

**Kyle Chandler**
9150 Wilshire Blvd. #350
Beverly Hills, CA 90212
"Actor"

**Otis Chandler**
1421 Emerson
Oxnard, CA 93033
"Publisher"

**Michael Chang**
1751 Pinnacle Drive #1500
McLean, VA 22102
"Tennis Player"

**Stockard Channing**
1122 S. Robertson Blvd. #15
Los Angeles, CA 90035
"Actress"

**Rosalind Chao**
6500 Wilshire blvd. #2200
Los Angeles, CA 90048
"Actress"

**Doug Chapin**
9911 W. Pico Blvd. PH 1
Los Angeles, CA 90035
"Film Producer"

**Tom Chapin**
1414 Pennsylvania Avenue
Pittsburgh, PA 15233
"Singer"

**Geraldine Chaplin**
Manoir de Bau
CH-1800 Vevey SWITZERLAND
"Actress"

**Lonny Chapman**
3973 Goodland Avenue
Studio City, CA 91604
"Actor"

**Mark David Chapman**
#81 A 3860
Attica State Prison, Box 149
Attica, NY 14011
"John Lennon's Killer"

**Tracy Chapman**
307 - 7th Avenue #807
New York, NY 10001
"Singer"

**Dave Chappelle**
P.O. Box 5617
Beverly Hills, CA 90210
"Actor"

**Cyd Charisse**
10724 Wilshire Blvd. #1406
Los Angeles, CA 90024
"Actress, Dancer"

**HRH Prince Charles**
Highgrove House
Doughton, Tetbury
GL8 8TN ENGLAND
"Royalty"

**Ray Charles**
2107 W. Washington Blvd. #200
Los Angeles, CA 90018
"Singer, Pianist"

**Suzette Charles**
2705 Cricket Hollow Court
Hendersonville, NV 89014
"Former Miss America"

**Leslie Charleson**
c/o ABC-TV General Hospital
4151 Prospect Avenue
Los Angeles, CA 90027
"Actress"

**Tony Charmoli**
1271 Sunset Plaza Drive
Los Angeles, CA 90069
"Director, Choreography"

**Charo**
151 El Camino Drive
Beverly Hills, CA 90212
"Singer"

**Melanie Chartoff**
10380 Tennessee Avenue
Los Angeles, CA 90064
"Actress"

**David Charvet**
151 El Camino Drive
Beverly Hills, CA 90212
"Actor"

**Julio Ceasar Chavez**
1 Hall of Fame Drive
Canastota, NY 13032
"Boxer"

**Chevy Chase**
8500 Wilshire Blvd. #700
Beverly Hills, CA 90211
"Actor, Writer"

**Lorraine Chase**
68 Old Brompton Road
London SW7 ENGLAND
"Actress"

**Brandi Chastain**
3613 Londonderry
Santa Clara, CA 95090
"Soccer Player"

**Benjamin Chavis**
P.O. Box 1661
Ellicott City, MD 21041
"Ex-N.A.A.C.P. Director"

**Chayanne**
1717 N. Bayshore Drive, #2146
Miami, FL 33132
"Actor"

**Don Cheadle**
13428 Maxella Avenue, PMB 476
Marina del Rey, CA 90292
"Actor"

**Cheap Trick**
509 Hartnell Street
Monterey, CA 93940
"Rock & Roll Group"

**Maree Cheatham**
8787 Shoreham Drive
West Hollywood, CA 90069
"Actress"

**Chubby Checker**
320 Fayette Street #200
Conshohocken, PA 19426
"Singer, Songwriter"

**Molly Cheek**
11365 Ventura Blvd. #100
Studio City, CA 91604
"Actress"

**Joan Chen**
2601 Filbert Street
San Francisco, CA 94123
"Actress"

**Joie Chen**
c/o CNN
P.O. Box 105366
Atlanta, GA 30348
"News Anchor, Reporter"

**Julie Chen**
51 West 52nd Street
New York, NY 10019
"TV Show Host"

**Mrs. Anna Chenault**
2510 Virgina Avenue NW #1404
Washington, DC 20005
"Author, Journalist"

**Dick Cheney**
6613 Madison Drive
McLean, VA 22101
"Vice President"

**Cher**
8942 Wilshre Blvd.
Beverly Hills, CA 90211
"Actress, Singer"

**Colby Chester**
5757 Wilshire Blvd. #473
Los Angeles, CA 90048
"Actor"

**Mark Chestnut**
1106 16th Avenue South
Nashville, TN 37212
"Singer"

**Morris Chestnut**
9830 Wilshire Blvd.
Beverly Hills, CA 90212
"Actor"

**Sam Chew, Jr.**
8075 West 3rd Street #303
Los Angeles, CA 90048
"Actor"

**Hank Cheyne**
3172 Dona Susana Drive
Studio City, CA 91604
"Actor"

**Michael Chiklis**
4310 Sutton Place
Sherman Oaks, CA 91413
"Actor"

**Julia Child**
103 Irving Street
Cambridge, MA 02138
"TV Personality"

**Linden Chiles**
2521 Skyline
Topanga, CA 90290
"Actor"

**Lois Chiles**
9200 Sunset Blvd. #1130
Los Angeles, CA 90069
"Actress"

**Jacques Chirac**
Palais de l'Elysses
55 rue du Faubourg-St.-Honore
F-75008 Paris FRANCE
"President of France"

**Shirley Chisholm**
3344 Newbliss Circle
Ormond Beach, FL 32174
"Politician"

**Joey Chitwood**
4410 West Alva Street
Tampa, FL 33614
"Race Car Driver"

**Anna Chlumsky**
641 West Lake Street #402
Chicago, IL 60661
"Actress"

**Margaret Cho**
1815 Butler Avenue #120
Los Angeles, CA 90025
"Actress"

**Chocolate Milk**
P.O. Box 82
Great Neck, NY 11021
"R&B Group"

**David Chokachi**
11433 Berwick Street
Los Angeles, CA 90049
"Actor"

**Rae Dawn Chong**
4526 Wilshire Blvd.
Los Angeles, CA 90010
"Actress"

**Thomas Chong**
1625 Casale Road
Pacific Palisades, CA 90272
"Actor, Writer, Director"

**Deepak Chopra**
948 Granvis Altamira
Palos Verdes, CA 90274
"Author"

**Raymond Chow**
23 Barker Road
Craigside Mansion #5B
HONG KONG (BCC)
"Film Director"

**Jean Chretien**
24 Sussex Drive
Ottawa, Ontario
K1M OMS CANADA
"Prime Minister"

**Hayden Christensen**
P.O. Box 2459
San Rafeal, CA 94912
"Actor"

**Helena Christensen**
43 King Street
London WC2E 8JS ENGLAND
"Model, Actress"

**Todd Christensen**
991 Sunburst Lane
Alpine, UT 84004
"ex-Football Player"

**Claudia Christian**
8491 Sunset Blvd. #140
Los Angeles, CA 90069
"Actress"

**Julie Christie**
23 Linden Gardens
London W2 4HD ENGLAND
"Actress"

**Lou Christie**
P.O. Box 2172
Hillside Manor, NY 11040
"Singer"

**Dennis Christopher**
5757 Wilshire Blvd. #473
Los Angeles, CA 90036
"Actor"

**Warren Christopher**
1701 Coldwater Canyon
Beverly Hills, CA 90210
"Ex-Secretary of State"

**William Christopher**
10100 Santa Monica Blvd. #2490
Los Angeles, CA 90067
"Actor"

**Connie Chung**
c/o CNN
5 Pennsylvania Plaza
New York, NY 10109
"News Correspondent"

**Thomas Haden Church**
15260 Ventura Blvd. #1040
Sherman Oaks, CA 91403
"Actor"

**Eddie Cibrian**
4434-C Moorpark Way
Toluca Lake, CA 91602
"Actor"

**"Cicciolina"**
Via Cassia 1818
I-00123 Rome ITALY
"Actress, Politician"

**Joseph Cicippio**
2107 - 3rd Street
Norristown, PA 19401
"Ex-Hostage"

**Michael Cimino**
9015 Alta Cedro
Beverly Hills, CA 90210
"Writer, Producer"

**Cinderella**
9200 Susnet Blvd. #2500
Los Angeles, CA 90067
"Rock & Roll Group"

**Charles Cioffi**
10100 Santa Monica Blvd. #2500
Los Angeles, CA 90067
"Actor"

**Liz Claiborne**
650 Fifth Avenue
New York, NY 10019
"Fashion Designer"

**Clancy Brothers**
177 Woodland Avenue
Westwood, NJ 07675
"Folk Group"

**Tom Clancy**
1638 Lee Drive
Edgewater, MD 20137
"Novelist"

**Gordon Clapp**
9300 Wilshire Blvd. #555
Beverly Hills, CA 90212
"Actor"

**Eric Clapton**
46 Kensington Court
London W8 5DP ENGLAND
"Singer, Guitarist"

**Jillian Clare**
859 Hollywood Way #344
Burbank, CA 91505
"Actress"

**Candy Clark**
13775-A Mono Way #220
Sonora, CA 95370
"Actress"

**Dick Clark**
3003 West Olive Avenue
Burbank, CA 91505
"Ex-TV Show Host, Producer"

**Doran Clark**
6399 Wilshire Blvd. #414
Los Angeles, CA 90048
"Actress"

**Joe Clark**
707-7th Avenue SW #1300
Calgary, Alb. T2P 3H6 CANADA
"Ex-Prime Minister"

**Marcia Clark**
4343 Lankershim Blvd.
Universal City, CA 91602
"Attorney"

**Mary Higgins Clark**
210 Central Park South
New York, NY 10019
"Writer"

**Oliver Clark**
2781 La Castana Drive
Los Angeles, CA 90046
"Actor"

**Petula Clark**
15 Chemin Rieu, CH-1208
Geneva SWITZERLAND
"Singer, Actress"

**Ramsey Clark**
36 East 12th Street
New York, NY 10003
"Politician"

**Roy Clark**
1800 Forrest Blvd.
Tulsa, OK 74114
"Singer, Guitarist"

**Susan Clark**
7943 Woodrow Wilson Drive
Los Angeles, CA 90046
"Actress"

**General Wesley K. Clark**
GTN
150 Fifth Avenue
New York, NY 10011
"Military Leader"

**Will Clark**
1000 Papworth Avenue
Metairie, LA 70005
"Baseball Player"

**Angela Clarke**
7557 Mulholland Drive
Los Angeles, CA 90046
"Actress"

**Arthur C. Clarke**
25 Barnes Place
Colombo 7 SRI LANKA
"Author"

**Bob Clarke**
127 Rivershore Drive
Seaford, DE 19973
"Cartoonist"

**Brian Patrick Clarke**
333-D Kenwood
Burbank, CA 91505
"Actor"

**Stanley Clarke**
9200 Sunset Blvd. #900
Los Angeles, CA 90069
"Guitarist, Composer"

**Patricia Clarkson**
1741 North Ivar Street
Hollywood, CA 90028
"Actress"

**Robert Clary**
10001 Sun Dial Lane
Beverly Hills, CA 90210
"Actor"

**The Clash**
268 Camden Road
London NW1 ENGLAND
"Rock & Roll Group"

**Andrew Dice Clay**
836 North La Cienega Blvd. #202
Los Angeles, CA 90069
"Comedian, Actor"

**Jill Clayburgh**
P.O. Box 432
Lakeville, CT 06039
"Actress"

**Jane Clayson**
524 West 57th Street
New York, NY 10019
"TV Show Host"

**John Cleese**
115 Hazlebury Road
London SW6 2LX ENGLAND
"Actor, Writer"

**Roger Clemens**
11535 Quall Hollow
Houston, TX 77024
"Baseball Player"

**David Clennon**
954 - 20th Street #B
Santa Monica, CA 90403
"Actor"

**Van Cliburn**
455 Wilder Place
Shreveport, LA 71104
"Pianist"

**Jimmy Cliff**
51 Lady Musgrove Road
Kingston JAMAICA
"Singer"

**Linda Clifford**
1560 Broadway #1308
New York, NY 10036
"Singer"

**Eleanor Clift**
1750 Pennsylvania Ave. N.W.
Suite #1220
Washington, DC 20001
"News Correspondent"

**Debra Clinger**
1206 Chickasaw Drive
Brentwood, TN 37027
"Actress"

**Bill Clinton**
15 Old House Lance
Chappaqua, NY 10413
"Ex-President of United States"

**Chelsea Clinton**
15 Old House Lane
Chappaqua, NY 10514
"Daughter of the President"

**Hillary Rodham-Clinton**
15 Old House Lance
Chappaqua, NY 10413
"Senator"

**Roger Clinton**
22616 Juniper Avenue
Torrance, CA 90505
Former President's Brother"

**John Clive**
4 Court Lodge, Chelsea
London SW3 AJA ENGLAND
"Actor, Writer"

**Kristen Cloke**
1450 South Robertson Blvd.
Los Angeles, CA 90035
"Actress"

**George Clooney**
10866 Wilshire Blvd., #1100
Los Angeles, CA 90024
"Actor"

**Glenn Close**
9830 Wilshire Blvd.
Beverly Hills, CA 90212
"Actress"

**The Coasters**
1780 SW McAllister Lane
Port St. Lucie, FL 34953
"Vocal Group"

**Phyllis Coates**
P.O. Box 1969
Boyes Hot Springs, CA 95416
"Actress"

**Dan Coats**
1300 South Harrison Street #3158
Ft. Wayne, IN 46802
"Politician"

**Julie Cobb**
1801 Avenue of the Stars #902
Los Angeles, CA 90067
"Actress"

**Hank Cochran**
350 Hunter's Lane
Hendersonville, TN 37075
"Singer, Songwriter"

**Johnnie Cochran, Jr.**
4929 Wilshire Blvd., Suite #1010
Los Angeles, CA 90010
"Attorney"

**Bruce Cockburn**
1775 Broadway #501
New York, NY 10019
"Singer, Songwriter"

**Joe Cocker**
16830 Ventura Blvd. #501
Encino, CA 91436
"Singer"

**David Allan Coe**
783 Rippling Creek
Nixa, MO 65714
"Singer, Songwriter"

**Sebastian Coe**
Starswood
High Barn Road
Effingham
Leatherhead KT24 5PW EN-
GLAND
"Runner"

**Susie Coelho**
3500 West Olive Avenue #1400
Burbank, CA 91505
"Actress, Model"

**Joel Coen**
9560 Wilshire Blvd. #516
Beverly Hills, CA 90212
"Film Director"

**Paul Coffey**
633 Hawthorne Street
Birmingham, MI 48009
"Hockey Player"

**Frank "Junior" Coghlan**
28606 Rey Court
Saugus, CA 95062
"Actor"

**Larry Cohen**
2111 Coldwater Canyon
Beverly Hills, CA 90210
"Writer, Producer"

**Leonard Cohen**
121 Leslie Street
No. York, Ontario
M3C 2J9 CANADA
"Singer, Songwriter"

**Sasha Cohen**
c/o Ice Palace
13211 Brooks Drive #A
Baldwin Park, CA 91706
"Ice Skater"

**Dennis Cole**
13701 Riverside drive #201
Sherman Oaks, CA 91423
"Actor"

**Gary Cole**
1122 S. Robertson Blvd. #15
Los Angeles, CA 90035
"Actor"

**George Cole**
Donnelly
Newham Hill Bottom
Nettleford Oxon, ENGLAND
"Actor"

**Michael Cole**
6332 Costello Avenue
Van Nuys, CA 91401
"Actor"

**Mrs. Marie Cole**
South House
Tyringham, MA 01264
"Widow of Nat Cole"

**Natalie Cole**
1801 Avenue of the Stars #1105
Los Angeles, CA 90067
"Singer"

**Tina Cole**
1540 Castec Drive
Sacremento, CA 95864
"Actress"

**Dabney Coleman**
360 North Kenter Avenue
Los Angeles, CA 90049
"Actor"

**Durell Coleman**
800 S. Robertson Blvd. #5
Los Angeles, CA 90035
"Actor"

**Gary Coleman**
4710 Don Miguel Drive
Los Angeles, CA 90008
"Actor"

**Jack Coleman**
11333 Moorpark Street #PMB 156
Studio City, CA 91602
"Actor"

**Lisa Coleman**
3575 Cahuenga Blvd. #450
Hollywood, CA 90068
"Actress"

**Margaret Colin**
130 West 42nd Street, #612
New York, NY 10036
"Actress"

**Toni Collette**
Box 478, Kings Cross
2011 NSW AUSTRALIA
"Actress"

**Mark Collie**
3017 Poston Avenue
Nashville, TN 37203
"Guitarist"

**Clifton C. Collins, Jr.**
1505 10th Street
Santa Monica, CA 90401
"Actor"

**Gary Collins**
2751 Hutton Drive
Beverly Hills, CA 90210
"Actor, TV Show Host"

**Jackie Collins**
P.O. Box 3717
Redondo Beach, CA 90277
"TV Show Host, Author"

**Joan Collins**
9255 Doheny Road
Los Angeles, CA 90069
"Actress, Producer"

**Judy Collins**
450 Seventh Avenue #603
New York, NY 10123
"Singer"

**Kate Collins**
1410 York Avenue #4-D
New York, NY 10021
"Actress"

**Lewis Collins**
15 Maiden Lane
London WC2 7NG ENGLAND
"Actor"

**Marva Collins**
4146 West Chicago Avenue
Chicago, IL 60651
"Educator"

**Phil Collins**
252-260 Regent Street
London W1B 3BX ENGLAND
"Singer, Drummer"

**Stephen Collins**
10390 Santa Monica Blvd. #300
Los Angeles, CA 90025
"Actor"

**Sen. Susan Collins (ME)**
Senate Russell Building #172
Washington, DC 20510
"Politicain"

**Scott Colomby**
1425 N. Queens Road
Los Angeles, CA 90069
"Actor"

**Miriam Colon**
51 West 52nd Street
New York, NY 10019
"Actress"

**Color Me Badd**
9850 Sandalfoot Blvd. #458
Boca Raton, FL 33428
"Music Group"

**Charles Colson**
P.O. Box 17500
Washington, DC 20041
"Author"

**Jessie Colter**
1117-17th Avenue South
Nashville, TN 37212
"Singer"

**Chi Coltrane**
5955 Tuxedo Terrace
Los Angeles, CA 90068
"Singer"

**Robbie Coltrane**
19 Sydney Mews
London SW3 6HL ENGLAND
"Actor"

**Franco Columbu**
1732 South Sepulveda Blvd.
Los Angeles, CA 90064
"Actor, Bodybuilder"

**Chris Columbus**
P.O. Box 3000
Leavesden, Waterford
WD25 7LT ENGLAND
"Screenwriter"

**Nadia Comaneci**
3214 Bart Conner Drive
Norman, OK 73072
"Gymnast"

**Holly Marie Combs**
1120 South Robertson Blvd. #15
Los Angeles, CA 90035
"Actress"

**Jeffrey Combs**
1875 Century Park East #2250
Los Angeles, CA 90067
"Actor"

**Sean "P Diddy" Combs**
1540 Broadway, 30th Floor
New York, NY 10036
"Rap Singer"

**Paul Comi**
2395 Ridgeway Road
San Marino, CA 91108
"Actor"

**Cristi Conaway**
334 Huntley Drive
Los Angeles, CA 90048
"Actress"

**Jeff Conaway**
4519 Greenbush Avenue
Sherman Oaks, CA 91423
"Actor"

**Dave Conception**
Urb. Los Caobos Botalon 5d
Piso-Maracay 5 VENEZUELA
"Ex-Baseball Player"

**Gary A. Condit**
2509 Acorn Lane
Ceres, CA 95307
"Former US Congressman"

**David Cone**
17080 Harbour point Drive
Ft. Myers, FL 33908
"Baseball Player"

**Gino Conforti**
1440 Veteran Avenue #603
Los Angeles, CA 90024
"Actor"

**John Conlee**
38 Music Square East #117
Nashville, TN 37203
"Singer, Songwriter"

**Darlene Conley**
7800 Beverly Blvd. #3371
Los Angeles, CA 90036
"Actress"

**Earl Thomas Conley**
657 Baker Road
Smyrna, TN 37167
"Singer, Songwriter"

**Joe Conley**
P.O. Box 6487
Thousand Oaks, CA 91359
"Actor"

**Didi Conn**
1901 Ave. of the Stars #1450
Los Angeles, CA 90067
"Actress"

**Terri Conn**
1268 East 14th Street
Brooklyn, NY 11230
"Actress"

**Jennifer Connelly**
8942 Wilshire Blvd.
Beverly Hills, CA 90211
"Actress"

**Bart Conner**
3214 Bart Conner Drive
Norman, OK 73072
"Athlete"

**Dennis Conner**
1011 Anchorage Lane
San Diego, CA 92106
"Yachtsman"

**Jason Connery**
5410 Wilshire Blvd. #708
Los Angeles, CA 90036
"Actor"

**Harry Connick, Jr.**
323 Broadway
Cambridge, MA 02139
"Pianist, Singer"

**Billy Connolly**
The Boat House
Crabtree Lane
London SW6 6LU ENGLAND
"Actor"

**Patrick Connor**
3 Spring Bank
New Mills nr. Stockport
SK12 4AS ENGLAND
"Actor"

**Carol Connors**
1709 Ferrari Drive
Beverly Hills, CA 90210
"Songwriter"

**Jimmy Connors**
1962 East Valley Road
Santa Barbara, CA 93108
"Tennis Player"

**Mike Connors**
4810 Louise Avenue
Encino, CA 91316
"Actor"

**Barnaby Conrad**
3530 Pine Valley Drive
Sarasota, FL 34239
"Author, Painter"

**Kimberly Conrad**
10236 Charing Cross Road
Los Angeles, CA 90077
"Mrs. Hugh Hefner"

**Paul Conrad**
28649 Crestridge Road
Palos Verdes, CA 90274
"Cartoonist"

**Robert Conrad**
11300 West Olympic Blvd. #610
Los Angeles, CA 90064
"Actor, Writer"

**Shane Conrad**
9255 Sunset Blvd. #620
Los Angeles, CA 90069
"Actor"

**Kevin Conroy**
9301 Wilshire Blvd. #312
Beverly Hills, CA 90210
"Actor"

**John Considine**
10100 Santa Monica Blvd. #2490
Los Angeles, CA 90067
"Actor, Writer"

**Tim Considine**
3708 Mountain View Avenue
Los Angeles, CA 90066
"Actor, Writer, Director"

**Michel Constantin**
17 Blvd. Bartole Beauvallon
83120 Sainte Maxime, FRANCE
"Actor"

**Ex-King Constantine**
4 Linnell Drive
Hampstead Way
London NW11 ENGLAND
"Royalty"

**Michael Constantine**
1604 Bern Street
Reading, PA 19604
"Actor"

**John Conte**
75600 Beryl Drive
Indian Wells, CA 92260
"Actor"

**Bill Conti**
117 Fremont Place
Los Angeles, CA 90005
"Composer, Arranger"

**Tom Conti**
123a Kings Road
London SW3 4PL ENGLAND
"Actor"

**Frank Converse**
10100 Santa Monica Blvd. #2490
Los Angeles, CA 90067
"Actor"

**Gary Conway**
11240 Chimney Rock Road
Paso Robles, CA 93446
"Actor"

**Kevin Conway**
25 Central Park West
New York, NY 10023
"Actor"

**Tim Conway**
P.O. Box 17047
Encino, CA 91416
"Actor, Director"

**Rep. John Conyers (MI)**
House Rayburn Bldg. #2426
Washington, DC 20515
"Politician"

**Ry Cooder**
326 Entrada Drive
Santa Monica, CA 90402
"Guitarist, Songwriter"

**Carole Cook**
8829 Ashcroft Avenue
Los Angeles, CA 90048
"Actress"

**Fielder Cook**
180 Central Park South
New York, NY 10019
"TV Writer, Producer"

**Robin Cook**
4601 Gulf Shore Blvd. #P4
Naples, FL 33940
"Screenwriter"

**Alistair Cook**
Nassau Point
Cutchogue, NY 11935
"Journalist, TV Announcer"

**Danny Cooksey**
9460 Wilshire Blvd. #300
Beverly Hills, CA 90212
"Singer"

**Peter Cookson**
30 Norfolk Road
Southfield, MA 01259
"Actor"

**Dr. Denton Cooley**
3014 Del Monte Drive
Houston, TX 77019
"Heart Surgeon"

**Jennifer Coolidge**
9465 Wilshire Blvd. #600
Beverly Hills, CA 90212
Actress"

**Martha Coolidge**
2129 Coldwater Canyon
Beverly Hills, CA 90210
"Director"

**Rita Coolidge**
11684 Ventura Blvd. #899
Studio City, CA 91604
"Singer, Actress"

**Coolio**
GLP, Huetteldorfstr. 259
Vienna 1140 AUSTRIA
"Singer"

**Pat Coombs**
5 Wendela Court
Harrow-On-The-Hill
Middlesex ENGLAND
"Actress"

**Gerry Cooney**
22501 Linden Blvd.
Jamaica, NY 11411
"Boxer"

**Alice Cooper**
4135 East Keim Drive
Paradise Valley, AZ 85253
"Singer, Songwriter"

**Chris Cooper**
9465 Wilshire Blvd. #212
Beverly Hills, CA 90210
"Actor"

**Henry Cooper**
5 Ledway Drive
Webley
Middlesex ENGLAND
"TV Personality"

**Jeanne Cooper**
8401 Edwin Drive
Los Angeles, CA 90046
"Actress"

**L. Gordon Cooper**
1338 Nathan Lane
Ventura, CA 93001
"Astronaut"

**Joan Copeland**
88 Central Park West
New York, NY 10023
"Actress"

**Stewart Copeland**
1 Water Lane
Camded Town
London NW1 8NZ ENGLAND
"Drummer"

**Teri Copley**
5003 Coldwater Canyon Avenue
Sherman Oaks, CA 91423
"Actress"

**David Copperfield**
11777 San Vicente Blvd. #601
Los Angeles, CA 90049
"Magician"

**Francis Coppola**
916 Kearny Street
San Francisco, CA 94133
"Writer, Producer"

**Gretchen Corbett**
1801 Avenue of the Stars #902
Los Angeles, CA 90067
"Actress"

**John Corbett**
1327 Brinkley Avenue
Los Angeles, CA 90049
"Actor"

**Michael Corbett**
8730 Sunset Blvd. #220
Los Angeles, CA 90069
"Actor"

**Ronnie Corbett**
57 Gt. Cumberland Place
London W1H 7LJ ENGLAND
"Comedian"

**Barry Corbin**
2113 Greta Lane
Ft. Worth, TX 76120
"Actor"

**Kevin Corcoran**
8617 Balcom
Northridge, CA 91325
"Actor"

**Mara Corday**
P.O. Box 800393
Valencia, CA 91355
"Actress"

**Angel Cordero**
P.O. Box 90
Jamaica, NY 11411
"Horse Jockey"

**Chick Corea**
2635 Griffith Park Blvd.
Los Angeles, CA 90039
"Musician"

**Angel Corella**
890 Broadway
New York, NY 10003
"Dancer"

**Al Corley**
3323 Corinth Avenue
Los Angeles, CA 90066
"Singer"

**Roger Corman**
11600 San Vicente Blvd.
Los Angeles, CA 90049
"Writer, Producer"

**Cornelius Bros. & Sister Rose**
2 Professional Drive, #240
Gaithersburg, TN 30879
"R&B Group"

**Don Cornelius**
600 Sanders Road
Birmingham, AL 35226
"TV Show Host"

**Helen Cornelius**
P.O. Box 121089
Nashville, TN 37212
"Singer"

**Don Cornell**
100 Bayview Drive #1521
North Miami, FL 33160
"Singer"

**Lydia Cornell**
8075 West Third Street #303
Los Angeles, CA 90048
"Actress, Model"

**Leanza Cornett**
3504 Grand View Blvd.
Los Angeles, CA 90066
"TV Show Host"

**Nick Cornish**
3393 Barham Blvd.
Los Angeles, CA 90068
"Actor"

**Georges Corraface**
1 rue Gueneguard
F-75006 Paris ENGLAND
"Actor"

**Adrienne Corri**
2-4 Noel Street
London W1V 3RB ENGLAND
"Actress"

**Bud Cort**
6500 Wilshire Blvd. #2200
Los Angeles, CA 90048
"Actor"

**Dan Cortese**
28873 Via Venezia
Malibu, CA 90265
"Actor"

**Joe Cortese**
4724 Poe Avenue
Woodland Hills, CA 91364
"Actor"

**Valentina Cortese**
Piazza Sant' Erasmo 9
I-20121 Milan, ITALY
"Actress"

**Norman Corwin**
c/o USC
3551 Ironside Parkway
Los Angeles, CA 90089
"Writer, Producer"

**Bill Cosby**
P.O. Box 4049
Santa Monica, CA 90411
"Actor, Comedian"

**Daniel Cosgrove**
3500 West Olive Avenue #920
Burbank, CA 91505
"Actress"

**Pierre Cosso**
13 Rue Madelieine Michelis 92200
Neuillly, FRANCE
"Film Producer"

**Mary Costa**
3340 Kingston Pike, Unit 1
Knoxville, TN 37919
"Soprano"

**Constantin Costa-Gavras**
244 rue Saint-Jacques
75005 Paris, FRANCE
"Filmwriter, Director"

**Midge Costanza**
11811 West Olympic Blvd.
Los Angeles, CA 90064
"Ex-President Aide"

**Bob Costas**
1100 Avenue of the Americas
New York, NY 10036
"Sportscaster"

**Elvis Costello**
125 Parkway
London NW1 1PS ENGLAND
"Singer"

**Mariclare Costello**
12250 Addison Street
Valley Village, CA 91607
"Actress"

**Nicholas Coster**
1624 North Gardner
Los Angeles, CA 90046
"Actor"

**Kevin Costner**
9830 Wilshire Blvd.
Beverly Hills, CA 90212
"Actor"

**David Coulier**
9150 Wilshire Blvd. #350
Beverly Hills, CA 90212
"Actor"

**Catherine Coulter**
P.O. Box 17
Mill Valley, CA 94942
"Authoress"

**Fred Couples**
5609 Cradlerock Circle
Plano, TX 75093
"Golfer"

**Katherine Couric**
30 Rockefeller Plaza #388-E
New York, NY 10112
"TV Show Host"

**Jim Courier**
1 Erieview Plaza #1300
Cleveland, OH 44114
"Tennis Player"

**Hazel Court-Taylor**
100 North Arlington #100
Reno, NV 89503
"Actress"

**Tom Courtenay**
13 Shorts Gardens
London SW15 1PW ENGLAND
"Actor"

**Jerome Courtland**
1837 Westleigh Drive
Glenview, IL 60025
"Film Director"

**Robin Cousins**
174-178 North Gower Street
London NW1 2NB ENGLAND
"Ice Skater"

**Jean-Michel Cousteau**
7 rue d'Estaing
F-75116 Paris FRANCE
"Underwater Explorer"

**Bob Cousy**
459 Salisbury Street
Worchester, MA 01609
"Basketball Player"

**Franklin Cover**
1422 North Sweetzer #402
Los Angeles, CA 90069
"Actor"

**Archibald Cox**
78 Condon Point Road
Brooksville, ME 04617
"Politician"

**Bobby Cox**
1575 Reids Ferry Way
Marietta, GA 30062
"Baseball Manager"

**Courteney Cox**
1122 S. Robertson Blvd. #15
Los Angeles, CA 90035
"Actress"

**Ronny Cox**
13948 Magnolia Blvd.
Sherman Oaks, CA 91423
"Actor, Film Producer"

**Peter Coyote**
774 Marin Drive
Mill Valley, CA 94941
"Actor"

**Cuffy Crabbe**
11216 North 74th Street
Scottsdale, AZ 85260
"Actor"

**Billy "Crash" Craddock**
P.O. Box 428
Portland, TN 37148
"Singer, Songwriter"

**Jenny Craig**
11355 North Torrey Pines Road
La Jolla, CA 92078
"Physical Fitness Director"

**Jim Craig**
15 Jyre Lane
North Easton, MA 02356
"Hockey Player"

**Wendy Craig**
29 Roehampton Gate
London SW15 5JR ENGLAND
"Actress"

**Yvonne Craig**
P.O. Box 827
Pacific Palisades, CA 90272
"Actress"

**Jeanne Crain**
1029 Arbolado Road
Santa Barbara, CA 93103
"Actress"

**Douglass Cramer**
738 Sarbonne Road
Los Angeles, CA 90077
"TV Writer, Producer"

**Barbara Crampton**
8436 West Third Street #740
Los Angeles, CA 90048
"Actress"

**Gemma Craven**
42 Hazelbury Road
London SW6 2ND ENGLAND
"Actress"

**Matt Craven**
5033 Campo Road
Woodland Hills, CA 91364
"Actor"

**Wes Craven**
7920 Sunset Blvd.
Los Angeles, CA 90069
"Writer, Producer"

**Christina Crawford**
7 Springs Farm Sanders Road
Tensed, ID 83870
"Authoress"

**Cindy Crawford**
1122 South Robertson Blvd. #15
Los Angeles, CA 90035
"Model"

**Johnny Crawford**
2440 El Contento Drive
Los Angeles, CA 90068
"Actor"

**Michael Crawford**
114 St. Martin's Lane
London WC2N 4BE ENGLAND
"Actor"

**Randy Crawford**
1924 Spring Street
Paso Robles, CA 93446
"Singer"

**Robert Cray**
P.O. Box 170429
San Francisco, CA 94117
"Band Leader"

**Ben Crenshaw**
1800 Nueces Street
Austin, TX 78701
"Golfer"

**Marshall Crenshaw**
110 W. 57th Street #300
New York, NY 10019
"Singer, Songwriter"

**The Crew-Cuts**
29 Cedar Street
Creskill, NJ 07626
"Vocal Group"

**Michael Crichton**
433 N. Camden Drive #500
Beverly Hills, CA 90210
"Filmwriter, Director"

**The Cricketts**
2 Music Circle South #212
Nashville, TN 37203
"Rock & Roll Group"

**Peter Criss**
4905 S. Atlanta Avenue
Daytona Beach, FL 32127
"Drummer, Singer"

**Judith Crist**
180 Riverside Drive
New York, NY 10024
"Film Critic"

**Linda Cristal**
9129 Hazen Drive
Beverly Hills, CA 90210
"Actress"

**James Cromwell**
1801 Avenue of the Stars #902
Los Angeles, CA 90067
"Actor"

**David Cronenberg**
217 Avenue Road
Toronto, Ontario
M5R 2J3 CANADA
"Film Writer, Director"

**Regina Cronenweth**
5410 Wilshire Blvd. #227
Los Angeles, CA 90036
"Actress"

**Walter Cronkite**
51 West 52nd Street #1934
New York, NY 10019
"Broadcast Journalist"

**Hume Cronyn**
40 West 57th Street
New York, NY 10019
"Actor"

**Annette Crosbie**
76 Oxford Street
London W1D 1BS ENGLAND
"Actress"

**Cathy Lee Crosby**
1223 Wilshire Blvd. #404
Santa Monica, CA 90403
"Actress"

**David Crosby**
P.O. Box 9008
Solvang, CA 93464
"Singer, Songwriter"

**Denise Crosby**
8242 Blackburn Avenue
Los Angeles, CA 90048
"Actor"

**Mrs. Kathryn Crosby**
P.O. Box 85
Genda, NV 89411
"Widower of Bing Crosby"

**Norm Crosby**
5750 Wilshire Blvd. #580
Los Angeles, CA 90036
"Comedian, Actor"

**Philip Crosby**
21801 Providencia
Woodland Hills, CA 91364
"Actor"

**Ben Cross**
13 Randor Walk
London SW3 4BP ENGLAND
"Actor"

**Christopher Cross**
P.O. Box 5156
Santa Barbara, CA 93150
"Singer, Songwriter"

**Marcia Cross**
10340 Santa Monica Blvd. #2500
Los Angeles, CA 90025
"Actress"

**Andrae Crouch**
20265 Wells Drive
Woodland Hills, CA 91364
"Singer"

**Lindsay Crouse**
15115 1/2 Sunset Blvd. #A
Pacific Palisades, CA 90272
"Actress"

**Sheryl Crow**
10345 West Olympic Blvd., #200
Los Angeles, CA 90064
"Singer"

**Cameron Crowe**
1016 Amalfi Drive
Pacific Palisades, CA 90272
"Filmwriter, Producer"

**Rodney Crowell**
4405 Belmont Park Terrace
Nashville, TN 37215
"Singer, Songwriter"

**Mart Crowley**
8955 Beverly Blvd.
Los Angeles, CA 90048
"Writer"

**Billy Crudup**
9830 Wilshire Blvd.
Beverly Hills, CA 90212
"Actor"

**Tom Cruise**
8500 Wilshire Blvd. #700
Beverly Hills, CA 90211
"Actor"

**Denny Crumm**
12038 Hunting Crest Road
Prospect, KY 40059
"ex-Basketball Coach"

**Brandon Cruz**
706 Pismo Court
San Diego, CA 92109
"Actor"

**Jon Cryer**
9560 Wilshire Blvd. #500
Beverly Hills, CA 90212
"Actor"

**Billy Crystal**
151 El Camino Drive
Beverly Hills, CA 90212
"Actor"

**Kieran Culkin**
9830 Wilshire Blvd.
Beverly Hills, CA 90212
"Actor"

**Macaulay Culkin**
704 Broadway
New York, NY 10003
"Actor"

**Brett Cullen**
2229 Glyndon Avenue
Venice, CA 90291
"Actor"

**Robert Culp**
2260 Bowmont Drive
Beverly Hills, CA 90210
"Actor, Writer, Director"

**Michael Culver**
29 Tibbets Close
London SW19 6EF ENGLAND
"Actor"

**Molly Culver**
2658 Griffith Park Blvd. #284
Los Angeles, CA 90039
"Actress"

**Randall Cunningham**
2035 Helm
Las Vegas, NV 89119
"Football Player"

**ex Secy. Andrew Cuomo**
787 Seventh Avenue
New York, NY 10019
"ex-Government Official"

**Mario Cuomo**
50 Sutton Place So. #11-G
New York, NY 10022
"Ex-Governor"

**Mike Curb**
3907 West Alameda Avenue
Burbank, CA 91505
"Record Producer"

**The Cure**
133 West 25th Street
5th Floor
New York, NY 10001
"Rock & Roll Band"

**Kevin Curren**
5808 Back Court
Austin, TX 78764
"Tennis Player"

**Cherie Currie**
3050 North Chandelle Road
Los Angeles, CA 90046
"Singer"

**Louise Currie**
1317 Del Resto Drive
Beverly Hills, CA 90210
"Actress"

**Mark Curry**
9200 Sunset Blvd. #900
Los Angeles, CA 90069
"Actor"

**Jane Curtin**
P.O. Box 1070
Sharon, CT 06069
"Actress"

**Valerie Curtin**
15622 Meadowgate Road
Encino, CA 91316
"Actress, Writer"

**Dan Curtis**
143 S. Rockingham Avenue
Los Angeles, CA 90049
"Actor"

**Jamie Lee Curtis**
955 South Carrillo Drive #200
Los Angeles, CA 90048
"Actress"

**Tony Curtis**
2778 Scotts Valley Drive
Henderson, NV 89052
"Actor, Director"

**Vondie Curtis-Hall**
9465 Wilshire Blvd. #650
Beverly Hills, CA 90212
"Actor"

**Joan Cusack**
8500 Wilshire Blvd. #700
Beverly Hills, CA 90211
"Actress"

**John Cusack**
321 North Clark Street #3400
Chicago, IL 60610
"Actor"

**Clive Cussier**
P.O. Box 5059
Scottsdale, AZ 85261
"Novelist"

**Lise Cutter**
4526 Wilshire Blvd.
Los Angeles, CA 90010
"Actress"

**Jon Cypher**
9229 Sunset Blvd. #315
Los Angeles, CA 90069
"Actor"

**Billy Ray Cyrus**
309 - 10th Avenue #120
Nashville, TN 37203
"Singer"

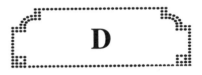

**Da Brat**
685 Lambert Drive, NE
Atlanta, GA 30324
"Singer"

**Augusta Dabney**
North Mountain Road
Dobbs Ferry, NY 10522
"Actress"

**Maryan d'Abo**
32 Tavistock Street
London WC2E 7PB ENGLAND
"Actress"

**Olivia d'Abo**
1122 S. Robertson Blvd. #15
Los Angeles, CA 90035
"Actress"

**Mark Dacascos**
P.O. Box 1549
Studio City, CA 91604
"Actor"

**Tim Daggett**
1750 East Boulder Street
Colorado Springs, CO 80909
"Gymnast"

**Arlene Dahl**
P.O. Box 116
Sparkill, NY 10976
"Actress"

**Eva Dahlbeck**
Box 27126
102 52 Stockholm SWEDEN
"Actress"

**Bill Dailey**
1331 Park Avenue SW.
Albuquerque, NM 87104
"Actor"

**Janet Dailey**
1947 Lakeshore Drive
Branson, MO 65616
"Author"

**Elizabeth Daily**
1122 "B" Street #308
Hayward, CA 94541
"Actress"

**John Dalancie**
1313 Brunswick Avenue
South Pasadena, CA 91030
"Actor"

**Dick Dale**
P.O. Box 1713
Twenty Nine Palms, CA 92277
"Singer, Guitarist"

**Jim Dale**
28 Berkeley Square
London W1X 6HD ENGLAND
"Actor"

**The Dalai Lama**
Thekchen Choling
McLeod Gunji, Hangra Dist.
Himachal Pradesh, INDIA
"Religious Leader"

**Richard M. Daley**
121 North Main Street
Chicago, IL 60602
"Mayor of Chicago"

**Dallas Cowboys Cheerleaders**
1 Cowboy Parkway
Irving, TX 75063
"Cheerleading Team"

**Joe Dallesandro**
521 West Briar Place #505
Chicago, IL 60657
"Actor"

**Abby Dalton**
P.O. Box 100
Mammoth Lakes, CA 93546
"Actress"

**Audrey Dalton**
22461 Labrusca
Mission Viejo, CA 92692
"Actress"

**Lacy J. Dalton**
820 Cartwright Road
Reno, NV 89511
"Singer"

**Timothy Dalton**
76 Oxford Street
London W1N OAX ENGLAND
"Actor"

**Roger Daltry**
18/21 Jermyn Street #300
London SW1Y 6HP ENGLAND
"Singer, Actor"

**Carson Daly**
9701 Wilshire Blvd., 10th Floor
Beverly Hills, CA 90212
"MTV Personality"

**John Daly**
112 TPC Blvd.
Ponte Verde Beach, FL 32082
"Golfer"

**Rad Daly**
5670 Wilshire Blvd. #820
Los Angeles, CA 90048
"Actor"

**Timothy Daly**
11718 Barrington Court #252
Los Angeles, CA 90049
"Actor"

**Tyne Daly**
272 South Lasky Drive #402
Beverly Hills, CA 90212
"Actress"

**Jacques D'Amboise**
594 Broadway #805
New York, NY 10012
"Choreographer"

**Michael Damian**
3500 W. Olive Avenue #1400
Burbank, CA 91505
"Actor"

**Marcus D'Amico**
26 Ashwood Mews
London SW7 4DE ENGLAND
"Actor"

**Mark Damon**
2781 Benedict Canyon
Beverly Hills, CA 90210
"Actor"

**Stuart Damon**
367 North Van Ness Avenue
Los Angeles, CA 90004
"Actor"

**Vic Damone**
25864 Tournament Road #L
Valencia, CA 91355
"Singer"

**Bill Dana**
P.O. Box 1792
Santa Monica, CA 90406
"Actor, Comedian"

**Justin Dana**
16830 Ventura Blvd. #300
Encino, CA 91436
"Actor"

**Charles Dance**
76 Oxford Street
London W1D 1BS ENGLAND
"Actor"

**Eric Dane**
8899 Beverly Blvd. #510
Los Angeles, CA 90048
"Actor"

**Claire Danes**
9 Desbrosses Street #200
New York, NY 10013
"Actress"

**Shera Danese**
1801 Avenue of the Stars #902
Los Angeles, CA 90067
"Actress"

**Beverly D'Angelo**
301 West 57th Street #16C
New York, NY 10017
"Actress"

**Rodney Dangerfield**
10580 Wilshire Blvd. #21-NE
Los Angeles, CA 90024
"Comedian, Actor"

**Charlie Daniels**
14410 Central Pike
Mt. Juliet, TN 37122
"C&W Group"

**Erin Daniels**
1122 S. Roxbury Drive
Los Angeles, CA 90035
"Actress"

**Jeff Daniels**
137 Park Street
Chelsea, MI 48118
"Actor"

**Margaret Truman Daniels**
830 Park Avenue
New York, NY 10021
"Daughter of Pres. Truman"

**William Daniels**
12805 Hortense Street
Studio City, CA 91604
"Actor"

**Nicholas Daniloff**
2400 "N" Street NW
Washington, DC 20037
"News Correspondent"

**Sybil Danning**
1438 North Gower Street
Bldg. 35, Box 5, #171
Los Angeles, CA 90028
"Actress"

**Danny & The Juniors**
P.O. Box 1017
Turnersville, NJ 08012
"Vocal Group"

**Linda Dano**
1010 Nautilus
Mamaroneck, NY 10543
Actress"

**Ted Danson**
955 South Carrillo Drive #300
Los Angeles, CA 90048
"Actor"

**Joe Dante**
2321 Holly Drive
Los Angeles, CA 90068
"Film Director"

**Tony Danza**
151 El Camino Drive
Beverly Hills, CA 90212
"Actor"

**Mariah D'Aprile**
1268 East 14th Street
Brooklyn, NY 11230
"Actress"

**Patti D'Arbanville**
125 Main Avenue
Sea Cliff, NY 11579
"Actress"

**Terence Trent D'Arby**
10 Great Marlborough Street
London W1V 2LP ENGLAND
"Singer"

**Mireille Darc**
78 Blvd. Malesherbes
75008 Paris FRANCE
"Actress"

**Georgine Darcy**
7044 Los Tilos Road
Los Angeles, CA 90068
"Actress"

**Christopher Darden**
5215 Shenandoah Avenue
Los Angeles, CA 90056
"Attorney"

**Alvin Dark**
103 Cranberry Way
Easley, SC 29640
"Ex-Baseball Player"

**Johnny Dark**
1100 North Alta Loma #707
Los Angeles, CA 90069
"Comedian"

**Jennifer Darling**
P.O. Box 57593
Sherman Oaks, CA 91403
"Actress"

**Joan Darling**
P.O. Box 6700
Tesuque, NM 87574
"Writer, Director"

**Ron Darling**
19 Woodland Street
Millbury, MA 01527
"Baseball Player"

**James Darren**
P.O. Box 1088
Beverly Hills, CA 90213
"Actor, Singer"

**Danielle Darrieux**
1 Rue Alfred de Vingnu
F-75008 Paris, FRANCE
"Actress"

**Henry Darrow**
10561 Missouri Avenue #1
Los Angeles, CA 90025
"Actor"

**Mark Dacasos**
P.O. Box 1549
Studio City, CA 91604
"Actor"

**Sen. Tom Daschle (SD)**
509 Hart Office Buliding
Washington, DC 20510
"Politician"

**Sam Dash**
110 Newlands
Chevy Chase, MD 20815
"Watergate Participate"

**Jules Dassin**
8 Athinalon Efivon St.
Athens 11521 GREECE
"Actor, Director"

**Brad Daugherty**
2923 Streetsboro Road
Richfield, OH 44286
"Basketball Player"

**Elyssa Davalos**
2934 1/2 Beverly Glen Circle #53
Los Angeles, CA 90077
"Actress"

**Richard Davalos**
2311 Vista Gordo Road
Los Angeles, CA 90048
"Actor, Director"

**Nigel Davenport**
2 Condult Street
London W1R 9TG ENGLAND
"Actor"

**Robert Davi**
10044 Calvin Avenue
Northridge, CA 91324
"Actor"

**Marty Davich**
1044 Armada Drive
Pasadena, CA 91103
"Actor"

**Craig David**
21 Heathermans Road, Unit F
London SW6 4TJ ENGLAND
"Singer"

**Hal David**
12711 Ventura Blvd. #420
Studio City, CA 91604
"Lyricist"

**Joanna David**
25 Maida Avenue
London W2 ENGLAND
"Actress"

**Keith David**
1134 West 105th St.
Los Angeles, CA 90044
"Actor"

**Lolita Davidovich**
15200 Friends Street
Pacific Palisades, CA 90272
"Actress"

**Doug Davidson**
c/o CBS/Y&R
7800 Beverly Blvd. #3305
Los Angeles, CA 90036
"Actor"

**Eileen Davidson**
11300 West Olympic Blvd. #610
Los Angeles, CA 90064
"Actress"

**Gordon Davidson**
165 Mabery Road
Santa Monica, CA 90406
"Film Director"

**John Davidson Jr.**
21243 Ventura Blvd. #101
Woodland Hills, CA 91364
"Singer, Actor"

**Tommy Davidson**
3800 Weslin Avenue
Sherman Oaks, CA 91423
"Actor"

**Embeth Davidtz**
9465 Wilshire Blvd. #820
Beverly Hills, CA 90212
"Actress"

**Geraint Wyn Davies**
438 Queen Street East
Toronto, Ont. M5A 1T4 CANADA
"Actor"

**Lane Davies**
P.O. Box 2053
Thousand Oaks, CA 91358
"Actor"

**Tamara Davies**
c/o CBS/B&B
7800 Beverly Blvd. #3371
Los Angeles, CA 90036
"Actress"

**Al Davis**
1220 Harbor Bay Parkway
Alameda, CA 94502
"Football Team Owner"

**Ann B. Davis**
23315 Eagle Gap
San Antonio, TX 78255
"Actress"

**Billy Davis, Jr.**
P.O. Box 7905
Beverly Hills, CA 90212
"Singer"

**Clifton Davis**
9200 Sunset Blvd. #900
Los Angeles, CA 90069
"Actor, Clergyman"

**Gov. Gray Davis (CA)**
999 N. Doheny Drive, #803
Los Angeles, CA 90069
"Politician"

**Hope Davis**
574 West End Avenue, #4
New York, NY 10024
"Actress"

**Geena Davis**
1301 Belfast Drive
Los Angeles, CA 90069
"Actress"

**Glenn Davis**
47-650 Eisenhower Drive
La Qunita, CA 92253
"Actor"

**Jeff Davis**
9560 Wilshire Blvd. #516
Beverly Hills, CA 90212
"Radio & TV Personality"

**Jim Davis**
4330 East Country Road #450W
New Albany, IN 47320
"Cartoonist"

**Judy Davis**
8942 Wilshire Blvd.
Beverly Hills, CA 90212
"Actress"

**Kristin Davis**
c/o Endeavor
9701 Wilshire Blvd.
Beverly Hills, CA 90212
"Actress"

**Mac Davis**
9100 Wilshire Blvd. #1000W
Beverly Hills, CA 90212
"Singer, Actor"

**Martha Davis**
333 Valencia #450
San Francisco, CA 94103
"Singer"

**Marvin Davis**
1120 Schuyler Road
Beverly Hills, CA 90210
"Film Executive"

**Matthew Davis**
2133 Holly Drive
Los Angeles, CA 90068
"Actor"

**Ossie Davis**
44 Cortland Avenue
New Rochelle, NY 10801
"Actor, Writer, Director"

**Patti Davis**
688 St. Cloud Road
Los Angeles, CA 90077
Daughter of Ex-President"

**Phyllis Davis**
29330 SE Hillyard Drive
Boring, OR 97009
"Actress"

**Skeeter Davis**
309 Seward Road
Brentwood, TN 37027
"Singer"

**Tyrone Davis**
1995 Broadway #501
New York, NY 10023
"Singer"

**Willie Davis**
7532 Vista Del Mar
Venice, CA 90291
"Ex-Football Player"

**Bruce Davison**
P.O. Box 57593
Sherman Oaks, CA 91403
"Musician"

**Peter Davison**
18-21 Jermyn Street #300
London SW1Y 6HP ENGLAND
"Actor"

**Pam Dawber**
2236-A Encinitas Blvd
Encinitas, CA 92024
"Actress"

**Dominique Dawes**
129 Ritchie Avenue
Silver Spring, MD 20910
"Gymnast"

**Pete Dawkins**
178 Rumson Road
Rumson, NJ 07760
"Former Politician"

**Adria Dawn**
9300 Wilshire Blvd. #555
Beverly Hills, CA 90212
"Actress"

**Andre Dawson**
6770 SW 101st Street
Miami, FL 33156
"Ex-Baseball Player"

**Len Dawson**
2121 George Halas Drive NW
Canton, OH 44708
"Sportscaster"

**Richard Dawson**
1117 Angelo Drive
Beverly Hills, CA 90210
"Ex-TV Show Host, Actor"

**Rosario Dawson**
1635 N. Cahuenga Blvd. #500
Hollywood, CA 90028
"Actress"

**Roxann Dawson**
1635 N. Cahuenga Blvd. #500
Hollywood, CA 90028
"Actress"

**Doris Day**
P.O. Box 223163
Carmel, CA 93922
"Actress"

**Laraine Day**
10313 Lauriston Avenue
Los Angeles, CA 90025
"Actress"

**Daniel Day-Lewis**
65 Connaught Street
London W2 ENGLAND
"Actor"

**Taylor Dayne**
P.O. Box 413
Bridgewater, CT 05672
"Singer"

**Brian Deacon**
85 Gladstone Road
London SW19 ENGLAND
"Actor"

**Billy Dean**
2908 Poston Avenue
Nashville, TN 37203
"Singer"

**Erin J. Dean**
129 W. Wilson Street #202
Costa Mesa, CA 92627
"Actress"

**Jimmy Dean**
8000 Centerview Parkway #400
Cordova, TN 38018
"Singer"

**John Dean**
9496 Rembert Lane
Beverly Hills, CA 90210
"Author"

**Robin Deardan**
4659 Ethel Avenue
Sherman Oaks, CA 91423
"Actress"

**Blossom Dearie**
P.O. Box 21
East Durham, NY 12423
"Singer"

**Justin Deas**
10100 Santa Monica Blvd. #2500
Los Angeles, CA 90067
"Actor"

**Michael K. Deaver**
4 Chaparrel Lane
Palos Verdes, CA 90274
"Ex-Government Official"

**Dr. Michael De Bakey**
One Baylor Plaza #A-902
Houston, TX 77030
"Heart Surgeon"

**Burr De Benning**
4235 Kingfisher Road
Calabasas, CA 91302
"Actor"

**Nicole deBoer**
3401 Lawrence Ave. East #577
Scarborough, Ontario M1H 1B2
CANADA
"Actress"

**Ryan DeBoer**
510 West Hastings Street #1404
Vancouver BC V6B 1L8 CANADA
"Actor"

**Dorothy DeBorba**
P.O. Box 2723
Livermore, CA 94550
"Actress"

**Chris De Burge**
Bargy Castle, Tonhaggard
Wesxord, IRELAND
"Singer, Guitarist"

**Yvonne DeCarlo**
13701 Riverside Drive #201
Sherman Oaks, CA 91423
"Actress"

**Mary Decker Slaney**
2923 Flintlock Street
Eugene, OR 97401
"Track Athlete"

**Joey Dee**
P.O. Box 8770
Endwell, NY 13762
"Singer"

**Ruby Dee**
44 Cortland Avenue
New Rochelle, NY 10801
"Actress"

**Sandra Dee**
880 Hilldale Avenue #15
Los Angeles, CA 90069
"Actress"

**Dee-Lite**
428 Cedar Street NW
Washington, DC 20012
"Singer"

**Mickey Deems**
13114 Weddington Street
Van Nuys, CA 91401
"Actor, Director"

**Deep Pruple**
P.O. Box 254
Sheffield S6 IDF ENGLAND
"Rock & Roll Group"

**Morris Dees**
Rolling Hills Ranch
Route #1
Mathews, AL 36052
"Attorney"

**Rick Dees**
3400 Riverside Drive #800
Burbank, CA 91505
"Radio-TV Personality"

**Eddie Deezen**
8205 Santa Monica Blvd. #1-316
West Hollywood, CA 90046
"Actor"

**Def Leppard**
27A Floral Street 3300
London WC2E 0DQ ENGLAND
"Rock & Roll Group"

**William Defoe**
c/o WMA
1325 Avenue of the Americas
New York, NY 10019
"Actor"

**Ellen DeGeneres**
9465 Wilshire Blvd. #444
Beverly Hills, CA 90211
"Actress"

**Hubert De Givenchy**
3 Avenue George V
75008 Paris, FRANCE
"Fashion Designer"

**Gloria DeHaven**
420 North Palm Drive
Beverly Hills, CA 90210
"Actress"

**Penny DeHaven**
P.O. Box 83
Brentwood, TN 37027
"Singer"

**Olivia DeHavilland**
Boite Postale 156-16
Paris, Cedex 16-75764
FRANCE
"Actress"

**Deja Vu**
1 Touchstone Lane
Chard, Somerset
TA20 IRF ENGLAND
"Rock & Roll Group"

**Frederick W. deKlerk**
120 Plein Street, Priv. Bag X-999
Capetown 8000
REP. OF SOUTH AFRICA
"Politician"

**Kim Delaney**
1640 S. Sepulveda Blvd. #218
Los Angeles, CA 90025
"Actress"

**Raven De La Croix**
5022 Denny Avenue
North Hollywood, CA 91601
"Actress, Model"

**John deLancie**
1313 Brunswick Avenue
South Pasadena, CA 91030
"Actor"

**Dana Delany**
3435 Ocean Park Blvd. #112-N
Santa Monica, CA 90405
"Actress"

**Oscar de la Renta**
Brook Hill Farm
Skiff Mountain Road
Kent, CT 06757
"Fashion Designer"

**De La Soul**
2697 Heath Avenue
Bronx, NY 10463
"Music Group"

**Frances De La Tour**
15 Golden Square #315
London S1R 3AG ENGLAND
"Actress"

**Rep. Tom Delay (TX)**
Connon House Office Building 341
Washington, DC 20515
"Politicain"

**Marieh Delfino**
9300 Wilshire Blvd. #555
Beverly Hills, CA 90212
"Actress"

**Michael Dell**
One Dell Way
Round Rock, TX 78682
"Dell Computers Founder"

**Myrna Dell**
12958 Valley Heart Drive #4
Studio City, CA 91604
"Actress"

**Ken Delo**
844 South Masselin
Los Angeles, CA 90048
"Singer"

**Alan Delon**
Rt. de Malagnous 170
CH-1224 Chene-Bougeries
SWITZERLAND
"Actor"

**Nathalie Delon**
3 Qual Malaquais
75006 Paris, FRANCE
"Actor"

**John Z. DeLorean**
P.O. Box 1092
Bedminster, NJ 07921
"Automobile Builder"

**Michael DeLorenzo**
12250 Addison Street
Valley Village, CA 91607
"Actor"

**Daniele Delorme**
16 rue de Marignan
75008 Paris, FRANCE
"Actor"

**Victoria De Los Angeles**
East Magnini, Paseo de Gracia
87-7-D Barcelona SPAIN
"Soprano"

**Vanessa Del Rio**
285 Fifth Avenue #324
Brooklyn, NY 11215
"Actress"

**Milton De Lugg**
2740 Claray Drive
Los Angeles, CA 90024
"Composer, Conductor"

**Drea De Matteo**
9150 Wilshire Blvd. #350
Beverly Hills, CA 90212
"Actress"

**Lynsey De Paul**
21A Clifftown Road
Southend-on-Sea
Essex SS1 1AB ENGLAND
"Singer"

**Benicio Del Toro**
8730 Sunset Blvd. #490
Los Angeles, CA 90069
"Actor"

**Dom Deluise**
1186 Corsica Drive
Pacific Palisades, CA 90272
"Actor, Director"

**Michael Deluise**
1186 Corsica Drive
Pacific Palisades, CA 90272
"Actor"

**Peter Deluise**
1223 Wilshire Blvd. #411
Santa Monica, CA 90403
"Actor"

**Alex Delvecchio**
21186 Bridge Street, Box 526
Southfield, MI 48034
"Hockey Player"

**The Del Vikings**
P.O. Box 770850
Orlando, FL 32877
"Music Group"

**Don Demetral**
6240 S. Country Club Drive
Oklahoma City, OK 73159
"Actor"

**Jonathan Demme**
c/o Clinica Estetico
127 W. 24th St., 7th Fl.
New York, NY 10011
"Director"

**Rebecca De Mornay**
1122 South Robertson Blvd.
Los Angeles, CA 90035
"Actress"

**Patrick Dempsey**
8347 Sunset View
Los Angeles, CA 90069
"Actor"

**Nigel Dempster**
10 Buckingham Street
London WC2 ENGLAND
"Writer"

**Dame Judi Dench**
46 Albermarle Street
London W1X 4PP ENGLAND
"Actress"

**Catherine Deneuve**
76 rue Bonaparte
F-75006 Paris FRANCE
"Actress"

**Maurice Denham**
44 Brunswick Gardens #2
London W8 ENGLAND
"Actor"

**Lydie Denier**
270 North Canon Drive #1811
Beverly Hills, CA 90210
"Actress"

**Robert DeNiro**
375 Greenwich
New York, NY 10013
"Actor"

**Anthony John Denison**
10100 Santa Monica Blvd. #1060
Los Angeles, CA 90067
"Actor"

**Brian Dennehy**
121 North San Vincente Blvd.
Beverly Hills, CA 90211
"Actor"

**Martin Denny**
6770 Hawaii Kai Drive #402
Honolulu, HI 96825
"Composer"

**Reginald Denny**
844 N. Vernon Avenue
Azusa, CA 91702
"L.A. Riot Beating Victim"

**John Densmore**
49 Halderman Raod
Santa Monica, CA 90402
"Musician"

**Bucky Dent**
8895 Indian River Run
Boynton Beach, FL 33457
"Ex-Baseball Player"

**Catherine Dent**
244 West 57th Street #707
New York, NY 10019
"Actress"

**Tylor Dent**
596 Broadway #701
New York, NY 10012
"Tennis Player"

**Jamie Denton**
436 Thunderbird Court
Fullerton, CA 92835
"Author"

**Bob Denver**
P.O. Box 269
Princeton, WV 24740
"Actor"

**Brian De Palma**
8942 Wilshire Blvd.
Beverly Hills, CA 90212
"Writer, Producer"

**Gerard Depardieu**
4 Place de la Chapelle
F-75800 Bougival, FRANCE
"Actor"

**Suzanne De Passe**
1100 North Altal Loma #805
Los Angeles, CA 90069
"TV Writer"

**Johnny Depp**
9100 Wilshire Blvd. #725-E
Beverly Hills, CA 90212
"Actor"

**Bo Derek**
P.O. Box 1149
Santa Ynez, CA 93460
"Actress"

**Bruce Dern**
P.O. Box 1581
Santa Monica, CA 90406
"Actor"

**Laura Dern**
9830 Wilshire Blvd.
Beverly Hills, CA 90212
"Actress"

**Cleavant Derricks**
480 Burano Court
Agoura Hills, CA 91301
"Actor"

**Alan Dershowitz**
1563 Massachusetts Avenue
Cambridge, MA 02138
"Attorney, Professor"

**Jean Desailly**
53 quai des Grand Augistina
F-75006 Paris, FRANCE
"Actor"

**Robert Desiderio**
1475 Sierra Vista Drive
Aspen, CO 81611
"Actor"

**Destiny's Child**
9898 Bissonnet #625
Houston, TX 77036
"R&B Group"

**George Deukmejian**
555 W. 5th Street
Los Angeles, CA 90013
"Ex-Governor"

**Donna DeVarona**
1750 E. Boulder Street
Colorado Springs, CO 80909
"Ice Skater"

**Gail Devers**
950 Herrington Road #217
Lawrenceveille, GA 30044
"Track & Field"

**Loretta Devine**
5816 Ernest Avenue
Los Angeles, CA 90034
"Actress"

**Danny Devito**
P.O. Box 491246
Los Angeles, CA 90049
"Actor"

**Devo**
P.O. Box 6868
Burbank, CA 91510
"Rock & Roll Group"

**Duchess of Devonshire**
Chatsworth, Bakewell
Derbyshire ENGLAND
"Royalty"

**Duke of Devonshire**
Chatsworth, Bakewell
Derbyshire ENGLAND
"Royalty"

**Susan Dey**
1640 South Seulveda Blvd. #530
Los Angeles, CA 90025
"Actress"

**Cliff DeYoung**
481 Savona Way
Oak Park, CA 91377
"Actor & Singer"

**The Diamonds**
561 Keystone Avenue #224
Reno, NV 89503
"50s Band"

**Diamond Rio**
2908 Poston Avenue
Nashville, TN 37203
"Music Group"

**Bobby Diamond**
5309 Comercio Way
Woodland Hills, CA 91364
"Actor"

**Neil Diamond**
P.O. Box 3357
Los Angeles, CA 90028
"Singer, Songwriter"

**Don Diamont**
125 S. Sycamore Avenue
Los Angeles, CA 90036
"Actor"

**John Diaquino**
151 El Camino Drive
Beverly Hills, CA 90212
"Actor"

**Cameron Diaz**
9465 Wilshire Blvd. #212
Beverly Hills, CA 90212
"Actress"

**Rob Dibbie**
54 Summit Farms Road
Southington, CT 06489
"Baseball Player"

**Leonardo DiCaprio**
9465 Wilshire Blvd. #519
Beverly Hills, CA 90212
"Actor"

**George Di Cenzo**
156 - 5th Street #820
New York, NY 10010
"Actor"

**Andy Dick**
337 North Croft Avenue
West Hollywood, CA 90046
"Actor"

**Douglas Dick**
604 Gretna Green Way
Los Angeles, CA 90049
"Actor"

**Dick & Dee Dee**
P.O. Box 1875
Gretna, LA 70054
"Vocal Duo"

**Jimmy Dickens**
5010 West Concord Road
Brentwood, TN 37027
"Singer"

**Angie Dickinson**
1715 Carla Ridge Drive
Beverly Hills, CA 90210
"Actress"

**Bo Diddley**
1560 Broadway #1308
New York, NY 10036
"Singer, Guitarist"

**John Diehl**
10100 Santa Monica Blvd. #2500
Los Angeles, CA 90025
"Actor"

**Dena Dietrich**
1155 North La Cienega Blvd. #302
Los Angeles, CA 90069
"Actress"

**Michael Dietz**
c/o CBS/B&B
7800 Beverly Blvd. #3371
Los Angeles, CA 90036
"Actor"

**Joe Diffie**
901 - 18th Avenue South
Nashville, TN 37212
"Singer"

**Taye Diggs**
9107 Wilshire Blvd. #650
Beverly Hills, CA 90212
"Actor"

**Barry Diller**
USA Interactives, Inc.
152 West 57th Street
New York, NY 10018
"Business Executive"

**Phyllis Diller**
163 South Rockingham Avenue
Los Angeles, CA 90049
"Actress, Comedienne"

**Bradford Dillman**
770 Hot Springs Road
Santa Barbara, CA 93103
"Actor"

**C. Douglas Dillon**
169 S. Beach Road
Hobe Sound, FL 33455
"Banker, Diplomat"

**Denny Dillon**
350 West 57th Street #16A
New York, NY 10019
"Actress"

**Kevin Dillon**
49 West 9th Street #5B
New York, NY 10011
"Actor"

**Matt Dillon**
9465 Wilshire Blvd. #600
Beverly Hills, CA 90212
"Actor"

**Melinda Dillon**
1505 10th Street
Santa Monica, CA 90401
"Actress"

**Dion Di Mucci**
1650 Broadway #503
New York, NY 10019
"Singer"

**Rep. John D. Dingell (MI)**
House Rayburn Bldg. #2328
Washington, DC 20515
"Politician"

**David Dinkins**
c/o Columbia University
420 West 118th Street
New York, NY 10017
"Ex-Mayor"

**Celine Dion**
2540 Daniel Johnson #744
Laval, PQ H70 2S3 CANADA
"Singer"

**Christian Dior**
St. Anna-Platz 2
80538 Munich, GERMANY
"Fashion Designer"

**Dire Straits**
16 Lambton Place
London W11 2SH  ENGLAND
"Rock & Roll Group"

**The Dirt Band**
P.O. Box 1915
Aspen, CO 81611
"Music Group"

**Bob Dishy**
20 East 9th Street
New York, NY 10003
"Actor, Writer"

**Roy Disney**
500 South Buena Vista Street
Burbank, CA 91521
"Writer, Producer"

**Sacha Distal**
20 rue de Fosses-Saint Jaques
F-75005 Paris, FRANCE
"Singer"

**Mike Ditka**
2121 George Halas Drive
Canton, OH 44708
"Football Coach"

**Donna Dixon**
8955 Norma Place
Los Angeles, CA 90069
"Actress"

**Ivan Dixon**
27350 Barkes Way
Tehachapl, CA 93561
"Actor, Director"

**Jesse Dizon**
P.O. Box 8933
Universal City, CA 91608
"Actor, Writer"

**Lou Dobbs**
c/o CNN
820 - 1st Street NE
Washington, DC 20002
"News Anchor & Reporter"

**Alan Dobie**
Pontus, Molash
Kent CT4 8HW ENGLAND
"Actor"

**Kevin Dobson**
685 Miramonte Drive
Santa Barbara, CA 93109
"Actor"

**Peter Dobson**
1640 S. Sepulveda Blvd. #218
Los Angeles, CA 90025
"Actor"

**Tamara Dobson**
40 West 57th Street
New York, NY 10019
"Actress"

**Larry Doby**
P.O. Box 193
Massapequa, NY 11758
"Baseball Manager"

**Carol Doda**
P.O. Box 387
Fremont, CA 94537
"Dancer"

**Sen. Christopher Dodd (CT)**
Senate Russell Building #444
Washington, DC 20510
"Politicain"

**Bobby Doerr**
33705 Illahe Agness Road
Agness, OR 97406
"Ex-Baseball Player"

**Shannen Doherty**
9560 Wilshire Blvd. #516
Beverly Hills, CA 90212
"Actress"

**Elizabeth Dole**
700 New Hampshire Ave. NW
Washington, DC 20037
"Ex- Govt. & Red Cross Official"

**Robert J. Dole**
700 New Hampshire Ave. NW
Washington, DC 20037
"Ex-Senator"

**Ami Dolenz**
14336 Ventura Blvd. #200
Sherman Oaks, CA 91423
"Actress"

**Mickey Dolenz**
P.O. Box 1821
Ojai, CA 93204
"Musician, Actor"

**Sen. Pete Domenici**
402 - 15th Street NW
Albuquerque, NM 87104
"Politician"

**Placido Domingo**
Staatsoper, Opernring 2
1010 Vienna Austria
"Tenor"

**Fats Domino**
5515 Marais Street
New Orleans, LA 70117
"Singer, Pianist"

**Phil Donahue**
420 East 54th St. #22-F
New York, NY 10022
"TV Show Host"

**Troy Donahue**
11918 Laurelwood
Studio City, CA 91604
"Actor"

**Sam Donaldson**
1125 Crest Lane
McLean, VA 22101
"Broadcast Journalist"

**Peter Donat**
P.O. Box 5617
Beverly Hills, CA 90210
"Actor"

**Stanley Donen**
30 West 63rd Street #25
New York, NY 10023
"Film Director"

**Donfeld**
13949 Ventura Blvd. #309
Sherman Oaks, CA 91423
"Costume Designer"

**Clive Donner**
1466 North Kings Road
Los Angeles, CA 90069
"Film Director"

**Jorn Donner**
Pohjoisranta 12
SF-00170 Helsinki
FINLAND
"Film Director"

**Robert Donner**
3828 Glenridge Drive
Sherman Oaks, CA 91423
"Actor"

**Mary Agnes Donoghue**
427 Alta Avenue
Santa Monica, CA 90402
"Writer"

**Terry Donohue**
11918 Laurelwood
Studio City, CA 91604
"College Football Coach"

**Donovan**
151 El Camino Drive
Beverly Hills, CA 90212
"Singer, Songwriter"

**Art Donovan**
1512 Jeffers Road
Baltimore, MD 21204
"Ex-Football Player"

**Doobie Brother**
15140 Sonoma Highway
Glen Ellen, CA 95442
"Rock & Roll Group"

**James Doohan**
P.O. Box 2800
Redmond, WA 98073
"Actor"

**Vince Dooley**
P.O. Box 1472
Athens, GA 30603
"Football Coach"

**Karin Dor**
Nordliche Munchner Street 43
0-82031 Grunwald GERMANY
"Actress"

**Stephen Dorff**
9560 Wilshire Blvd. #500
Beverly Hills, CA 90212
"Actor"

**Dolores Dorn**
8831 Sunset Blvd. #402
Los Angeles, CA 90069
"Actress"

**Michael Dorn**
3751 Multiview Drive
Los Angeles, CA 90068
"Actor"

**Patrick Dorn**
11365 Ventura Blvd. #100
Box 7403
Studio City, CA 91604
"Actor"

**Tony Dorsett**
2121 George Halis Drive NW
Canton, OH 44708
"Ex-Football Player"

**David Dortort**
133 Udine Way
Los Angeles, CA 90024
"Writer, Producer"

**Roy Dotrice**
6 Meadow Lane
Leasingham, Seaford
Lincs. NB34 8L2 ENGLAND
"Actor"

**Doug E. Doug**
4024 Radford Avenue #3
Studio City, CA 91604
"Rap Singer"

**Brandon Douglas**
112 South Almont Drive
Los Angeles, CA 90048
"Actor"

**Donna Douglas**
P.O. Box 1511
Huntington Beach, CA 92647
"Actress, Singer"

**Eric Douglas**
9000 Sunset Blvd. #405
Los Angeles, CA 90069
"Actor"

**Illena Douglas**
9560 Wilshire Blvd. #500
Beverly Hills, CA 90212
"Actress"

**James "Buster" Douglas**
465 Waterbury Court #A
Gahanna, OH 43230
"Boxer"

**Jerry Douglas**
17336 Rancho Street
Encino, CA 91316
"Actor"

**Kirk Douglas**
805 North Rexford Drive
Beverly Hills, CA 90210
"Actor, Director"

**Michael Douglas**
151 Central Park West
New York, NY 10023
"Actor, Producer"

**Robyn Douglass**
1301 S. Federal Street
Chicago, IL 60605
"Actress"

**Gary Dourdan**
10100 Santa Monica Blvd. #2500
Los Angeles, CA 90067
"Actor"

**Brad Dourif**
125 S. Robertson Blvd. #126
Beverly Hills, CA 90211
"Actor"

**Peggy Dow**
2121 S. Yorkstown Avenue
Tulsa, OK 74114
"Actress"

**Doris Dowling**
9026 Elevado Avenue
Los Angeles, CA 90069
"Actress"

**Lesley-Anne Down**
P.O. Box 57593
Sherman Oaks, CA 91403
"Actress"

**Robert Downey, Jr.**
20 Waterside Plaza #28D
New York, NY 10010
"Actor"

**Roma Downey**
55 West 900 South
Salt Lake City, UT 84101
"Actress"

**Big Al Downing**
10 Luanita Lane
Newport News, VA 23606
"Singer"

**Dave Dravecky**
13840 Gleneagle Drive
Colorado Springs, CO 80921
"Ex-Baseball Player"

**Dr. Hook**
P.O. Box 398
Flagler Beach, FL 32136
"Actor"

**Tom Dreesen**
14570 Benefit Street #201
Sherman Oaks, CA 91403
"Comedian"

**Fran Drescher**
2400 Whitman Place
Los Angeles, CA 90068
"Actress"

**Griffen Drew**
P.O. Box 16753
Beverly Hills, CA 90209
"Actress"

**Clyde Drexler**
University of Houston Basketball
Houston, TX 77277
"Ex-Basketball Player"

**Richard Dreyfuss**
14820 Valley Vista Blvd.
Sherman Oaks, CA 91403
"Actor"

**Burkhard Driest**
Alter Militarring 8
50933 Koln GERMANY
"Actor"

**The Drifters**
2756 N. Green Valley Pkwy. #449
Las Vegas, NV 89014
"Vocal Group"

**Minnie Driver**
1122 S. Robertson Blvd. #15
Los Angeles, CA 90035
"Actress"

**Jon Drummond**
6601 Hannum Avenue
Culver City, CA 90230
"Sprinter"

**Allen Drury**
P.O. Box 647
Tiburon, CA 94920
"Author"

**James Drury**
100 Spring Lake Drive
Montgomery, TX 77356
"Actor"

**Roy Drusky**
131 Trivett Drive
Portland, TN 37148
"Singer, Songwriter"

**Fred Dryer**
4117 Radford Avenue
Studio City, CA 91604
"Actor, Football Player"

**Ja'Net DuBois**
8306 Wilshire Blvd. #189
Beverly Hills, CA 90211
"Actress"

**Peter Duchin**
305 Madison Avenue #956
New York, NY 10165
"Pianist"

**David Duchovny**
1122 S. Robertson #15
Los Angeles, CA 90035
"Actor"

**Rick Ducommun**
15821 Ventura Blvd. #235
Encino, CA 91436
"Comedian"

**Michael Dudikoff**
2954 Palos Verdes Drive North
Rolling Hills, CA 90274
"Actor"

**Peter Duffell**
29 Roehampton Gate
London SW15 5JR ENGLAND
"TV Writer, Director"

**Julia Duffy**
9255 Sunset Blvd. #1010
Los Angeles, CA 90069
"Actress, Director"

**Patrick Duffy**
Caller Service 001
Eagle Point, OR 97524
"Actor, Director"

**Dennis Dugan**
15611 Royal Oak Drive
Encino, CA 91436
"Actor"

**Josh Duhamel**
c/o All My Children
71 West 66th Street
New York, NY 10023
"Actor"

**Kitty Dukakis**
85 Perry Street
Brookline, MA 02146
"Author, Wife of Michael"

**Michael Dukakis**
85 Perry Street
Brookline, MA 02146
"Ex-Govornor"

**Olympia Dukakis**
684 Broadway #7-E
New York, NY 10012
"Actress"

**Bill Duke**
7510 Sunset Blvd. #523
Los Angeles, CA 90046
"Actor"

**Patty Duke**
5110 E. Dodd Road
Hayden, ID 83835
"Actress"

**The Dukes**
11 Chartfield Square
London SW15 ENGLAND
"Rock & Roll Group"

**Keir Dullea**
310 West 72nd Street #9B
New York, NY 10023
"Actor"

**Troy Dumais**
201 South Capitol Ave. #430
Indianapolis, IN 46225
"Olympic Diver"

**Melvin Dummar**
Dummar's Restaurant
Gabbs, NV 89409
"Alleged in Howard Hughes' Will"

**Faye Dunaway**
901 N. Spaulding Avenue
Los Angeles, CA 90046
"Actress"

**Sandy Duncan**
61 West 90th Street
New York, NY 10024
"Actress"

**Angelo Dundee**
450 N. Park Road #800
Hollywood, FL 33021
"Boxing Trainer"

**Tony Dungy**
c/o Baltimore Ravens
333 West Camden Street
Balitore, MD 21201
"Football Coach"

**Stephen Dunham**
9701 Wilshire Blvd.
10th Floor
Beverly Hills, CA 90212
"Actor"

**Susan Dunlap**
840 Carmel Avenue
Albany, CA 94706
"Author"

**Holly Dunn**
20 Herrada Road
Santa Fe, NM 87506
"C&W Singer"

**Dominick Dunne**
155 East 49th Street
New York, NY 10017
"Author, Producer"

**Griffin Dunne**
1501 Broadway #2600
New York, NY 10036
"Actor, Producer"

**Murphy Dunne**
4400 Encinal Canyon Road
Malibu, CA 90265
"Actor"

**Debbe Dunning**
P.O. Box 2748
Toluca Lake, CA 91610
"Actress"

**Kirsten Dunst**
151 El Camino Drive
Beverly Hills, CA 90212
"Actress"

**Pierre duPont**
Patterns
Rockland, DE 19732
"Ex-Govenor"

**Duran Duran**
93A Westbourne Park Villas
London W2 5ED ENGLAND
"Rock & Roll Group"

**Roberto Duran**
Nuevo Reperto
El Carmen PANAMA
"Boxer"

**Margie Durante**
511 North Beverly Drive
Beverly Hills, CA 90210
"Mrs. Jimmy Durante"

**Deanna Durbin-David**
B.P. 3315
75123 Paris Cedex 03
FRANCE
"Actress"

**Charles Durning**
10590 Wilshire Blvd. #506
Los Angeles, CA 90024
"Actor"

**Kevin Durrand**
1450 S. Robertson Blvd.
Los Angeles, CA 90035
"Actor"

**Marj Dusay**
320 West 66th Street
New York, NY 10023
"Actress"

**Eliza Dushku**
1122 S. Robertson Blvd. #15
Studio City, CA 91604
"Actress"

**Nancy Dussault**
12211 Iredell Street
Studio City, CA 91604
"Actress"

**Deborah Dutch**
850 N. Kings Road #109
W. Hollywood, CA 90069
"Actress"

**Charles Dutton**
10061 Riverside Drive #821
Toluca Lake, CA 91602
"Actor"

**Robert Duvall**
1122 South Robertson Blvd. #15
Los Angeles, CA 90035
"Actor"

**Shelley Duvall**
Rt. 1, Box, 377-A
Blanco, TX 78606
"Actress"

**Dale Dye**
18208 Herbold Street
Northridge, CA 91325
"War Film Consultant"

**John Dykstra**
15060 Encanto Drive
Sherman Oaks, CA 91403
"Special Effects Cameraman"

**Lenny Dykstra**
2672 Ladbrook Way
Thousand Oaks, CA 91403
"Baseball Player"

**Bob Dylan**
P.O. Box 870
Cooper Station
New York, NY 10276
"Singer, Songwriter"

**Richard Dysart**
654 Copeland Court
Santa Monica, CA 90405
"Actor"

**George Dzundza**
19320 Wells Drive
Tarzana, CA 91356
"Actor"

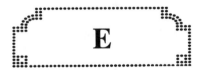

**E**

**Lawrence Eagleburger**
1450 Osensville Road
Charlottesville, VA 22901
"Ex-Government Official"

**The Eagles**
1100 Glendon Avenue #2000
Los Angeles, CA 90024
"Rock & Roll Group"

**Thomas F. Eagleton**
1 Mercantitle Center
St. Louis, MO 63101
"Former Senator"

**Earth, Wind & Fire**
9830 Wilshire Blvd.
Beverly Hills, CA 90212
"R&B Group"

**Tony Eason**
1000 Fulton Road
Hempstead, NY 11550
"Football Player"

**Jeff East**
99 Spindrift Drive
Rancho Palos Verdes, CA 90275
"Actor"

**Leslie Easterbrook**
5218 Bellingham Avenue
Valley Village, CA 91607
"Actress"

**Richard Eastham**
1529 Oriole Lane
Los Angeles, CA 90069
"Actor"

**Michael Easton**
2810 Baseline Trail
Los Angeles, CA 90068
"Actor"

**Robert Easton**
9300 Wilshire Blvd. #555
Beverly Hills, CA 90212
"Actor"

**Sheena Easton**
18136 Califa Street
Tarzana, CA 91356
"Singer, Songwriter"

**Clint Eastwood**
P.O. Box 4366
Carmel, CA 93921
"Actor"

**Kyle Eastwood**
2049 Century Park East #3500
Los Angeles, CA 90067
"Actor"

**Debb Eaton**
1040 Milan Road
Milan, NH 03588
"TV Survivor Contestant"

**Meredith Eaton**
121 N. San Vicente Blvd.
Beverly Hills, CA 90211
"Actor"

**Fred Ebb**
146 Central Park West #14D
New York, NY 10023
"Lyricist"

**Christine Ebersole**
1244A - 11th Street
Santa Monica, CA 90401
"Actress"

**Roger Ebert**
P.O. Box 146366
Chicago, IL 60614
"Film Critic"

**Bonnie Ebsen**
P.O. Box 356
Agoura, CA 91301
"Actress"

**Buddy Ebsen**
12250 Addison Street
Valley Village, CA 91607
"Actor"

**Dennis Eckersley**
39 Plympton Road
Sudbury, MA 01776
"Baseball Player"

**Aaron Eckhart**
9830 Wilshire Blvd.
Beverly Hills, CA 90212
"Actor"

**Steven Eckholdt**
c/o IA
1505 10th Street
Santa Monica, CA 90401
"Actor"

**James Eckhouse**
4222 Murietta Avenue
Sherman Oaks, CA 91423
"Actor"

**Duane Eddy**
P.O. Box 770850
Orlando, FL 33827
"Singer, Guitarist"

**Barbara Eden**
P.O. Box 5556
Sherman Oaks, CA 91403
"Actress"

**Gertrude Ederle**
4464 SW 37th Avenue
Fort Lauderdale, FL 33312
"Swimmer"

**David Edgar**
917 NE 16th Avenue #13
Ft. Lauderdale, FL 33312
"Playwright"

**HRH The Prince Edward**
Bagshot Park
Bagshot Surrey GU19 5PN EN-
GLAND
"Royalty"

**Anthony Edwards**
9560 Wilshire Blvd. #516
Beverly Hills, CA 90212
"Actor"

**Blake Edwards**
P.O. Box 491668
Los Angeles, CA 90049
"Writer, Producer, Director"

**Gail Edwards**
651 North Kilkea Drive
Los Angeles, CA 90048
"Actress"

**Jennifer Edwards**
4123 Saint Clair
Studio City, CA 91604
"Actress"

**Luke Edwards**
6212 Banner
Los Angeles, CA 90038
"Actor"

**Ralph Edwards**
818 North Doheny Drive #1401
West Hollywood, CA 90069
"TV Show Host, Producer"

**Ronnie Claire Edwards**
4900 Los Feliz Blvd.
Los Angeles, CA 90027
"Actress"

**Stacy Edwards**
10100 Santa Monica Blvd. #2500
Los Angeles, CA 90067
"Actress"

**Steve Edwards**
3980 Royal Oaks Place
Encino, CA 91436
"TV Show Host"

**Susan Egan**
211 S. Beverly Drive #208
Beverly Hills, CA 90212
"Actress"

**Julie Ege**
Vestre Nostegate 29
3300 Hokksund NORWAY
"Actress"

**Samantha Eggar**
345 N. Maple Drive #302
Beverly Hills, CA 90210
"Actress"

**Nicole Eggert**
4526 Wilshire Blvd.
Los Angeles, CA 90010
"Actress"

**Marta Eggerth**
Park Drive North
Rye, NY 10508
"Actress, Singer"

**Lisa Eichorn**
1501 Broadway #2600
New York, NY 10036
"Actress"

**Jill Eikenberry**
197 Oakdale Avenue
Mill Valley, CA 94941
"Actress"

**Cynthia Eilbacher**
P.O. Box 8920
Universal City, CA 91608
"Actress"

**Lisa Eilbacher**
4600 Petit Avenue
Encino, CA 91436
"Actress"

**Hallie Eisenberg**
275 - 7th Avenue #2600
New York, NY 10001
"Child Actress"

**Kate Eisenberg**
9200 Sunset Blvd. #1130
Los Angeles, CA 90069
"Actress"

**Susan Eisenhower**
1050 17th Street NW #600
Washington, DC 20030
"Granddaughter of Pres. Eisenhower"

**Michael Eisner**
500 South Buena Vista
Burbank, CA 91521
"Disney Executive"

**Britt Ekland**
68 Old Brompton Road
London SW7 3LQ ENGLAND
"Actress"

**Jack Elam**
1257 Sisklyou Blvd. #222
Ashland, OR 97520
"Actor"

**Dana Elcar**
1180 South Beverly Drive #301
Los Angles, CA 90035
"Actor, Director"

**Lee Elder**
1440 South Ocean Blvd. #3C
Pompano Beach, FL 33062
"Golfer"

**Dr. Joycelyn Elders**
800 Marshall Street
Little Rock, AR 72202
"Ex-Surgeon General"

**Carmen Electra**
1122 S. Robertson Blvd. #15
Los Angeles, CA 90035
"Actress"

**Electric Light Orchestra**
P.O. Box 770850
Orlando, FL 32877
"Rock & Roll Group"

**Erika Eleniak**
2029 Century Park East #300
Los Angeles, CA 90067
"Actress"

**Danny Elfman**
3236 Primera
Los Angeles, CA 90068
"Write Music for Films"

**Jenna Elfman**
6920 Los Tilos Road
Los Angeles, CA 90068
"Actress"

**Larry Elgart**
2065 Gulf of Mexico Drive
Longboat Key, FL 34228
"Composer"

**Christine Elise**
4526 Wilshire Blvd.
Los Angeles, CA 90010
"Actress"

**Kimberly Elise**
8383 Wilshire Blvd. #550
Beverly Hills, CA 90211
"Actress"

**HRH Elizabeth II**
Buckingham Palace
London SW1 ENGLAND
"Royalty

**Shannon Elizabeth**
7336 Santa Monica Blvd., PMB 690
Los Angeles, CA 90046
"Actress"

**Hector Elizando**
15030 Ventura Blvd. #751
Sherman Oaks, CA 91403
"Actor"

**Linda Ellerbee**
96 Morton Street
New York, NY 10014
"Journalist"

**Alecia Elliott**
P.O. Box 3075
Muscle Shoals, AL 35661
"Singer"

**Allison Elliot**
1505 10th Street
Santa Monica, CA 90401
"Actress"

**David James Elliott**
5555 Melrose Avenue
Clara Bow 204
Los Angeles, CA 90038
"Actor"

**Gordon Elliott**
555 West 57th Street
New York, NY 10019
"TV Show Host"

**Sam Elliott**
151 El Camino Drive
Beverly Hills, CA 90212
"Actor"

**Sean Elliott**
P.O. Box 530
San Antonio, TX 78292
"Basketball Player"

**Stephen Elliott**
3948 Woodfield Drive
Sherman Oaks, CA 91403
"Actor"

**Hunter Ellis**
9899 Santa Monica Blvd., PMB
2002
Beverly Hills, CA 90212
"TV Survivor Contestant"

**Harlan Ellison**
P.O. Box 55548
Sherman Oaks, CA 91423
"Actor"

**Daniel Ellsberg**
90 Norwood Avenue
Kensington, CA 94707
"Author"

**Elvira (Cassandra Peterson)**
P.O. Box 38246
Los Angeles, CA 90038
"Actress"

**John Elway**
10030 E. Arapahoe Road
Englewood, CO 80112
"Football Player"

**Joe Ely**
P.O. Box 91479
Austin, TX 78709
"Singer, Songwriter"

**Kelly Emberg**
10353 Glenbarr Avenue
Los Angeles, CA 90064
"Model"

**Ethan Embry**
9560 Wilshire Blvd. #516
Beverly Hills, CA 90212
"Actor"

**Joan Embry**
13036 Willow Road
Lakeside, CA 95040
"Actress"

**Eminem**
270 Lafayette Street #805
New York, NY 10012
"Rap Singer"

**Emir of Bahrain**
721 Fifth Avenue, 60th Floor
New York, NY 10022
"Royalty"

**Emir of Kuwait**
Banyan Palace
Kuwait City Kuwait
"Royalty"

**Emmanuel**
1406 Georgette Street
Santurce PUERTO RICO 00910
"Fashion Designer"

**Noah Emmerich**
151 El Camino Drive
Beverly Hills, CA 90212
"Actor"

**Roy Emmerson**
Private Bag 6060
Richmond South
Victoria 3121 AUSTRALIA
"Tennis Player"

**Dick Enberg**
1605 El Camino Del Teatro
La Jolla, CA 92037
"Sportscaster"

**Georgia Engel**
350 West 57th Street #10E
New York, NY 10019
"Actress"

**Susan Engel**
43A Princess Road
Regent's Park
London NW1 8JS ENGLAND
"Actress"

**England Dan**
P.O. Box 82
Great Neck, NY 10021
"Singer, Songwriter"

**Audie England**
6100 Wilshire Blvd. #1170
Los Angeles, CA 90048
"Actress"

**Robert Englund**
1278 Glenneyre, PMB 73
Laguna Beach, CA 92651
"Actor"

**Bill Engvall**
8380 Melrose Avenue #310
Los Angeles, CA 90069
"Actor"

**Brian Eno**
330 Harrow Road
London W9 ENGLAND
"Singer, Producer"

**Russell Enoch**
43A Princess Road
Regent's Park
London NW1 8JS ENGLAND
"Actor"

**Philippe Entremont**
Schwarzenbergplatz 10/7
A-1040 Vienna, AUSTRIA
"Pianist"

**John Entwhistle**
P.O. Box 251
Lake Peekskill, NY 10537
"Musician, Singer"

**Nora Ephron**
2211 Broadway #1 - J
New York, NY 10024
"Screenwriter"

**Omar Epps**
9701 Wilshire Blvd. 10th Floor
Beverly Hills, CA 90212
"Actor"

**Kathryn Erbe**
1964 Westwood Blvd. #400
Los Angeles, CA 90025
"Actress"

**Richard Erdman**
5655 Greenbush Avenue
Van Nuys, CA 91401
"Actor, Director"

**John Ericson**
7 Avnida Vista Grande, PMB 310
Santa Fe, NM 87508
"Actor"

**Carl Erskine**
6214 South Madison Avenue
Anderson, IN 46013
"Ex-Baseball Player"

**Julius Erving**
P.O. Box 914100
Longwood, FL 32791
"Ex-Basketball Player"

**Bill Erwin**
12324 Moorpark Street
Studio City, CA 91604
"Actor"

**Christoph Eschenbach**
2 Avenue d'Alena
75016 Paris, FRANCE
"Pianist"

**"Boomer" Esiason**
25 Heights Road
Plandome, NY 11030
"Ex-Football Player"

**Carl Esmond**
576 Tigertail Road
Los Angeles, CA 90049
"Actor"

**Giancarlo Esposito**
1505 10th Street
Santa Monica, CA 90401
"Actor"

**Mike Espy**
154 Deertrail Lane
Madison, MS 39110
"Former Government Official"

**David Essex**
5 Stratford Saye, 20-20 Wellington
Bourmemouth, Dorset BG8 8JN
ENGLAND
"Singer, Actor"

**Gloria Estefan**
420 Jefferson Avenue
Miami Beach, FL 33139
"Singer"

**Bob Estes**
4408 Long Champ Drive #21
Austin, TX 78746
"Golfer"

**Rob Estes**
1122 S. Robertson Blvd. #15
Los Angeles, CA 90035
"Actor"

**Simon Estes**
General-Wille-Str. 284
8706 Meilen SWITZERLAND
"Singer"

**Emilio Estevez**
P.O. Box 4041
Malibu, CA 90264
"Actor, Writer"

**Ramon Estevez**
837 Ocean Avenue #101
Santa Monica, CA 90402
"Actor"

**Renee Estevez**
617 South Olive Avenue #510
Los Angeles, CA 90014
"Actress"

**Erik Estrada**
3768 Eureka Drive
Studio City, CA 91604
"Actor"

**Joe Eszterhas**
151 El Camino Drive
Beverly Hills, CA 90212
"Screenwriter"

**Melissa Etheridge**
9830 Wilshire Blvd.
Beverly Hills, CA 90212
"Singer"

**Bob Eubanks**
5900 Highridge Road
Hidden Hills, CA 91302
"TV Show Host"

**Kevin Eubanks**
173 Brighton Avenue
Boston, MA 02134
"Band leader"

**Wesley Eure**
9460 Wilshire Blvd. #300
Beverly Hills, CA 90212
"Actor"

**Europe**
Box 22036
S-10422 Stockholm SWEDEN
"Rock & Roll Group"

**Eurythmics**
151 El Camino Drive
Beverly Hills, CA 90212
"Rock & Roll Group"

**Evan & Jaron**
1775 Broadway 3430
New York, NY 10019
"Twin Recording Artists"

**Linda Evangelista**
121 rue Legendre
F-75017 Paris FRANCE
"Model"

**Andrea Evans**
8075 West Third Street #303
Los Angeles, CA 90048
"Actress"

**Evans Evans**
3114 Abington Drive
Beverly Hills, CA 90210
"Actress"

**Janet Evans**
8 Barneburg
Dove Canyon, CA 92679
"Swimmer"

**Linda Evans**
6714 Villa Madera Drive, SW
Tacoma, WA 98499
"Actress"

**Mary Beth Evans**
P.O. Box 50105
Pasadena, CA 91115
"Actress"

**Mike Evans**
12530 Collins Street
North Hollywood, CA 91605
"Actor"

**Ronald E. Evans**
6134 East Mescal
Scottsdale, AZ 85254
"Columnist"

**Trevor Eve**
76 Oxford Street
London W1N OAX ENGLAND
"Actor"

**Dame Edna Everage**
5 Soho Square
London W1V 5DE ENGLAND
"Investigative Journalist"

**Chad Everett**
5472 Island Forest Place
Westlake Village, CA 91362
"Actor"

**Rupert Everett**
76 Oxford Street
London, W1N 0AX ENGLAND
"Actor"

**Nancy Everhart**
11365 Ventura Blvd. #100-7403
Studio City, CA 91604
"Actress"

**Angie Everhart**
6500 Wilshire Blvd. #2200
Los Angeles, CA 90048
"Model"

**Don Everly**
P.O. Box 56
Dunmore, KY 42339
"Singer"

**Phil Everly**
P.O. Box 56
Dunmore, KY 42339
"Singer"

**Charles Evers**
1072 Lynch Street
Jackson, MS 39203
"Civil Rights Worker"

**Jason Evers**
232 North Crescent Drive #101
Beverly Hills, CA 90210
"Actor"

**Myrlie Evers-Williams**
15 Colorado Avenue SW #310
Bend, OR 97702
"NAACP Ex-Director"

**Cory Everson**
23705 Vanowen Street #209
West Hills, CA 91307
"Actress"

**Chris Evert**
6181 Hollows Lane
Delray Beach, FL 33483
"Tennis Player"

**Greg Evigan**
5070 Arundel Drive
Woodland Hills, CA 91364
"Actor, Singer"

**Patrick Ewing**
10 Greenway Plaza E.
Houston, TX 77046
"ex-Basketball Player"

**Exile**
P.O. Box 1547
Goodlettsville, TN 37070
"Music Group"

**Extreme**
189 Carlton Street
Toronto, Ontario
M5A 2K7 CANADA
"Music Group"

**Richard Eyer**
2739 Underwood Lane
Bishop, CA 93514
"Actor"

**Shelley Fabares**
P.O. Box 6010-909
Sherman Oaks, CA 91413
"Actress"

**Ava Fabian**
13775-A Mono Way #220
Sonora, CA 95370
"Actress, Model"

**Nanette Fabray**
13834 Magnolia Blvd.
Sherman Oaks, CA 91423
"Actress"

**HM King Fahd**
Royal Palace
Riyadh, SAUDI ARABIA
"Royalty"

**Jeff Fahey**
8306 Wilshire Blvd. #438
Beverly Hills, CA 90211
"Actor"

**Barbara Fairchild**
P.O. Box 2287
Branson, MO 65615
"Singer"

**Morgan Fairchild**
P.O. Box 57593
Sherman Oaks, CA 91403
"Actress"

**Adam Faith**
76 Oxford Street
London W1N OAX ENGLAND
"Singer, Actor"

**Marianne Faithfull**
235 Footscray Road
New Eltham
London SE9 2EL ENGLAND
"Singer, Songwriter"

**Lola Falana**
1201 "N" Street NW #A-5
Washington, DC 20005
"Singer, Dancer, Actress"

**Nick Faldo**
21 World Golg Place
Saint Augustine, FL 32092
"Golfer"

**Peter Falk**
100 Universal City Plaza
Universal City, CA 91608
"Actor, Director"

**Jinx Falkenburg**
P.O. Box 405
Mill Neck, NY 11765
"Actress, Model"

**Rev. Jerry Falwell**
1971 University Blvd.
Lynchburg, VA 24502
"Evangelist"

**Keith Famie**
5433 Bently Road #104
West Bloomfield, MI 48332
"Chef & Survivor Contestant"

**Hampton Fancher III**
115 S. Topanga Canyon Blvd. #180
Topanga, CA 90290
"Screenwriter"

**Dakota Fanning**
4343 Lankershim Blvd. #100
Universal City, CA 91602
"Child Actress"

**Stephanie Faracy**
8765 Lookout Mountain Road
Los Angeles, CA 90046
"Actress"

**Debrah Farentino**
1505 - 10th Street
Santa Monica, CA 90401
"Actress"

**James Farentino**
1340 Londonderry Place
Los Angeles, CA 90069
"Actor"

**Linda Farentino**
112 South Almont Drive
Los Angeles, CA 90048
"Actress"

**Donna Fargo**
P.O. Box 150527
Nashville, TN 37215
"Singer"

**Dennis Farina**
217 Edgewood Avenue
Clearwood, FL 33755
"Actor"

**Anna Faris**
9615 Brighton Way #300
Beverly Hills, CA 90210
"Actress"

**Lillian Farley**
84 Kenneth Avenue
Huntington, NY 11743
"Model"

**Art Farmer**
49 East 96th Street
New York, NY 10128
"Jazz Musician"

**Shannon Farnon**
12743 Milbank Street
Studio City, CA 91604
"Actress"

**Jamie Farr**
53 Ranchero
Bell Canyon, CA 91307
"Actor, Director"

**Louis Farrakhan**
4855 So. Woodlawn Ave.
Chicago, IL 60615
"Religious Leader"

**Mike Farrell**
P.O. Box 6010-826
Sherman Oaks, CA 91413
"Actor, Writer, Director"

**Sharon Farrell**
369 South Doheny Drive, PMB 507
Beverly Hills, CA 90211
"Actress"

**Shea Farrell**
1180 South Beverly Drive #301
Los Angeles, CA 90035
"Actor"

**Terry Farrell**
6500 Wilshire Blvd. #2200
Los Angeles, CA 90048
"Actress"

**Peter Farrelly**
9830 Wilshire Blvd.
Beverly Hills, CA 90212
"Director, Producer"

**Amy Farrington**
8675 West Washington Blvd. #203
Culver City, CA 90232
"Actress"

**Mia Farrow**
124 Henry Sanford Road
Bridgewater, CT 06752
"Actress"

**Dante Fascell**
6300 SW 99th Terrace
Miami, FL 33156
"Politician"

**Howard Fast**
65 Bleaker Street
New York, NY 10012
"Author"

**Fat Boys**
250 W. 57th Street #1723
New York, NY 10107
"Rap Group"

**David Faustino**
8075 West 3rd Street #303
Los Angeles, CA 90048
"Actor"

**Dan Fauts**
4020 Murphy Canyon Road
San Diego, CA 92123
"Ex-Football Player"

**Suzy Favor-Hamilton**
P.O. Box 120
Indianapolis, IN 46206
"Runner"

**Brett Favre**
3071 Gothic Court
Green Bay, WI 54313
"Football Player"

**Jon Favreau**
9560 Wilshire Blvd., #516
Beverly Hills, CA 90212
"Actor"

**Allen Fawcett**
8436 W. Third Street #740
Los Angeles, CA 90048
"Actor, TV Show Host"

**Farrah Fawcett**
10580 Wilshire Blvd. #14-NE
Los Angeles, CA 90024
"Actress, Model"

**Brad Faxon**
77 Rumstick Road
Barrington, RI 02806
"Golfer"

**Melinda Fee**
12315 Moorpark Street #11
Sherman Oaks, CA 91423
"Actress"

**Dr. Feelgood**
3 East 54th Street
New York, NY 10022
"Singer"

**Joe Feeney**
32630 Concord Drive
Madison Heights, MI 48071
"Singer"

**Jules Feiffner**
325 West End Avenue #12A
New York, NY 10023
"Writer"

**Sen. Russell Feingold (WI)**
7114 Donna Drive
Middleton, WI 53562
"Politician"

**Alan Feinstein**
9229 Sunset Blvd. #311
Los Angeles, CA 90069
"Actor"

**Sen. Dianne Feinstein (CA)**
1825 Kalorama Square #4
Washington, DC 20008
"Politician"

**Michael Feinstein**
4647 Kingswell Avenue #110
Los Angeles, CA 90027
"Actor"

**Don Felder**
P.O. Box 6051
Malibu, CA 90265
"Singer, Songwriter"

**Barbara Feldon**
14 E. 74th Street
New York, NY 10021
"Actress, Model"

**Tovah Feldshuh**
322 Central Park West #11B
New York, NY 10025
"Actor"

**Martin Feldstein**
147 Clifton Street
Belmont, MA 02178
"Economist"

**Jose Feliciano**
297-101 Kinderkamack Road
Oradell, NJ 07649
"Singer, Guitarist"

**Bob Feller**
P.O. Box 157
Gates Mills, OH 44040
"Ex-Baseball Player"

**Edith Fellows**
2016 1/2 North Vista Del Mar
Los Angeles, CA 90068
"Actress"

**Narvel Felts**
2005 Narvel Felts Avenue
Malden, MO 63863
"Singer"

**John Femia**
1650 Boradway #714
New York, NY 10019
"Singer"

**Freddy Fender**
6438 Revolution Drive
Corpus Christi, TX 78413
"Singer, Songwriter"

**Cathy Ferguson**
21861 Oceanview Lane
Huntington Beach, CA 92646
"Gold Medalists Swimmer"

**Colin Ferguson**
10100 Santa Monica Blvd. #2500
Los Angeles, CA 90067
"Actor"

**Jay Ferguson**
560 "N" Street SW #304
Washington, DC 20024
"Composer, Songwriter"

**Maynard Ferguson**
P.O. Box 1821
Ojai, CA 93024
"Trumpeter"

**Alejandro Fernandez**
11002 Rocks Road
Whitter, CA 90601
"Singer, Songwriter"

**Mary Jo Fernandez**
6040 SW 104th Street
Miami, FL 33156
"Tennis Player"

**Vince Ferragamo**
6713 Horeshoe Road
Orange, CA 92669
"Football Player"

**Ferrante & Teicher**
12224 Avila Drive
Kansas City, MO 64145
"Piano Duo"

**Adam Ferrara**
P.O. Box 5617
Beverly Hills, CA 90210
"Comic Actor"

**Cristina Ferrare**
1280 Stone Canyon
Los Angeles, CA 90077
"Actress, Model"

**Geraldine Ferraro**
218 Lafayette Street
New York, NY 10012
"Ex-Congresswoman"

**Conchata Ferrell**
1335 N. Seward Street
Hollywood, CA 90028
"Actress"

**Will Ferrell**
237 West 35th Street #400
New York, NY 10001
"Actor"

**Andrea Ferreol**
10 Avenue George V
F-75008 Paris FRANCE
"Actress"

**Mel Ferrer**
6590 Camino Carreta
Carpenteria, CA 93013
"Actor"

**Miguel Ferrer**
2710 Nichols Canyon
Los Angeles, CA 90046
"Actor"

**Lou Ferrrigno**
621 17th Street
Santa Monica, CA 90402
"Actor, Bodybuilder"

**Brian Ferry**
59A Chesson Road
London W14 9QS ENGLAND
"Singer, Songwriter"

**Debra Feuer**
9560 Wilshire Blvd. #500
Beverly Hills, CA 90212
"Actress"

**Mark Fidrych**
260 West Street
Northboro, MA 01532
"Ex-Baseball Player"

**John Fiedler**
225 Adams Street #10B
Brooklyn, NY 11201
"Actor"

**Chelsea Field**
P.O. Box 5617
Beverly Hills, CA 90210
"Actress"

**Sally Field**
12307 7th Helena Drive
Los Angeles, CA 90049
"Actress"

**Shirley Anne Field**
2-4 Noel Street
London W1V 2RB ENGLAND
"Actress"

**Sylvia Field**
3263 Via Alta Mira
Fallbrook, CA 92028
"Actress"

**Freddie Fields**
8899 Beverly Blvd. #918
Los Angeles, CA 90048
"Motion Picture Producer"

**Mrs. Fields**
462 Bearcat Drive
Salt Lake City, UT 84115
"Cookie Executive"

**Ralph Fiennes**
91 Regent Street
London W1R 7TB ENGLAND
"Actor"

**Harvey Fierstein**
1479 Carla Ridge Drive
Beverly HIlls, CA 90210
"Dramatist, Actor"

**Elizabeth Filarski**
39 Perennial Drive
Cranston, RI 02920
"Survivor II Contestant"

**Nathan Fillion**
9460 Wilshire Blvd. #700
Beverly Hills, CA 90212
"Actor"

**Jon Finch**
2-4 Noel Street
London W1V 3RB ENGLAND
"Actor"

**Travis Fine**
c/o Talent Enterprises
9111 Wilshire Blvd.
Beverly Hills, CA 90212
"Actor"

**Rollie Fingers**
P.O. Box 230729
Las Vegas, NV 89123
"Ex-Baseball Player"

**Fyvush Finkel**
155 East 50th Street #6E
New York, NY 10022
"Actor"

**Albert Finney**
45 - 51 Whitfield Street
London W1 ENGLAND
"Actor"

**Jennifer Finnigan**
7800 Beverly Blvd. #3371
Los Angeles, CA 90036
"Actress"

**Ann Firbank**
76 Oxford  Street
London W1N 0AX ENGLAND
"Actress"

**Eddie Firestone**
303 South Crescent Heights
Los Angeles, CA 90048
"Actor"

**The Firm**
57A Great Titchfield Street
London W1P 7FL ENGLAND
"Rock & Roll Group"

**Colin Firth**
76 Oxford Street
London W1D 1BS ENGLAND
"Actor"

**Jonathan Firth**
4 Windmill Street
London W1T 7FL ENGLAND
"Actor"

**Bobby Fischer**
186 Route 9-W
New Windsor, NY 12550
"Chess Player"

**Dietrich Fischer-Diskau**
Lindenalle 22 D-14050
Berlin, GERMANY
"Baritone"

**Larry Fishburne**
4116 W. Magnolia Blvd. #101
Burbank, CA 91505
"Actor"

**Carrie Fisher**
1700 Coldwater Canyon
Beverly Hills, CA 90210
"Actress"

**Eddie Fisher**
10000 North Point Street #1802
San Francisco, CA 94109
"Actor, Singer"

**Frances Fisher**
8730 Sunset Blvd. #490
Los Angeles, CA 90069
"Actress"

**Joely Fisher**
9465 Wilshire Blvd. #430
Beverly Hills, CA 90212
"Actress"

**Terry Louise Fisher**
5314 Pacific Avenue
Marina del Rey, CA 90292
"TV Writer, Producer"

**Todd Fisher**
3435 Ocean Park Blvd. #206
Santa Monica, CA 90405
"Actor"

**Michael Fishman**
P.O. Box 133226
Big Bear Lake, CA 92315
"Actor"

**Carlton Fisk**
P.O. Box 590
Cooperstown, NY 13326
"Ex-Baseball Player"

**Christian Fittipaldi**
282 Alphaville Baruei, 064500
Sao Paulo BRAZIL
"Race Car Driver"

**Emerson Fittipaldi**
735 Crandon Blvd. #503
Miami, FL 33149
"Race Car Driver"

**Rick Fitts**
1903 Dracena Drive
Los Angeles, CA 90068
"Actor"

**Geraldine Fitzgerald**
50 East 79th Street
New York, NY 10019
"Actress"

**Roberta Flack**
330 East 43rd Street #102
New York, NY 10017
"Singer, Songwriter"

**Fanny Flagg**
1569 Miramar Lane
Santa Barbara, CA 93108
"Actress"

**Rick Flair**
7205 Piper Point Lane
Charlotte, NC 28270
"Wrestler"

**The Flamingos**
2375 Tropicanna Avenue #304
Las Vega, NV 89119
"Vocal Group"

**Fionnula Flanagan**
118 S. Beverly Drive #201
Beverly Hills, CA 90212
"Actress"

**Susan Flannery**
6977 Shepard Mesa Drive
Santa Barbara, CA 93103
"Actress"

**Jennifer Flavin**
30 Beverly Park
Beverly Hills, CA 90210
"Model"

**Fleetwood Mac**
5901 Warner Avenue #462
Huntington Beach, CA 92649
"Rock & Roll Group"

**Mick Fleetwood**
5901 Warner Avenue #462
Huntington Beach, CA 92649
"Drummer, Songwriter"

**Charles Fleischer**
749 North Crescent Heights Blvd.
Los Angeles, CA 90038
"Actor"

**Heidi Fleiss**
P.O. Box 271831
Los Angeles, CA 90027
"Hollywood Madam"

**Peggy Fleming**
1122 S. Robertson Blvd. #15
Los Angeles, CA 90035
"Ice Skater"

**Louise Fletcher**
6500 Wilshire Blvd. #2200
Los Angeles, CA 90048
"Actress"

**Lucy Lee Flippin**
1753 Canfield Avenue
Los Angeles, CA 90035
"Actress"

**Calista Flockhart**
9100 Wilshire Blvd. #725E
Beverly Hills, CA 90212
"Actress"

**Flock of Seagulls**
P.O. Box 1821
Ojai, CA 93024
"Rock & Roll Group"

**Myron Floran**
26 Georgeff Road
Rolling Hills, CA 90274
"Composer"

**Dann Florek**
145 West 45th Street #1204
New York, NY 10036
"Actor"

**Tom Flores**
11220 N.E. 53rd Street
Kirkland, WA 98033
"Football Executive"

**Ray Floyd**
231 Royal Palm Way #100
Palm Beach, FL 33480
"Golfer"

**Doug Flutie**
268 Newbury Street
Boston, MA 02116
"Football Player"

**Larry Flynt**
9211 Robin Drive
Los Angeles, CA 90069
"Publisher"

**Nina Foch**
P.O. Box 1884
Beverly Hills, CA 90213
"Actress"

**Dan Fogelberg**
9200 Sunset Blvd. #530
Los Angeles, CA 90069
"Singer, Songwriter"

**John Fogerty**
7009 penbrook Drive
Franklin, TN 37069
Singer, Songwriter"

**Jeremy Foley**
P.O. Box 70025
Houston, TX 77270
"Actor"

**Tom Foley**
601 West 1st Ave. #2W
Spokane, WA 99204
"Ex-Congressman"

**Ken Follett**
P.O. Box 4
Knebworth SG3 6UT ENGLAND
"Author"

**Meg Follows**
121 North San Vicente Blvd.
Beverly Hills, CA 90211
"Actress"

**Bridget Fonda**
c/o AMG
9465 Wilshire Blvd.
Beverly Hills, CA 90212
"Actress"

**Jane Fonda**
P.O. Box 5840
Atlanta, GA 31107
"Actress, Writer"

**Peter Fonda**
Route 38 Box 2024
Livingston, MT 59047
"Actor, Writer, Director"

**Shirlee Fonda**
110 East 57th Street
New York, NY 10022
"Mrs. Henry Fonda"

**Joan Fontaine**
P.O. Box 222600
Carmel, CA 93922
"Actress"

**D.J. Fontana**
P.O. Box 262
Carteret, NJ 07008
"Drummer"

**Horton Foote**
95 Horatio Street #332
New York, NY 10014
"Screenwriter"

**Shelby Foote**
542 East Parkway South
Memphis, TN 38104
"Historian"

**June Foray**
22745 Erwin Street
Woodland Hills, CA 91367
"Actress"

**Brian Forbes**
Seven Pines
Wentworth, Surrey, ENGLAND
"Writer, Director"

**Steve Forbes**
60 Fifth Avenue
New York, NY 10011
"Magazine Publisher"

**Raymond Forchion**
4680 Van Noord Avenue
Sherman Oaks, CA 91423
"Actor"

**Mrs. Betty Ford**
40365 San Dune Road
Rancho Mirage, CA 92270
"Ex-First Lady, Author"

**Charlotte Ford**
25 Sutton Place
New York, NY 10023
"Daughter of Henry Ford II"

**Doug Ford**
6128 Bear Creek Circle
Lake Worth, FL 33467
"Golfer"

**Eileen Ford**
344 East 59th Street
New York, NY 10022
"Talent Agent"

**Faith Ford**
9560 Wilshire Blvd. #500
Beverly Hills, CA 90211
"Actress, Model"

**Frankie Ford**
7200 France Avenue #330
Edina, MN 55435
"Singer, Songwriter"

**Gerald R. Ford**
40365 San Dune Road
Rancho Mirage, CA 92270
"Former President"

**Glenn Ford**
911 Oxford Way
Beverly Hills, CA 90210
"Actor"

**Harrison Ford**
3555 North Moose Wilson Road
Jackson, WY 83001
"Actor"

**Maria Ford**
8281 Melrose Avenue #200
Los Angeles, CA 90046
"Actress"

**Mick Ford**
47 Courtfield Road #9
London SW7 4DB
ENGLAND
"Actor"

**Ruth Ford**
1 West 72nd Street
New York, NY 10023
"Actress"

**Sen. Wendell Ford (KY)**
Senate Russell Building #173A
Washington, DC 20510
"Politicain"

**Whitey Ford**
38 Schoolhouse Lane
Lake Success, NY 11020
"Ex-Baseball Player"

**Foreigner**
1 Conduit Street
London W1R 9T9 ENGLAND
"Rock & Roll Group"

**George Foreman**
7639 Pine Oak Drive
Humble, TX 77397
"Boxer"

**Forester Sisters**
3322 West End Avenue
Nashville, TN 37203
"C&W Group"

**Milos Forman**
c/o Lantz Office
200 West 57th Street
New York, NY 10019
"Film Director"

**Frederic Forrest**
11300 West Olympic Blvd. #610
Los Angeles, CA 90064
"Actor"

**Sally Forrest**
1125 Angelo Drive
Beverly Hills, CA 90210
"Actress"

**Steve Forrest**
1605 Michael Lane
Pacific Palisades, CA 90272
"Actor"

**Constance Forslund**
853 - 7th Avenue #9A
New York, NY 10019
"Actress"

**Brian Forster**
16172 Flamstead Drive
Hacienda Heights, CA 91745
"Actor"

**Robert Forster**
8550 Holloway Drive
Los Angeles, CA 90069
"Actor"

**Bruce Forsyth**
Kent House
Upper Ground
London SE1 ENGLAND
"TV Personality"

**Frederick Forsyth**
61-63 Oxbridge Rd., Ealing
London W5 5SA ENGLAND
"Writer"

**Bill Forsythe**
20 Winton Drive
Glasgow G12 OQA SCOTLAND
"Guitarist"

**John Forsythe**
3849 Roblar Avenue
Santa Ynez, CA 93460
"Actor"

**Rosemary Forsythe**
1591 Benedict Canyon
Beverly Hills, CA 90210
"Actress"

**Fabian Forte**
6671 Sunset Blvd. #1502
Los Angeles, CA 90028
"Actor, Singer"

**Larry Fortensky**
31682 Avenida Evita
San Juan Capistrano, CA 92675
"Elizabeth Taylor's Ex-husband"

**Dick Fosbury**
709 Canyon Run, Box 1791
Ketchum, ID 83340
"Track Athlete"

**Gen. Joe Foss**
P.O. Box 5051
Scottsdale, AZ 85261
"Firearms Assoc. Executive"

**Brigitte Fossey**
18 rue Troyon
75017 Paris, FRANCE
"Actress"

**Jodie Foster**
21515 Hawthorne Blvd. #1250
Torrance, CA 90503
"Actress"

**Meg Foster**
606 N. Larchmont Blvd. #309
Los Angeles, CA 90004
"Actress"

**Radney Foster**
1908 Wedgewood
Nashville, TN 37212
"Singer"

**Pete Fountain**
237 North Peters Street #400
New Orleans, LA 71030
"Clarienetist"

**Four Aces**
2011 Ferry Avenue #U-19
Camden, NJ 08104
"Vocal Group"

**Four Lads**
11761 East Speedway Blvd.
Tucson, AZ 85748
"Vocal Group"

**The Four Seasons**
9200 Sunset Blvd. #900
Los Angeles, CA 90069
"Rock & Roll Group"

**Four Tops**
40 West 57th Street
New York, NY 10019
"R & B Group"

**John Fowles**
52 Floral Street
London WC2E 9DA ENGLAND
"Author"

**Fox Brothers**
Rt. 6, Bending Chestnut
Franklin, TN 37064
"Gospel Group"

**Bernard Fox**
6601 Burnet Avenue
Van Nuys, CA 91405
"Actor"

**Edward Fox**
25 Maida Avenue
London W2 1ST ENGLAND
"Actor"

**Jamie Fox**
9830 Wilshire Blvd.
Beverly Hills, CA 90212
"Actor"

**Michael J. Fox**
62 Chelsea Piers #303
New York, NY 10011
"Actor, Director"

**Samantha Fox**
50 City Business Center
Lower Road
London SE16 2XB ENGLAND
"Singer, Model"

**Vivica Fox**
P.O. Box 572529
Taranza, CA 91357
"Actress"

**Jeff Foxworthy**
3310 West End Avenue #500
Nashville, TN 37203
"Actor"

**Robert Foxworth**
9720 Wilshire Blvd. #300
Beverly Hills, CA 90212
"Actor"

**A.J. Foyt**
19480 Stokes Road
Waller, TX 77484
"Race Car Driver"

**Don Frabotta**
5036 Riverton Avenue #2
N. Hollywood, CA 91601
"Actor"

**Jonathan Frakes**
9135 Hazen Drive
Beverly Hills, CA 90210
"Actor"

**Peter Frampton**
1016 - 17th Avenue South
Nashville, TN 37212
"Singer, Guitarist"

**Tony Franciosa**
567 Tigertail Road
Los Angeles, CA 90049
"Actor"

**Anne Francis**
P.O. Box 5608
Santa Barbara, CA 93105
"Actress"

**Connie Francis**
6413 West 102nd Terrace
Parkland, FL 33105
"Singer, Actress"

**Dick Francis**
P.O. Box 30866
7 Mile Beach
Grand Cayman WEST INDIES
"Author"

**Freddie Francis**
12 Ashley Drive
Jersey Road, Osterley
Middlesex TW7 5QA ENGLAND
"TV Director"

**Genie Francis**
9135 Hazen Drive
Beverly Hills, CA 90210
"Actress"

**Nancy Frangione**
280 S. Beverly Drive #400
Beverly Hills, CA 90212
"Actress"

**Rep. Barney Frank (MA)**
House Rayburn Bldg. #2210
Washington, DC 20515
"Politician"

**Gary Frank**
1644 Palisades Drive
Pacific Palisades, CA 90272
"Actor"

**Joanna Frank**
1274 Capri Drive
Pacific Palisades, CA 90272
"Actress"

**Al Franken**
345 North Maple Drive #302
Beverly Hills, CA 90210
"Comedian"

**Aretha Franklin**
8450 Linwood Street
Detroit, MI 48206
"Singer, Songwriter"

**Bonnie Franklin**
5757 Wilshire Blvd. #473
Beverly Hills, CA 90036
"Actress"

**Diane Franklin**
195 South Beverly Drive #400
Beverly Hills, CA 90212
"Actress"

**Don Franklin**
10101 Santa Monica Blvd. #2500
Los Angeles, CA 90067
"Actor"

**Gary Franklin**
7610 Beverly Blvd. #480820
Los Angeles, CA 90048
"Film Critic"

**Joe Franklin**
P.O. Box 1
Lynbrook, NY 11563
"TV Swow Host"

**Arthur Franz**
1736 Talon Avenue
Henderson, NV 89074
"Actor"

**Dennis Franz**
2300 Century Hill #75
Los Angeles, CA 90067
"Actor"

**Brendan Fraser**
2118 Wilshire Blvd. #513
Santa Monica, CA 90403
"Actor"

**Douglas Fraser**
800 East Jefferson Street
Detroit, MI 48214
"Ex-Union Leader"

**Linda Fratianne**
P.O. Box 151
Sun Valley, ID 83353
"Skater"

**Joe Frazier**
2917 North Broad Street
Philadelphia, PA 19132
"Ex-Boxer Champion"

**Sheila Frazier**
1179 S. Highland Avenue
Los Angeles, CA 90019
"Actress"

**Walt Frazier**
675 Flamingo Drive, Southwest
Atlanta, GA 30311
"Ex-Basketball Player"

**Cathy Freeman**
43 Fletcher Street
Essendon, Victoria 3040
AUSTRALIA
"Runner"

**Mona Freeman**
608 North Alpine Drive
Beverly Hills, CA 90210
"Actor"

**Morgan Freeman**
c/o William Morris
1325 Avenue of the Americas
New York, NY 10019
"Actor"

**Jim Fregosi**
1092 Copeland Court
Tarpon Springs, FL 34689
"Ex-Baseball Player"

**Leigh French**
1850 North Vista Avenue
Los Angeles, CA 90046
"Actor"

**Matt Frewer**
8942 Wilshire Blvd. #155
Beverly Hills, CA 90211
"Actor"

**Janie Fricke**
P.O. Box 1547
Goodlettsville, TN 37070
"Singer"

**Squire Fridell**
13563 Ventura Blvd. #200
Sherman Oaks, CA 91403
"Actor"

**William Friedkin**
10451 Bellagio Road
Los Angeles, CA 90077
"Film Director"

**Milton Friedman**
Quadrangle Office
Hoover Institute
Stanford University
Palo Alto, CA 94305
"Econominist"

**Sonya Friedman**
208 Harriston Road
Glen Rock, NJ 07452
"TV Show Host"

**Chuck Fries**
6922 Hollywood Blvd.
Los Angeles, CA 90028
"TV Executive"

**Daniel Frischman**
145 S. Fairfax Avenue #310
Los Angeles, CA 90036
"Actor"

**David Frizzell**
4694 East Robertson Road
Cross Plains, TN 37049
"Singer"

**Dominic Frontiere**
280 S. Beverly Drive #411
Beverly Hills, CA 90212
"Composer, Conductor"

**Georgia Frontiere**
375 Skyline Drive
Sedona, AZ 86336
"Football Team Owner"

**Sir David Frost**
BBC Centre
Wood Lane
LondonW12 7RJ ENGLAND
"TV Show Host"

**Mark Frost**
P.O. Box 1723
Studio City, CA 91604
"TV Writer"

**Soleil Moon Frye**
2713 North Keystone
Burbank, CA 91504
"Actress"

**Leo Fuchs**
609 North Kilkea Drive
Los Angeles, CA 90048
"Actor"

**Alan Fudge**
355 South Rexford Drive
Beverly Hills, CA 90212
"Actor"

**Daisy Fuentes**
12233 West Olympic Blvd. #170
Los Angeles, CA 90064
"MTV Host"

**The Fugees**
83 Riverside Drive
New York, NY 10024
"Hip-Hop Trio"

**Mark Fuhrman**
P.O. Box 141
Sandpoint, ID 83864
"Ex-Cop"

**Penny Fuller**
10100 Santa Monica Blvd. #2500
Los Angeles, CA 90067
"Actress"

**Robert Fuller**
5012 Auckland Avenue
North Hollywood, CA 91601
"Actor"

**Eileen Fulton**
524 West 57th Street, #5330
New York, NY 10019
"Actress"

**Annette Funicello**
16102 Sandy Lane
Encino, CA 91316
"Actress"

**John Furey**
400 South Beverly Drive #101
Beverly Hills, CA 90212
"Actor"

**Mira Furlan**
247 South Beverly Drive #102
Beverly Hills, CA 90212
"Actress"

**Edward Furlong**
9830 Wilshire Blvd.
Beverly Hills, CA 90212
"Actor"

**Stephen Furst**
3900 Huntercrest Court
Moopark, CA 93021
"Actor"

**George Furth**
235 South Reeves Drive #401
Beverly Hills, CA 90212
"Actor, Writer"

**Jim Furyk**
2561 west Ben Hogan Drive
Tucson, AZ 85742
"Golfer"

**Kenny G**
9830 Wilshire Blvd.
Beverly Hills, CA 90212
"Singer"

**Dan Gable**
University of Iowa
216 Field House
Iowa City, IA 52242
"Olympic Wrestling Coach"

**Princess Zsa Zsa Gabor**
1001 Bel Air Road
Los Angeles, CA 90077
"Actress"

**John Gabriel**
100 West 57th Street #5-Q
New York, NY 10019
"Actor"

**Peter Gabriel**
Box 35, Corsham
Wiltshire, London
SW13 8SZ ENGLAND
"Singer, Songwriter"

**Roman Gabriel**
P.O. Box 1676
Little River, SC 39565
"Ex-Football Player"

**Col. Moammar Gaddafi**
State Office
Tripoli, LIBYA
"Politician"

**Max Gail**
P.O. Box 4160
Malibu, CA 90265
"Actor"

**Boyd Gaines**
200 West 57th Street #1407
New York, NY 10019
"Actor"

**Silas Gaither**
9899 Santa Monica Blvd., PBM 2002
Beverly Hills, CA 90212
"Survivor III Contestant"

**John Kenneth Galbraith**
30 Francis Avenue
Cambridge, MA 02138
"Economist"

**Gallagher**
14984 Roan Court
West Palm Beach, FL 33414
"Comedian"

**Helen Gallagher**
260 West End Avenue
New York, NY 10023
"Actress"

**Megan Gallagher**
6500 Wilshire Blvd. #2200
Los Angeles, CA 90048
"Actress"

**Peter Gallagher**
2124 Broadway #131
New York, NY 10023
"Actor"

**Silvana Gallardo**
10637 Burbank Blvd.
No. Hollywood, CA 91601
"Actress"

**Gina Gallego**
6550 Murietta Avenue
Van Nuys, CA 91401
"Actress"

**Zack Galligan**
419 1/2 North Stanley
Los Angeles, CA 90036
"Actor"

**Joe Gallison**
P.O. Box 10187
Wilmington, NC 28405
"Actor"

**Don Galloway**
2501 Colorado Avenue #350
Santa Monica, CA 90404
"Actor"

**Rita Gam**
180 West 58th Street #8B
New York, NY 10019
"Actress"

**Sir Michael Gambon**
76 Oxford Street
London W1D 1BS ENGLAND
"Actor"

**Bruno Ganz**
Glattalstrasse 83
8052 Zurich SWITZERLAND
"Actor"

**Teresa Ganzel**
9460 Wilshire Blvd. #300
Beverly Hills, CA 90212
"Actress"

**Joe Garagiola**
7433 East Tuckey Lane
Scottsdale, AZ 85250
"TV Show Host, Sportscaster"

**Terri Garber**
4526 Wilshire Blvd.
Los Angeles, CA 90010
"Actress"

**Victor Garber**
488 Madison Avenue #8
New York, NY 10022
"Actor"

**Gil Garcetti**
139 North Cliffwood
Los Angeles, CA 90049
"District Attorney"

**Andy Garcia**
1122 S. Robertson #15
Los Angeles, CA 90035
"Actor"

**Jsu Garcia**
11300 West Olympic Blvd. #610
Los Angeles, CA 90064
"Actor"

**Randy Gardner**
4640 Glencove Avenue #6
Marina Del Rey, CA 90291
"Ice Skater"

**Colonel Guy S. Gardner**
316 South Taylor Street
Arlington, VA 22204
"Astronaut"

**Rulon Gardner**
P.O. Box 1242
Laramle, WY 82073
Wrestler"

**Art Garfunkel**
9 East 79th Street
New York, NY 10021
"Singer, Songwriter"

**Beverly Garland**
8014 Briar Summit Drive
Los Angeles, CA 90046
"Actress"

**ex-Sen Jake Garn**
210 South Main Street #600
Salt Lake City, UT 84111
"Ex-Senator"

**James Garner**
33 Oakmont Drive
Los Angeles, CA 90049
"Actor, Director"

**Jennifer Garner**
9701 Wilshire Blvd.
10th Floor
Beverly Hills, CA 90212
"Actress"

**Janeane Garofalo**
1122 South Robertson Blvd. #15
Los Angeles, CA 90035
"Actress"

**Teri Garr**
9150 Wilshire Blvd. #350
Beverly Hills, CA 90212
"Actress"

**Betty Garrett-Parks**
3231 Oakdell Road
Studio City, CA 91604
"Actress"

**Brad Garrett**
9615 Brighton Way #300
Beverly Hills, CA 90210
"Comedian"

**Leif Garrett**
9850 Sandalfoot Blvd. #1640
Los Angeles, CA 90067
"Musician"

**David Garrison**
630 Estrada Redona
Santa Fe, NM 87501
"Actor"

**Frank Garrison**
2715 Charles Road
Odessa, NY 14869
"Survivor III Contestant"

**Greg Garrison**
1655 Hidden Valley Road
Thousand Oaks, CA 91361
"Director"

**Zina Garrison**
P.O. Box 272305
Houston, TX 77277
"Tennis Player"

**Jennie Garth**
1122 South Robertson Blvd. #15
Los Angeles, CA 90035
"Actress"

**Kathy Garver**
620 Country Club Lane
Coronado, CA 92118
"Actress"

**Cyndy Garvey-Truhan**
13924 Panay Way #309
Marina del Rey, CA 90292
"Talk Show Host"

**Steve Garvey**
11718 Barrington Court #6
Los Angeles, CA 90049
"Ex-Baseball Player"

**Julie Garwood**
c/o Ballantine Books
201 East 50th Street
New York, NY 10022
"Author"

**Lorraine Gary**
1158 Tower Drive
Beverly Hills, CA 90210
"Actress"

**Daryl Gates**
756 Portola Terrace
Los Angeles, CA 90042
"Ex-Police Chief"

**William "Bill" Gates**
1 Microsoft Way
Redmond, WA 98052
"Microsoft Co-Founder"

**Larry Gatlin**
5100 Harris Avenue
Kansas City, MO 64133
"Singer, Songwriter"

**Jennifer Gatti**
1801 Avenue of the Stars #902
Los Angeles, CA 90067
"Actress"

**Willie Gault**
P.O. Box 10759
Marina del Rey, CA 90292
"Ex-Football Player"

**Cassandra Gava**
1745 Camino Palmero, #210
Los Angeles, CA 90046
"Actress"

**John Gavin**
2100 Century Park W. #10263
Los Angeles, CA 90067
"Actor"

**Rebecca Gayheart**
853-7th Avenue #9A
New York, NY 10019
"Actress"

**Crystal Gayle**
51 Music Square East
Nashville, TN 37203
"Singer"

**Mitch Gaylord**
P.O. Box 15001
Beverly Hills, CA 90209
"Olympic Gold Medalists"

**George Gaynes**
3344 Campanil Drive
Santa Barbara, CA 93109
"Actor, Director"

**Gloria Gaynor**
P.O. Box 4172
Warren, NJ 07059
"Singer"

**Mitzi Gaynor**
6310 San Vicente Blvd. #330
Los Angeles, CA 90048
"Actor, Dancer"

**Ben Gazzara**
8436 West 3rd Street #740
Los Angeles, CA 90048
"Actor"

**Cynthia Geary**
1640 South Sepulveda blvd. #218
Los Angeles, CA 90025
"Actress"

**Paul Geary**
92 High Street, Unit T-41
Medford, MA 02155
"Musician"

**Nicolei Gedda**
Valhavagen 128
S-11441 Stockholm, SWEDEN
"Tenor"

**Jason Gedrick**
8730 Sunset Blvd. #490
Los Angeles, CA 90069
"Actor"

**Ellen Geer**
21418 West Entrada Road
Topanga, CA 90290
"Actress"

**David Geffen**
100 Universal Plaza
Lakeside Building #601
Universal City, CA 91608
"Record Executive"

**Martha Gehman**
2488 Cheremoya Avenue
Los Angeles, CA 90068
"Actress"

**Larry Gelbart**
807 North Alpine Drive
Beverly Hills, CA 90210
"Writer, Producer"

**Sir Bob Geldof, KBE**
14 Clifford Street
Bond Street House
London W1X 2JD ENGLAND
"Singer"

**Sarah Michelle Gellar**
1122 South Robertson Blvd. #15
Los Angeles, CA 90035
"Actress"

**Uri Geller**
Sonning-on-Thames
Berkshire, ENGLAND
"Psychic"

**Michael Gelman**
7 Lincoln Square
New York, NY 10023
"Actor, Writer"

**The X Generation**
184 Glochester Place
London NW1 ENGLAND
"Rock & Roll Group"

**Genesis**
252 - 260 Regent Street #100
London W1B 3BX ENGLAND
"Rock & Roll Group"

**Hans-Dietrich Genscher**
Am Kottenforst 16
D-53343 Wachtberg-Pech
GERMANY
"Diplomat"

**Bryan Genesse**
9200 Sunset Blvd. #900
Los Angeles, CA 90069
"Actor"

**Peter Gent**
208 North Center Street
Bangor, ME 49013
"Author"

**Jan Gentry**
17803 Green Willow Drive
Tampa, FL 33647
"Survivor V Contestant"

**Boy George (O'Dowd)**
63 Grosvenor Street
London W1X 9DA ENGLAND
"Singer, Composer"

**Lynda Day George**
10310 Riverside Drive #104
Toluca Lake, CA 91602
"Actress"

**Melissa George**
9465 Wilshire Blvd. #600
Beverly Hills, CA 90212
"Actress"

**Susan George**
520 Washington Blvd. #187
Marina del Rey, CA 90292
"Actress"

**Wally George**
14155 Magnolia Blvd. #127
Sherman Oaks, CA 91423
"TV Show Host"

**Rep. Richard Gephardt (MO)**
1226 Cannon House Office Building
Washington, DC 20515
"Politician"

**Geraldo**
17337 Ventura Blvd. #208
Encino, CA 91316
"TV Show Host"

**Gil Gerard**
23679 Calabasas Road #325
Calabasas, CA 91302
"Actor"

**David Gerber**
10800 Chalon Road
Los Angeles, CA 90077
"TV Producer"

**Richard Gere**
14 East 4th Street #509
New York, NY 10012
"Actor"

**David Gergen**
1105 Alvord Court
McLean, VA 22102
"Journalist"

**Jack Germond**
1627 "K" Street NW #1100
Washington, DC 20006
"News Correspondent"

**Gerry & The Pacemakers**
294-296 Nether Street, Finchley
London N3 1RJ ENGLAND
"Music Group"

**Gina Gershon**
120 West 45th Street #3601
New York, NY 10036
"Actress"

**Jami Gertz**
8942 Wilshire Blvd.
Beverly Hills, CA 90211
"Actress"

**David Gest**
150 East 69th Street #21-G
New York, NY 10021
"Producer"

**Malcolm Gets**
155 Spring Street, 6th Floor
New York, NY 10012
"Actor"

**Balthazar Getty**
9460 Wilshire Blvd. #700
Beverly Hills, CA 90212
"Actor"

**Gordon Getty**
2880 Broadway
San Francisco, CA 94115
"Executive, Composer"

**Mrs. J. Paul Getty**
1535 North Beverly Drive
Beverly Hills, CA 90210
"Philanthropist"

**John Getz**
900 Galloway Street
Pacific Palisades, CA 90272
"Actor"

**Alice Ghostley**
3800 Reklaw Drive
North Hollywood, CA 91604
"Actress"

**Marcus Giamatti**
9200 Sunset Blvd. #900
Los Angeles, CA 90069
"Actor"

**Giancarlo Giannini**
Via della Giuliana 101
I-00195 Rome ITALY
"Actor"

**Barry Gibb**
20505 US 19 North #12-290
Clearwater, FL 34624
"Singer"

**Cynthia Gibb**
P.O. Box 1249
White River Junction, VT 05001
"Actress"

**Maurice Gibb**
20505 US 19 North #12-290
Clearwater, FL 34624
"Singer, Songwriter"

**Robin Gibb**
20505 US 19 North #12-290
Clearwater, FL 34624
"Singer, Songwriter"

**Leeza Gibbons**
151 El Camino Drive
Beverly Hills, CA 90212
"TV Show Host"

**Marla Gibbs**
3500 W. Manchester Blvd. #267
Inglewood, CA 90305
"Actress"

**Terri Gibbs**
312 Crawford Mill Lane
Grovetown, GA 30813
"Singer, Songwriter"

**Althea Gibson**
P.O. Box 76
East Orange, NJ 07019
"Tennis Player"

**Charles Gibson**
1965 Broadway #500
New York, NY 10023
"TV Show Host"

**Debbie Gibson**
666 Fifth Avenue #302
New York, NY 10103
"Singer"

**Don Gibson**
P.O. Box 50474
Nashville, TN 37205
"Singer, Songwriter"

**Henry Gibson**
26740 Latigo Shore Drive
Malibu, CA 90265
"Actress"

**Mel Gibson**
1888 Century Park East #500
Los Angeles, CA 90067
"Actor, Writer"

**Thomas Gibson**
6100 Wilshire Blvd. #203
Los Angeles, CA 90036
"Actor"

**Pamela Gidley**
6325 Ivarena Street
Los Angeles, CA 90068
"Actress"

**Frank Gifford**
140 West 57th Street #12A
New York, NY 10019
"Sportscaster"

**Kathie Lee Gifford**
140 West 57th Street #12A
New York, NY 10019
"ex-TV Show Host"

**Herschel Burke Gilbert**
2451 Nichols Canyon
Los Angeles, CA 90046
"Composer, Conductor"

**Melissa Gilbert**
P.O. Box 57593
Sherman Oaks, CA 57593
"Actress"

**Sara Gilbert**
51 West 52nd Street
New York, NY 10019
"Actress"

**Bob Gilder**
1917 NW Bonney Drive
Corvallis, OR 97330
"Golfer"

**Johnny Gill**
1995 Broadway #501
New York, NY 10023
"Singer, Songwriter"

**Vince Gill**
1908 Wedgewood
Nashville, TN 37212
"Singer, Songwriter"

**Ann Gillespie**
526 N. Larchmont Blvd. #210
Los Angeles, CA 90004
"Actress"

**Robert Gillespie**
10 Irving Road
London W14 0JS ENGLAND
"Actor, Director"

**Mickey Gilley**
P.O. Box 1242
Pasadena, TX 77501
"Singer, Songwriter"

**Burton Gilliam**
1427 Tascosa Court
Allen, TX 75013
"Actor"

**Terry Gilliam**
The Old Hall
South Grove Highgate
London N6 6BP ENGLAND
"Actor, Writer, Director"

**Richard Gilliland**
400 South Beverly Drive #102
Beverly Hills, CA 90212
"Actor"

**Billy Gilman**
209 10th Avenue #229
Nashville, TN 37212
C&W Singer"

**Dorothy Gilman**
15 Hill Lane
Westport, CT 06880
"Author"

**David Gilmore**
43 Portland Road
London, W11 4LJ ENGLAND
"Guitarist"

**Peri Gilpin**
9100 Wilshire Blvd. #1000W
Beverly Hills, CA 90212
"Actress"

**Frank Gilroy**
6 Magnin Road
Monroe, NY 10950
"Dramatist"

**Clarence Gilyard, Jr.**
24040 Camino Del Avion #A-239
Monarch Bay, CA 92629
"Actor"

**Jack Ging**
P.O. Box 1131
La Quinta, CA 92253
"Actor"

**Newt Gingrich**
3200 Windy Hill Road #900 West
Atlanta, GA 30339
"Neo-Conserative"

**Ruth Bader Ginsbury**
700 New Hampshire Avenue, NW
Washington, DC 20037
"Supreme Court Justice"

**William Ginsburg**
10100 Santa Monica Blvd., #800
Los Angeles, CA 90067
"Attorney"

**Robert Ginty**
280 S. Beverly Drive #400
Beverly Hills, CA 90212
"Actor"

**Carmine Giovinazzo**
9255 Sunset Blvd. #620
Los Angeles, CA 90069
"Actor"

**Annie Girardot**
20 Ave., Rapp
F-75007 Paris, FRANCE
"Actress"

**Greg Giraldo**
9200 Sunset Blvd. #900
Los Angeles, CA 90069
"Actor"

**Carlo Giuffre**
via Massimi 45
I-00136 Rome, ITALY
"Conductor"

**Rudy Giuliani**
787 Seventh Avenue
New York, NY 10019
"ex-Mayor"

**Hubert Givenchy**
3 Avenue George V
75008 Paris, FRANCE
"Fashion Designer"

**Robin Givens**
P.O. Box 118
Stone Ridge, NY 12484
"Actress"

**Glaser Brothers**
916-19th Avenue South
Nashville, TN 37212
"Music Group"

**Paul Michael Glaser**
1221 Ocean Avenue #1601
Santa Monica, CA 90401
"Actor, Director"

**Philip Glass**
38 East 3rd Street
New York, NY 10003
"Composer"

**Ron Glass**
2485 Wild Oak Drive
Los Angeles, CA 90068
"Actor"

**Glass Tiger**
238 Davenport #126
Toronto, Ontario M5R 1J6
CANADA
"Rock & Roll Group"

**Lola Glaudini**
9150 Wilshire Blvd. #350
Beverly Hills, CA 90212
"Actress"

**Joanna Gleason**
9560 Wilshire Blvd. #516
Beverly Hills, CA 90212
"Actress"

**Kel Gleason**
P.O. Box 1324
Copperas Cove, TX 76522
"Survivor II contestant"

**Paul Gleason**
8436 W. Third Street #740
Los Angeles, CA 90048
"Actor"

**Ex-Sen. John Glenn**
1747 College Road
400 Stillman Hall
Columbus, OH 43212
"Politician, Astronaut"

**Scott Glenn**
P.O. Box 1018
Ketchum, ID 83340
"Actor"

**Sharon Gless**
P.O. Box 48005
Los Angeles, CA 90048
"Actress"

**Bruce Glover**
11449 Woodbine Street
Los Angeles, CA 90066
"Actor"

**Crispin Glover**
3573 Carnation Avenue
Los Angeles, CA 90026
"Actor"

**Danny Glover**
41 Sutter Street #1648
San Francisco, CA 94104
"Actor"

**John Glover**
1505 - 10th Street
Santa Monica, CA 90401
"Actor"

**Julian Glover**
19 Ullswater Road
London SW13 ENGLAND
"Actor"

**Jean-Luc Godard**
15 rue du Nord
CH-1180 Rolle
SWITZERLAND
"Film Director"

**Dale Godboldo**
1850 N. Whitley Avenue #1201
Hollywood, CA 90028
"Actor"

**Mark Goddard**
Chamberlain School
P.O. Box 778
Middleboro, MA 02346
"Actor"

**Trevor Goddard**
9229 Sunset Blvd. #311
Los Angeles, CA 90069
"Actor"

**Alexander Goehr**
11 West Road
Cambridge, ENGLAND
"Composer"

**Bob Goen**
5555 Melrose Avenue, #1
Los Angeles, CA 90038
"TV Performer"

**Bernhard Goetz**
55 West 14th Street
New York, NY 10011
"Subway Shooter"

**Andrew Gold**
22207 Summit View Drive
Woodland Hills, CA 91367
"Singer, Songwriter"

**Elon Gold**
9560 Wilshire Blvd. #516
Beverly Hills, CA 90212
"Comedian"

**Missy Gold**
3500 West Olive Ave. #1400
Burbank, CA 91505
"Actress"

**Tracey Gold**
4619 Goodland Avenue
Studio City, CA 91604
"Actress"

**Adam Goldberg**
1505 10th Street
Santa Monica, CA 90401
"Actor"

**Gary David Goldberg**
25 Oakmont Drive
Los Angeles, CA 90049
"Writer, Producer"

**Leonard Goldberg**
235 Ladera Drive
Beverly Hills, CA 90210
"TV-Film, Producer"

**Whoopi Goldberg**
9171 Wilshire Blvd. #300
Beverly Hills, CA 90210
"Actress, Comedienne"

**Jeff Goldblum**
955 S. Carrillo Drive, #300
Los Angeles, CA 90048
"Actor"

**William Lee Golden**
Rt. 2, Saundersville Road
Hendersonville, TN 37075
"Singer, Songwriter"

**Ricky Paull Golin**
4526 Wilshire Blvd.
Beverly Hills, CA 90210
"Actor"

**William Goldman**
9830 Wilshire Blvd.
Beverly Hills, CA 90212
"Screenwriter"

**Lelia Goldoni**
15459 Wyandotte Street
Van Nuys, CA 91405
"Actress"

**Bobby Goldsboro**
P.O. Box 5250
Ocala, FL 32678
"Singer, Songwriter"

**Kelly Goldsmith**
P.O. Box 9735
Rancho Santa Fe, CA 92067
"Survivor III Contestant"

**Bobcat Goldthwait**
10061 Riverside Drive #760
Toluca Lake, CA 91602
"Actor, Comedian"

**Tony Goldwyn**
1741 North Ivar Street
Hollywood, CA 90028
"Actor"

**Valeria Golino**
9830 Wilshire Blvd.
Beverly Hills, CA 90212
"Actress"

**Arlene Golonka**
515 Ocean Avenue #308N
Santa Monica, CA 90402
"Actress"

**Richard Golub**
42 East 64th Street
New York, NY 10021
"Attorney"

**Panchito Gomez**
P.O. Box 7016
Burbank, CA 91510
"Actor"

**Juan Miguel & Elian Gonzalez**
Marcelo Salado
Cardenas CUBA
"Father & Son who returned to
Cuba"

**Lazaro & Marisleysis Gonzalez**
6341 SW 20th Street
Miami, FL 33155
"Sought custody of Elian Gonzalez"

**Pedro Gonzalez-Gonzalez**
1454 Charles Avenue
Culver City, CA 90230
"Wrestler"

**Dwight Gooden**
6700 - 30th Street So.
St. Petersburg, FL 33712
"Baseball Player"

**Grant Goodeve**
21416 N.E. 68th Court
Redmond, WA 98053
"Actor"

**Linda Goodfriend**
338 S. Beachwood Drive
Burbank, CA 91505
"Actress"

**Cuba Gooding, Jr.**
1122 S. Robertson Blvd., #15
Los Angeles, CA 90035
"Actor"

**Omar Gooding**
3500 West Olive Ave. #1400
Burbank, CA 91505
"Actor"

**Dody Goodman**
13701 Riv erside Drive #201
Sherman Oaks, CA 91423
"Actress"

**John Goodman**
619 Amalfi Drive
Pacific Palisades, CA 90272
"Actor"

**Gail Goodrich**
147 Byram Shore Road
Greenwich, CT 06830
"Ex-Basketball Player"

**Michael Goorjian**
7720 Sunset Blvd.
Los Angeles, CA 90046
"Actor"

**Mikhail S. Gorbachev**
49 Leningradsky Prospekt 209
Moscow, RUSSIA
"Former U.S.S.R. Chairman"

**Ekaterina Gordeeva**
P.O. Box 719
Simsbury, CT 06070
"Ice Skater"

**Barry Gordon**
1801 Avenue of the Stars #902
Los Angeles, CA 90067
"Actor"

**Bruce Gordon**
231-C Tano Road
Santa Fe, NM 87501
"Actor"

**Jeff Gordon**
1730 S. Federal Hwy.
Delray Beach, FL 33483
"Race Car Driver"

**Joey Gordon-Levitt**
4024 Radford Avenue
Building 3
Studio City, CA 91604
"Actor"

**Richard Gordon**
1 Craven Hill
London W2 3EP ENGLAND
"Writer"

**Robby Gordon**
P.O. Box 2037
Cornellius, NC 28031
"Race Car Driver"

**Berry Gordy**
6255 Sunset Blvd. #724
Hollywood, CA 90028
"Record Executive"

**V.P. Albert Gore, Jr.**
P.O. Box 2346
Alexandria, VA 22202
"Ex-Vice President U.S.A."

**Lesley Gore**
297 - 101 Kinderkamack Road
Oradell, NJ 07649
"Actress, Singer"

**Michael Gore**
15622 Royal Oak Road
Encino, CA 91436
"Composer"

**Tipper Gore**
P.O. Box 2346
Alexandria, VA 22202
"Wife of V.P. Albert Gore, Jr."

**Chris Gorham**
8730 Sunset Blvd. #480
Los Angeles, CA 90069
"Actor"

**Eydie Gorme**
944 Pinehurst Drive
Los Vegas, NV 89109
"Singer"

**Karen Lynn Gorney**
P.O. Box 230-1060
New York, NY 10023
"Actress"

**Frank Gorshin**
13701 Riverside Drive #201
Sherman Oaks, CA 91423
"Actor, Comedian"

**Vern Gosdin**
1415 River Landing Way
Woodstock, GA 30188
"Singer, Songwriter"

**Ryan Gosling**
9465 Wilshire Blvd. #212
Beverly Hills, CA 90212
"Actor"

**Mark Paul Gosselaar**
30853 Romero Canyon Road
Castaic, CA 91384
"Actor"

**Louis Gossett, Jr.**
8383 Wilshire Blvd. #550
Beverly Hills, CA 90211
"Actor, Director"

**Robert Gossett**
8306 Wilshire Blvd. #438
Beverly Hills, CA 90211
"Actor"

**Elliott Gould**
21250 Califa #201
Woodland Hills, CA 91367
"Actor"

**Harold Gould**
603 Ocean Avenue, 4 East
Santa Monica, CA 90402
"Actor"

**Robert Goulet**
3110 Monte Rosa
Las Vegas, NV 89120
"Singer"

**Curt Gowdy**
28 Graham Street
Leominster, MA 01453
"Sportscaster"

**Bud Grace**
P.O. Box 66
Oakton, VA 22124
"Cartoonist"

**Don Grady**
1887 Marview Drive
Thousand Oaks, CA 91362
"Actor"

**Steffi Graf**
8921 Andre Dr.
Las Vegas, NV 89113
"Tennis Player"

**Ilene Graff**
11455 Sunshine Terrace
Studio City, CA 91604
"Actress"

**Sue Grafton**
P.O. Box 41447
Santa Barbara, CA 93140
"Novilist"

**Rev. Billy Graham**
P.O. Box 779
Minneapolis, MN 55440
"Evangelist"

**ex-Sen. Bob Graham**
14814 Breckness Place
Miami Lakes, FL 33016
"Politician"

**Gary Graham**
4526 Wilshire Blvd.
Los Angeles, CA 90010
"Actor"

**Heather Graham**
c/o The Firm
9111 Wilshire Blvd. #100W
Los Angeles, CA 90069
"Actress"

**Lauren Graham**
1122 S. Robertson #15
Los Angeles, CA 90035
"Actress"

**Otto Graham**
2216 Riviera Drive
Saratoga, FL 34232
"Ex-Football Player"

**Nancy Grahn**
4910 Agnes Avenue
North Hollywood, CA 91607
"Actress"

**ex-Sen. Phil Gramm (TX)**
2323 Bryan #1500
Dallas, TX 75201
"Politician"

**Kelsey Grammer**
5555 Melrose Avenue, Bung L
Los Angeles, CA 90038
"Actor"

**Fred Grandy**
9417 Spruce Tree Circle
Bethesda, MD 20814
"Actor, Politician"

**Farley Granger**
15 West 72nd Street
New York, NY 10023
"Actor"

**Amy Grant**
9 Music Square South #214
Nashville, TN 37203
"Singer"

**Bud Grant**
8134 Oakmere Road
Bloomington, MN 55438
"Ex-Footboall Coach"

**Eddy Grant**
155-D Holland Park Drive
London W11 4UX ENGLAND
"Singer, Writer"

**Gogi Grant**
10323 Alamo Avenue #202
Los Angeles, CA 90064
"Singer"

**Hugh Grant**
36 Redcliffe Road
London SW10 9NJ ENGLAND
"Actor"

**Johnny Grant**
7000 Hollywood Blvd., PH
Hollywood, CA 90028
"TV Show Host"

**Lee Grant**
610 West End Avenue #7B
New York, NY 10024
"Actress, Director"

**Rodney A. Grant**
8430 Santa Monica Blvd. #200
W. Hollywood, CA 90069
"Actor"

**Guenther Grass**
Glockenglesserstr 21
D-23552 Lubeck GERMANY
"Author"

**Karen Grassle**
P.O. Box 913
Pacific Palisades 90272
"Actress"

**Sen. Charles E. Grassley (IA)**
Senate Hart Building #135
Washington, DC 20510
"Politicain"

**Shirley Ann Grau**
210 Baronne Street #1120
New Orleans, LA 70112
"Writer"

**Grateful Dead**
P.O. Box 1073-C
San Rafael, CA 94915
"Rock & Roll Group"

**Peter Graves**
1122 S. Robertson Blvd. #15
Los Angeles, CA 90035
"Actor"

**Billy Gray**
19612 Grandview Drive
Topanga, CA 90290
"Actor"

**Colleen Gray**
2337 Roscomare Road #2-112
Los Angeles, CA 90077
"Actress"

**Dulcie Gray**
44 Brunswick Gardens
Flat #2
London W8 ENGLAND
"Actress, Author"

**Erin Gray**
11288 Ventura Blvd. #900
Studio City, CA 91604
"Actress"

**Linda Gray**
P.O. Box 1370
Santa Clarita, CA 91386
"Actress, Director"

**Spalding Gray**
22 Wooster Street
New York, NY 10013
"Writer, Actor"

**William H. Gray III**
500 East 62nd Street
New York, NY 10021
"U.N.C.F. President"

**Kathryn Grayson**
2009 La Mesa Drive
Santa Monica, CA 90402
"Actress, Singer"

**Buddy Greco**
Land Title Bldg. #630
Philadelphia, PA 19110
"Singer"

**Green Day**
5337 College Avenue, #555
Oakland, CA 94618
"Musician"

**Al Green**
P.O. Box 456
Millington, TN 38083
"Singer, Clergy"

**Brian Austin Green**
5700 Wilshire Blvd. #575
Los Angeles, CA 90036
"Actor"

**Dallas Green**
548 Guernsey Road
West Grove, PA 19390
"Baseball Manager"

**Ellen Greene**
1505 10th Street
Santa Monica, CA 90401
"Actress, Singer"

**Graham Greene**
121 N. San Vicente Blvd.
Beverly Hills, CA 90211
"Author"

**James Greene**
60 Pope's Grove, Twickenham
Middlesex ENGLAND
"Actor"

**"Mean" Joe Greene**
2121 George Halas Dr. NW
Canton, OH 44708
"Ex-Football Player

**Michele Greene**
P.O. Box 29117
Los Angeles, CA 90029
"Actress"

**Shecky Greene**
1642 Laverne Way
Palm Springs, CA 92264
"Comedian"

**Jeff Greenfield**
1050 Techwood Drive, NW
Atlanta, GA 30318
"News Journalist"

**David Greenlee**
1811 North Whitley #800
Los Angeles, CA 90028
"Actor"

**Alan Greenspan**
2710 Chain Bridge Road, NW
Washington, DC 20016
"Federal Reserve Chairman"

**Bud Greenspan**
33 East 68th Street
New York, NY 10021
"Writer, Producer"

**Bruce Greenwood**
1465 Lindacrest Drive
Beverly Hills, CA 90210
"Actor"

**Lee Greenwood**
P.O. Box 6537
Sevierville, TN 37864
"Singer, Songwriter"

**Michael Greenwood**
14 Kingston House Prince Gate
London SW7 1LJ ENGLAND
"Actor"

**Brodie Greer**
300 S. Raymond Avenue #II
Pasadena, CA 91105
"Actor"

**Dabs Greer**
284 South Madison #102
Pasadena, CA 91101
"Actor"

**Dick Gregory**
P.O. Box 3270
Plymouth, MA 02361
"Activist, Comedian"

**Paul Gregory**
P.O. Box 38
Palm Springs, CA 92262
"Film Producer"

**Wayne Gretzky**
9100 Wilshire Blvd. #1000W
Beverly Hills, CA 90212
"Hockey Player"

**Joel Grey**
404 Park Avenue S., 10th Floor
New York, NY 10016
"Actor, Singer"

**Virginia Grey**
15101 Magnolia Blvd. #54
Sherman Oaks, CA 91403
"Actress"

**Richard Grieco**
2934 1/2 N. Beverly Glen Circle
Suite #252
Los Angeles, CA 90077
"Actor"

**Helmut Griem**
Klugstr. 36
D-80638 Munich GERMANY
"Actor"

**David Alan Grier**
9701 Wilshire Blvd., 10th Floor
Beverly Hills, CA 90212
"Actor"

**Pam Grier**
P.O. Box 370958
Denver, CO 80237
"Actress"

**Rosey Grier**
1250 -4th Street #600
Santa Monica, CA 90401
"Football Player"

**Ken Griffey, Jr.**
9935 Lake Louise Drive
Windemere, FL 34786
"Baseball Player"

**Ken Griffey, Sr.**
24606 Old Black Nugget Road
Issaquah, WA 98029
"Ex-Baseball Player"

**Archie Griffin**
4965 St. Andrews Drive
Westerville, OH 43082
"Ex-Football Player"

**Merv Griffin**
9876 Wilshire Blvd.
Beverly Hills, CA 90210
"Singer, Producer"

**Melanie Griffith**
3110 Main Street #205
Santa Monica, CA 90405
"Actress"

**Nancy Griffith**
509 Hartnell Street
Monterey, CA 93940
"Singer, Songwriter"

**Gary Grimes**
4578 West 165th Street
Lawndale, CA 90260
"Actor"

**Tammy Grimes**
10 East 44th Street #700
New York, NY 10017
"Actress"

**John Grisham**
c/o Randon House
201 East 50th Street
New York, NY 10022
"Author"

**George Grizzard**
400 East 54th Street
New York, NY 10022
"Actor"

**Dick Groat**
320 Beach Street
Pittsburgh, PA 15218
"Ex-Baseball Player"

**Charles Grodin**
9560 Wilshire Blvd. #500
Beverly Hills, CA 90212
"Actor"

**Ferde Grofe, Jr.**
18139 West Coastline
Malibu, CA 90265
"Writer"

**Steve Grogan**
8 Country Club Drive
Foxboro, MA 02035
"Ex-Football Player"

**David Groh**
247 S. Beverly Drive #102
Beverly Hills, CA 90212
"Actor"

**Sam Groom**
8730 Sunset Blvd. #440
Los Angeles, CA 90069
"Actor"

**Arye Gross**
112 South Almont Drive
Los Angeles, CA 90048
"Actor"

**Michael Gross**
888 7th Avenue #602
New York, NY 10106
"Actor"

**Michael Gross**
Paul-Ehrlich-Street 6, D-60596
Frankfurt, GERMANY
"Swimmer"

**Dave Grushin**
200 West Superior #202
Chicago, IL 60710
"Composer"

**Peter Guber**
10202 W. Washington Blvd.
Suite #1070
Culver City, CA 90232
"Film Producer"

**Bob Guccione**
11 Penn Plaza 12th Floor
New York, NY 10001
"Publisher"

**Pedro Guerrero**
435 S. Lafayette Park Place #308
Los Angeles, CA 90057
"Ex-Baseball Player"

**Christopher Guest**
9830 Wilshire Blvd.
Beverly Hills, CA 90212
"Actor, Writer"

**Lance Guest**
9229 Sunset Blvd. #311
Los Angeles, CA 90068
"Actor"

**Carla Gugino**
9830 Wilshire Blvd.
Beverly Hills, CA 90212
"Actress"

**Ron Guidry**
P.O. Box 666
Scott, LA 70583
"Ex-Baseball Player"

**Ann Guilbert**
550 Erskine Drive
Pacific Palisades, CA 90272
"Actress"

**Paul Guilfoyle**
8730 Sunset Blvd. #480
Los Angeles, CA 90069
"Actor"

**Robert Guillaume**
4709 Noeline Avenue
Encino, CA 91436
"Actor"

**John Guillerman**
309 S. Rockingham Avenue
Los Angeles, CA 90049
"Film Director"

**Cathy Guisewite**
4520 Main Street #700
Kansas City, MO 64111
"Cartoonist"

**Tito Guizar**
Sierra Madre
640 Lomas Drive Chaupultepec
Mexico City 10 09999 MEXICO
"Actor, Guitarist"

**Bryant Gumbel**
524 West 57th Street
New York, NY 10019
"TV Show Host"

**Greg Gumbel**
220 Heatherwood Court
Winter Springs, FL 33708
"Sports Anchor"

**Guns & Roses**
1229 Menlo Drive
Davis, CA 95616
"Rock & Roll Group"

**Dan Gurney**
2334 South Broadway
Santa Ana, CA 92707
"Race Car Drive"

**HM King Carl Gustav XVI**
Kungliga Slottet
11130 Stockholm SWEDEN
"Royalty"

**Arlo Guthrie**
55 North Street
Pittsfield, MA 01201
"Singer, Songwriter"

**Steve Guttenburg**
1401 Calle Del Jonella
Pacific Palisades, CA 90272
"Actor"

**Lucy Gutteridge**
76 Oxford Street
London W1N 0AX ENGLAND
"Actress"

**Jasmine Guy**
21243 Ventura Blvd. #101
Woodland Hills, CA 91364
"Actress, Singer"

**Tony Gwynn**
15643 Boulder Ridge Lane
Poway, CA 92064
"Baseball Player"

# H

**James "Gypsy" Haake**
1256 North Flores #1
Los Angeles, CA 90069
"Actor"

**Jay Haas**
4 Tuscany Center
Greer, SC 29650
"Golfer"

**Lukas Haas**
409 North Camden Drive #202
Beverly Hills, CA 90210
"Actor"

**Shelley Hack**
1208 Georgina
Santa Monica, CA 90402
"Actress, Model"

**Buddy Hackett**
800 North Whittier Drive
Beverly Hills, CA 90210
"Comedian, Actor"

**Gene Hackman**
9830 Wilshire Blvd.
Beverly Hills, CA 90212
"Actor"

**Brett Hadley**
5070 Woodley Avenue
Encino, CA 91436
"Actor"

**Jerry Hadley**
204 West 10th Street
New York, NY 10014
"Tenor"

**Molly Hagan**
9300 Wilshire Blvd. #555
Beverly Hills, CA 90212
"Actress"

**Sammy Hagar**
P.O. Box 5395
Novato, CA 94948
"Singer"

**Sen. Chuck Hagel**
11301 Davenport Street #2
Omaha, NE 68154
"Poiltician"

**Nina Hagen**
c/o Ariola Postfach
80 01 49 , D-81601
Munich, Germany
"Singer"

**Uta Hagen**
27 Washington Square N.
New York, NY 10011
"Actress"

**Julie Hagerty**
9465 Wilshire Blvd. #600
Beverly Hills, CA 90212
"Actress"

**Merle Haggard**
235 Murrell Meadows Drive #72
Sevierville, TN 37876
"Singer"

**Dan Haggerty**
5812 Comanche Avenue
Woodland Hills, CA 91367
"Actor"

**H.B. Haggerty**
10000 Riverside Drive #10
Toluca Lake, CA 91602
"Actor"

**Marvin Hagler**
c/o G. Webb
P.O. Box 282
Whitman, MA 02382
"Boxer"

**Larry Hagman**
9950 Sulpher Mountain Road
Ojai, CA 93023
"Actor, Director"

**Mayor James Hahn**
City Hall
200 North Spring Street
Los Angeles, CA 90012
"Politician"

**Jessica Hahn**
6345 Balboa Blvd. #375
Encino, CA 91316
"Radio Personality"

**Charles Haid**
4376 Forman Avenue
North Hollywood, CA 91602
"Actor, Producer"

**General Alexander Haig, Jr.**
685 Island Drive
Palm Beach, FL 32480
"Former Militay Leader"

**Arthur Hailey**
P.O. Box N-7776
Lyford Cay
Nassau, BAHAMAS
"Writer"

**Oliver Hailey**
11747 Canton Place
Studio City, CA 91604
"Screenwriter"

**Connie Haines**
880 Mandalay Avenue #3-109
Cleanwater Beach, FL 34630
"Singer"

**Randa Haines**
132 S. Rodeo Drive #300
Beverly Hills, CA 90212
"TV Director"

**Jester Hairston**
5047 Valley Ridge Avenue
Los Angeles, CA 90043
"Actor"

**Ron Hajak**
17420 Ventura Blvd. #4
Encino, CA 91316
"Actor"

**Khrystyne Haje**
P.O. Box 8750
Universal City, CA 91608
"Actress"

**David Halberstam**
c/o WMA
1325 Avenue of the Americas
New York, NY 10019
"Author"

**Barbara Hale**
P.O. Box 6061-261
Sherman Oaks, CA 91413
"Actress"

**Georgina Hale**
74A St. John's Wood
High Street
London NW8 ENGLAND
"Actress"

**Monte Hale**
4700 Western Heritage Way
Los Angeles, CA 90027
"Actor"

**Anthony Michael Hall**
8942 Wilshire Blvd. #219
Beverly Hills, CA 90211
"Actor"

**Arsenio Hall**
9701 Wilshire Blvd. #10th Flor
Beverly Hills, CA 90212
"TV Show Host, Actor"

**Diedre Hall**
11041 Santa Monica Blvd., PMB
715
Los Angeles, CA 90025
"Actress"

**Fawn Hall**
1568 Viewsite Drive
Los Angeles, CA 90069
"Secretary, Model"

**Jerry Hall**
471-473 Kings Road
London SW10 OLU ENGLAND
"Model"

**Lani Hall**
360 South La Clenega Blvd.
Los Angeles, CA 90048
"Singer, Songwriter"

**Michael C. Hall**
c/o Greenblatt & Janollari
1438 North Gower
Hollywood, CA 90028
"Actor"

**Monty Hall**
519 North Arden Drive
Beverly Hills, CA 90210
"TV Show Host"

**Regina Hall**
9255 Sunset Blvd. #210
Los Angeles, CA 90069
"Actress"

**Robert David Hall**
8087 Wilshire Blvd. #300
Los Angeles, CA 90036
"Actor"

**Tom T. Hall**
P.O. Box 198888
Nashville, TN 37219
"Singer, Songwriter"

**John Hallan**
51 Lansdowne Gardens
London, SW8 2EL, ENGLAND
"Actor"

**Tom Hallick**
13900 Tahiti Way #108
Marina del Rey, CA 90292
"Actor"

**Lori Hallier**
9255 Sunset Blvd. #920
West Hollywood, CA 90069
"Actress"

**Geri Halliwell**
19 - 21 Mortimer Street
London W1N 8DX ENGLAND
"Ex-Spice Girl"

**Jack Ham**
540 Lindbergh Drive
Moon Township, PA 15108
"Football Player"

**Alan Hamel**
P.O. Box 827
Monterey, CA 93942
"TV Personality"

**Veronica Hamel**
15821 Ventura Blvd. #235
Encino, CA 91436
"Actress"

**Dorothy Hamill**
P.O. Box 16286
Baltimore, MD 21210
"Ice Skater"

**Mark Hamill**
P.O. Box 124
Malibu, CA 90265
"Actor"

**Pete Hamill**
NY Daily News
220 East 42nd Street
New York, NY 10017
"Journalist & Author"

**George Hamilton IV**
203 SW Third Avenue
Gainesville, FL 32601
"Singer"

**Guy Hamilton**
22 Mont Port
E-07157 Port d'Andratx
Mallorca, SPAIN
"Film Director"

**Josh Hamilton**
151 El Camino Drive
Beverly Hills, CA 90212
"Actor"

**Rep. Lee Hamilton (IN)**
1201 East 10th Street, #107
Jeffersonville, IN 47130
"Politicain"

**Linda Hamilton**
8955 Norman Place
West Hollywood, CA 90069
"Actress"

**Lynn Hamilton**
P.O. Box 36012
Los Angeles, CA 90036
"Actress"

**Scott Hamilton**
13041 Ventura Blvd.
Studio City, CA 91604
"Ice Skater"

**Victoria Hamilton**
18/21 Jermyn Street, 3rd Floor
London SW1Y 6HP ENGLAND
"Actress"

**Harry Hamlin**
612 North Sepulveda Blvd. #10
Los Angeles, CA 90049
"Actor"

**Marvin Hamlisch**
970 Park Avenue #501
New York, NY 10028
"Composer, Pianist"

**Mia Hamm**
1801 South Prairie Avenue
Chicago, IL 60616
"Soccer Player"

**Hammer**
141 Dunbar Avenue
Fords, NJ 08863
"Rap Singer"

**John Hammond**
P.O. Box 170429
San Francisco, CA 94117
"Singer, Guitarist"

**Nicholas Hammond**
P.O. Box 386
Woollahra NSW 1350 AUSTRALIA
"Actor"

**Earl Hamner**
11575 Amanda Drive
Studio City, CA 91604
"TV Writer, Producer"

**Susan Hampshire**
123a Kings Road
London SW3 4PL ENGLAND
"Actress"

**James Hampton**
4251 Mary Ellen Avenue #E-8
Studio City, CA 91604
"Actor"

**Herbie Hancock**
88 Roxiticus Road
Far Hills, NJ 07931
"Pianist, Composer"

**Evan Handler**
252 North Larchmont Blvd. #200
Los Angeles, CA 9004
"Actor"

**Lee Haney**
105 Trall Point
Fairburn, GA 30213
"Singer"

**Tom Hanks**
8500 Wilshire Blvd. #700
Beverly Hills, CA 90211
"Actor"

**Bridget Hanley**
12021 Hesby Street
Valley Village, CA 91607
"Actress"

**Daryl Hannah**
1465 Lindacrest Drive
Beverly Hills, CA 90210
"Actress"

**Alyson Hannigan**
1122 S. Robertson Blvd. #15
Los Angeles, CA 90035
"Actress"

**Gunnar Hansen**
P.O. Box 368
North East Harbor, ME 04662
"Actor"

**Hanson**
1045 West 78th Street
Tulsa, OK 74132
"Music Trio"

**Curtis Hanson**
21 Eastwind Street
Marina del Rey, CA 90292
"Writer, Poet"

**Sir James Hanson**
180 Brompton Road
London SW3 1HF ENGLAND
"Film Director"

**Otto Harbach**
3455 Congress Street
Fairfield, CT 06430
"Lyricist"

**Anfernee "Penny" Hardaway**
P.O. Box 2132
Farmington Hills, MI 48333
"Basketball Player"

**Marcia Gay Harden**
1358 Woodbrook Lane
Southlake, TX 76092
"Actress"

**Melora Hardin**
3256 Hiloak Drive
Los Angeles, CA 90068
"Actress"

**Jerry Hardin**
3033 Vista Crest Drive
Los Angeles, CA 90068
"Actor"

**Kadeem Hardison**
19743 Valleyview Drive
Topanga, CA 90290
"Actor"

**Billy Hardwick**
1576 South White Station
Memphis, TN 38117
"Bowler"

**Robert Hardy**
123a Kings Street
London SW3 4PL ENGLAND
"Actor"

**Dorian Harewood**
2 Bearwood Drive
Toronto, Ont. M9A 4G4 CANADA
"Actress"

**Billy James Hargis**
Rose of Sharon Farm
Neosho, MO 64840
"Evangelist"

**Mariska Hargitay**
77 Park Avenue #15E
New York, NY 10016
"Actress"

**Dean Hargrove**
474 Halvern Drive
Los Angeles, CA 90049
"TV Writer, Producer"

**Marion Hargrove**
401 Monica Avenue #6
Santa Monica, CA 90403
"TV Writer"

**Susannah Harker**
55 Ashburnham Grove
Greenwich, London
SW10 8UJ ENGLAND
"Actress"

**Peter Harkey**
256 Orchard Street
Millis, MA 02054
"Survivor IV Contestant"

**Sen. Tom Harkin (IA)**
731 Hart Senate Office Building
Washington, DC 20510
"Politician"

**John Harkins**
121 N. San Vicente Blvd.
Beverly Hills, CA 90211
"Actor"

**Harlem Globetrotters**
400 East Van Buen #300
Phoenix, AZ 85004
"Comedy Basketball Team"

**Renny Harlin**
8800 Sunset Blvd. #400
Los Angeles, CA 90069
"Director"

**Katie Harman**
3631 NW First Court
Gresham, OH 97030
"Miss America 2002"

**Debbie Harmon**
13243 Valley Heart
Sherman Oaks, CA 91423
"Actress"

**Kelly Harmon**
13224 Old Oak Lane
Los Angeles, CA 90049
"Actress"

**Larry Harmon**
10509 Wilshire Blvd. #1604
Los Angeles, CA 90024
"Film Executive"

**Manny Harmon**
8350 Santa Monica Blvd.
Los Angeles, CA 90069
"Conductor"

**Mark Harmon**
2236 Encinitas Blvd. #A
Encinitas, CA 92024
"Actor"

**Winsor Harmon**
c/o CBS/B&B
7800 Beverly Blvd. #3371
Los Angeles, CA 90036
"Actor"

**Magda Harout**
13452 Vose Street
Van Nuys, CA 91405
"Actress"

**Bill Harper**
1180 South Beverly Drive #608
Los Angeles, CA 90035
"Humour Writer & Columnist"

**Heather Harper**
20 Milverton Road
London NW67AS ENGLAND
"Actress"

**Jessica Harper**
15430 Brownwood Place
Los Angeles, CA 90077
"Actress"

**Ron Harper**
13317 Ventura Blvd #1
Sherman Oaks, CA 91423
"Actor"

**Tess Harper**
8484 Wilshire Blvd. #500
Beverly Hills, CA 90211
"Actress"

**Valerie Harper**
P.O. Box 7187
Beverly Hills, CA 90212
"Actress"

**The Harptones**
55 West 119th Street
New York, NY 10026
"Vocal Group"

**Woody Harrelson**
9830 Wilshire Blvd.
Beverly Hills, CA 90212
"Actor"

**Curtis Harrington**
6286 Vine Way
Los Angeles, CA 90028
"Film Director"

**Pat Harrington**
730 Marzella Avenue
Los Angeles, CA 90049
"Actor, Writer"

**Bishop Barbara Harris**
138 Tremont Street
Boston, MA 02111
"Clergy"

**Ed Harris**
22031 Carbon Mesa
Malibu, CA 90265
"Actor"

**Emmylou Harris**
P.O. Box 158568
Nashville, TN 37215
"Singer, Songwriter"

**Estelle Harris**
9200 Sunset Blvd. #900
Los Angeles, CA 90069
"Actress"

**Franco Harris**
200 Chauser Court So.
Sewickley, PA 15143
"Ex-Football Player"

**Jared Harris**
259 West 6th Street
Claremont, CA 91711
"Actor"

**Julie Harris**
P.O. Box 1287
West Chatham, MA 02669
"Actress"

**Marilyn Harris**
217 North San Marino Avenue
San Gabriel, CA 91775
"Record Executive"

**Mel Harris**
5670 Wilshire Blvd., #8210
Los Angeles, CA 90048
"Actress"

**Neil Patrick Harris**
1122 South Robertson Blvd. #15
Los Angeles, CA 90035
"Actor"

**Sam Harris**
13701 Riverside Drive #201
Sherman Oaks, CA 91423
"Singer"

**Steve Harris**
8383 Wilshire Blvd. #550
Beverly Hills, CA 90211
"Actor"

**Susan Harris**
11828 La Grange #200
Los Angeles, CA 90025
"TV Producer"

**Gregory Harrison**
4526 Wilshire Blvd.
Los Angeles, CA 90010
"Singer, Songwriter"

**Linda Harrison**
16 Beverly Park
Beverly Hills, CA 90210
"Actress"

**Kathryn Harrold**
9200 Sunset Blvd. #1130
Los Angeles, CA 90069
"Actress"

**Lisa Harrow**
46 Albermarle Street
London W1X 4PP ENGLAND
"Actress"

**Deborah Harry**
8436 West Third Street #650
Los Angeles, CA 90048
"Singer"

**HRH Prince Harry**
Highgrove House
Gloucestershire ENGLAND
"Royalty"

**Ray Harryhausen**
2 Lichester Place
London W14 8AA ENGLAND
"Special Effect Technician"

**Bret "Hit Man" Hart**
435 Patina Place S.W.
Calgary Alberto
T3H 2P5 CANADA
"Wrestler"

**Corey Hart**
1445 Lambert Close #300
Montreal, Q H3H 1Z5
CANADA
"Singer, Songwriter"

**Mother Dolores**
(Dolores Hart)
Regina Laudis Convent
Bethlehem, CT 06751
"Actress, Nun"

**Freddie Hart**
317 N. Kenwood
Burbank, CA 91505
"Singer"

**Gary Hart**
950 - 17th Stree #2050
Denver, CO 80202
"Ex-Senator"

**Jim Hart**
207 Anthony Hall-SIUC
Carbondale, IL 62901
"Ex-Football Player"

**John Hart**
35109 Highway 79 #134
Warner Springs, CA 92086
"Actor"

**Mary Hart**
c/o ET
5555 Melrose Avenue #L
Los Angeles, CA 90038
"TV Show Host"

**Melissa Joan Hart**
10880 Wilshire Blvd. #1101
Los Angeles, CA 90024
"Actress"

**Mariette Hartley**
10110 Empyrean Way #304
Los Angeles, CA 90067
"Actress"

**Ted Hartley**
524 N. Rockingham Avenue
Los Angeles, CA 90049
" Actor"

**Jim Hartz**
475 L'Enfant Plaza
Washington, DC 20024
"TV Show Host"

**Anthony Harvey**
101 Park Avenue #4300
New York, NY 10107
"Film Director"

**Paul Harvey**
1035 Park Avenue
River Forest, IL 60305
"News Analyst"

**PJ Harvey**
535 Kings Road
The Plaza
London SW10 OS ENGLAND
"Singer"

**Steve Harvey**
9465 Wilshire Blvd. #517
Beverly Hills, CA 90212
"Comedian"

**Ernie Harwell**
c/o Comeria Park
Detroit, MI 48216
"Sportscaster"

**Eugene Hasenfus**
c/o General Delivery
Marinette, WI 54143
"Ex-Flight Master"

**Colleen Haskell**
9899 Santa Monica Blvd., PBM
2002
Beverly Hills, CA 90212
"CBS Survivor Contestant"

**Jimmie Haskell**
11800 Laughton Way
Northridge, CA 91326
"Composer, Conductor"

**Peter Haskell**
19924 Acre Street
Northridge, CA 91324
"Actor"

**Dennis Haskins**
345 N. Maple Drive #302
Beverly Hills, CA 90210
"Actor"

**David Hasselhoff**
5180 Louise Avenue
Encino, CA 91316
"Actor"

**Marilyn Hassett**
8905 Rosewood Avenue
Los Angeles, CA 90048
"Actress"

**Rep. J. Dennis Hastert (IL)**
2263 Rayburn House Office Bldg.
Washington, DC 20515
"Politicain"

**Rep. Alcee Hastings (FL)**
Longworth House Office Building
#1039
Washington, DC 20515
"Politicain"

**Bob Hastings**
620 S. Sparks Street
Burbank, CA 91505
"Actor"

**Don Hastings**
524 West 57th Street #5330
New York, NY 10019
"Actor"

**Sen. Orrin G. Hatch (UT)**
Senat Russell Bldg. #131
Washington DC 20510
"Politician"

**Richard Hatch**
P.O. Box 46519
Los Angeles, CA 90046
"Actor"

**Teri Hatcher**
10100 Santa Monica Blvd. #410
Los Angeles, CA 90067
"Actress"

**Juliana Hatfield**
1 Camp Street, #2
Cambridge, MA 02140
"Singer"

**Shawn Hatosy**
853 - 7th Avenue, #9A
New York, NY 10019
"Actor"

**Rutger Hauer**
20 Ocean Park Blvd. #25
Santa Monica, CA 90405
"Actor"

**Wings Hauser**
15821 Ventura Blvd. #235
Encino, CA 91436
"Actor"

**President Vaclav Havel**
Hradecek
CZ-11908  Prague
CZECHOSLOVAKIA REPUBLIC
"Politician"

**Richie Havens**
123 West 44th Street #11A
New York, NY 10036
"Singer, Guitarist"

**June Haver**
485 Halvern Drive
Los Angeles, CA 90049
"Actress"

**Nigel Havers**
125 Gloucester Road
London SW7 4TE ENGLAND
"Actor"

**June Havoc**
405 Old Long Ridge Road
Stamford, CT 06903
"Actress"

**Susan Hawk**
P.O. Box 36685
Las Vegas, NV 89133
"Actress"

**Ethan Hawke**
9460 Wilshire Blvd. #700
Beverly Hills, CA 90212
"Actor"

**Edwin Hawkins**
2041 Locust Street
Philadelphia, PA 19103
"Singer"

**Sophie B. Hawkins**
520 Washington Blvd. #337
Marina del Rey, CA 90292
"Singer"

**John Hawksworth**
24 Cottersmore Gardens #2
London W8 5PR ENGLAND
"TV Writer, Producer"

**Goldie Hawn**
8500 Wilshire Blvd. #700
Beverly Hills, CA 90211
"Actress"

**Tom Hayden**
152 Wadsworth
Santa Monica, CA 90405
"Politician"

**Julie Hayek**
5645 Burning Tree Drive
La Canada, CA 91011
"Actress, Model"

**Salma Hayek**
P.O. Box 57593
Sherman Oaks, CA 91403
"Actress"

**Bill Hayes**
4528 Beck Avenue
North Hollywood, CA 91602
"Actor"

**Billie Hayes**
P.O. Box 69493
Los Angeles, CA 90069
"Actress"

**Darren Hayes**
95 Buckley Avenue
Sausalito, CA 94965
"Singer"

**Elvin Hayes**
252 Piney Point Road
Houston, TX 77024
"Ex-Basketball Player"

**Isaac Hayes**
8942 Wilshire Blvd.
Beverly Hills, CA 90212
"Singer, Songwriter"

**Sean Hayes**
1122 S. Robertson Blvd. #15
Los Angeles, CA 90035
"Actor

**Susan Seaforth Hayes**
4528 Beck Avenue
North Hollywood, CA 91602
"Actress"

**Jim Haynie**
10100 Santa Monica Blvd. #2500
Los Angeles, CA 90067
"Actor"

**Robert Hays**
919 Victoria Avenue
Venice, CA 90291
"Actor"

**Dennis Haysbert**
1242 South Holt Avenue
Los Angeles, CA 90035
"Actor"

**Jonathan Haze**
3636 Woodhill Canyon
Studio City, CA 91604
"Actor"

**Glenne Headley**
8942 Wilshire Blvd.
Beverly Hills, CA 90211
"Actress"

**Mary Healy**
8641 Robinson Ridge Drive
Las Vegas, NV 89117
"Actress"

**George Hearn**
200 West 57th Street #900
New York, NY 10019
"Actor"

**Thomas Hearnes**
3165 Castle Canyon Avenue
Henderson, NV 89052
"Boxer"

**Patricia Hearst**
110-5th Street
San Francisco, CA 94103
"Author"

**Mrs. Victoria Hearst**
865 Comstock Avenue
Los Angeles, CA 90024
"Wife of William Hearst"

**Heart**
P.O. Box 3172
Beverly Hills, CA 90212
"Rock & Roll Group"

**Eric Heatherly**
P.O. Box 24895
Chattanooga, TN 37422
"Singer"

**Patricia Heaton**
8949 Sunset Blvd. #201
Los Angeles, CA 90069
"Actress"

**Heatwave**
6464 Sunset Blvd. #1010
Hollywood, CA 90028
"R&B Group"

**Anne Heche**
151 El Camino Dive
Beverly Hills, CA 90212
"Actress"

**Jessica Hecht**
1505 - 10th Street
Santa Monica, CA 90401
"Actress"

**Gina Hecht-Herskowitz**
5930 Foothill Drive
Los Angeles, CA 90068
"Actress"

**Tippi Hedren**
P.O. Box 189
Acton, CA 93510
"Actress"

**Hee Haw**
P.O. Box 140400
Nashville, TN 37214
"Comedy Show"

**Amy Heckerling**
1330 Schuyler Road
Beverly Hills, CA 90210
"Film Director"

**Dan Hedaya**
151 El Camino Drive
Beverly Hills, CA 90212
"Actor"

**David (Al) Hedison**
P.O. Box 1470
Beverly Hills, CA 90213
"Actor"

**Howell Heflin**
311 East 6th Street
Tuscumbia, AL 35674
"Politician"

**Christie Hefner**
680 North Lakeshore Drive
Chicago, IL 60611
"Hugh Hefner's Daughter"

**Hugh Hefner**
10236 Charing Cross Road
Los Angeles, CA 90077
"Publishing Executive"

**Neal Heftl**
9454 Wilshire Blvd. #405
Beverly Hills, CA 90212
"Composer"

**Robert Hegyes**
2404 Pacific Avenue
Venice, CA 90291
"Actor"

**Eric Heiden**
82 Sandburg Drive
Sacramento, CA 95819
"Skater"

**Katherine Heigl**
8436 West Third Street #650
Los Angeles, CA 90048
"Actress"

**Carol Heiss-Jenkins**
3183 Regency Plaza
Westlake, OH 44145
"Actress"

**Carl Held**
1817 Hillcrest Road #51
Los Angeles, CA 90068
"Actor"

**Annette Helde**
8430 Santa Monica Blvd. #200
Los Angeles, CA 90036
"Actress"

**Marg Helgenberger**
1122 S. Robertson Blvd. #15
Los Angeles, CA 90035
"Actress"

**Levon Helm**
160 Plochmann Lane
Woodstock, NY 12498
"Actor"

**Katherine Helmond**
151 El Camino Drive
Beverly Hills, CA 90212
"Actress"

**Leona Helmsley**
Park Lane Hotel
36 Central Park South
New York, NY 10019
"Hotel Executive"

**R.J. Helton**
7 North Mountain Avenue
Montclair, NJ 07042
"American Idol Finalist"

**Mariel Hemingway**
P.O. Box 2249
Ketchum, ID 83340
"Actress"

**Sherman Hemsley**
P.O. Box 5344
Sherman Oaks, CA 91413
"Actor"

**Florence Henderson**
P.O. Box 11295
Marina del Rey, CA 90295
"Singer, Actor"

**Rickey Henderson**
10561 Englewood Drive
Oakland, CA 94621
"Baseball Player"

**Skitch Henderson**
Hunt Hill Farm
RFD #3 Upland Road
New Milford, CT 06776
"Composer, Conductor"

**Thomas "Hollywood" Henderson**
7 Seafield Lane
Westhampton Beach, NY 11978
"Ex-Football Player"

**Lauri Hendler**
4034 Stone Canyon Avenue
Sherman Oaks, CA 91403
"Actress"

**Heike Henkel**
Tannenbergstr. 57
D-51373 Leverkusen
GERMANY
"Track Athlete"

**Marilu Henner**
151 El Camino Drive
Beverly Hills, CA 90212
"Actress"

**Linda Kaye Henning**
4342 Tujunga Avenue
Studio City, CA 91604
"Actress"

**Paul Henning**
4250 Navajo Street
Toluca Lake, CA 91602
"Actor"

**Tom Henrich**
1547 Albino Trail
Dewey, AZ 86327
"Ex-Baseball Player"

**Lance Henriksen**
1505 10th Street
Santa Monica, CA 90401
"Actor"

**Clarence "Frogman" Henry**
3309 Lawrence Street
New Orleans, LA 70114
"Singer, Guitarist"

**Buck Henry**
117 East 57th Street
New York, NY 10019
"Writer, Producer"

**Gloria Henry**
6442 Coldwater Canyon Ave. #206
North Hollywood, CA 91606
"Actress"

**Gregg Henry**
8956 Appian Way
Los Angeles, CA 90046
"Actor"

**Justin Henry**
1450 Franklin Street #A
Santa Monica, CA 90404
"Child Actor"

**Jon Hensley**
1505 10th Street
Santa Monica, CA 90401
"Actor"

**Pamela Hensley**
9526 Dalegrove Drive
Beverly Hills, CA 90210
"Actress"

**Natasha Henstridge**
1122 South Robertson Blvd. #15
Los Angeles, CA 90035
"Actress"

**Hans Werner Henze**
La Leprara
via Del Fontonile
00047 Marino ITALY
"Composer, Conductor"

**Richard Herd**
P.O. Box 56297
Sherman Oaks, CA 91413
"Actor"

**Jerry Herman**
1196 Cabrillo Drive
Beverly Hills, CA 90210
"Composer, Lyricist"

**Herman's Hermits**
P.O. Box 1821
Ojai, CA 93024
"Rock & Roll Group"

**Pee Wee Herman**
P.O. Box 29373
Los Angeles, CA 90029
"Actor"

**Keith Hernandez**
255 East 49th Street #28-D
New York, NY 10017
"Ex-Baseball Player"

**Willie Hernandez**
Calle C Buzon 125
Aguada PUERTO RICO 10017
"Baseball Player"

**Ty Herndon**
P.O. Box 128529
Nashville, TN 37212
"Actor"

**Lynn Herring**
4702 North 36th Street
Phoenix, AZ 85018
"Actress"

**Edward Herrmann**
1505 - 10th Street
Santa Monica, CA 90401
"Actor"

**Barbara Hershey**
8942 Wilshire Blvd., #219
Beverly Hills, CA 90211
"Actress"

**Maralyn Hershey**
37337 Green level Road
Wakefield, VA 23888
"CBS Survivor Contestant"

**Orel Hershiser**
5277 Isleworth Country Club Drive
Windemere, FL 34786
"Baseball Player"

**Jason Hervey**
1755 Seaview Trail
Los Angeles, CA 90046
"Actor"

**Eva Herzigova**
199 Lafayette Street #700
New York, NY 10012
"Model"

**Werner Herzog**
Turkenstr. 91
D-80799 Munich GERMANY
"Film Director"

**Whitey Herzog**
9426 Sappington Estates Dr.
St. Louis, MO 63127
"Baseball Manager"

**Howard Hesseman**
7146 La Presa
Los Angeles, CA 90068
"Actor, Director"

**Charlton Heston**
2859 Coldwater Canyon
Beverly Hills, CA 90210
"Actor, Director"

**Don Hewitt**
555 West 57th Street
New York, NY 10019
"Writer, Producer"

**Heather Hewitt**
6324 Tahoe Drive
Los Angeles, CA 90068
"Actress"

**Jennifer Love Hewitt**
14044 Ventura Blvd. #308
Sherman Oaks, CA 91423
"Actress"

**Martin Hewitt**
2396 Fitzgerald Road
Simi Valley, CA 93065
"Actor"

**Donald Hewlett**
King's Head House, Island Wall
Whitstable
Kent CT5 1EP ENGLAND
"Actor"

**Anne Heywood**
9966 Liebe Drive
Beverly Hills, CA 90210
"Actress"

**Dwayne Hickman**
P.O. Box 17226
Encino, CA 91416
"Actor"

**Catherine Hicks**
1122 South Robertson Blvd. #15
Los Angeles, CA 90035
"Actress"

**Dan Hicks**
P.O. Box 245
Sausalito, CA 94966
"Singer, Songwriter"

**Jack Higgins**
Septembertide
Mont De La Rocqque
Jersey Channel Islands
ENGLAND
"Writer"

**Joel Higgins**
9301 Wilshire Blvd. #300
Beverly Hills, CA 90210
"Actor"

**Gerald Hiken**
910 Moreno Avenue
Palo Alto, CA 94303
"Actor"

**Hildegarde**
Mary Manning Walsh Home
1339 York Avenue
New York, NY 10021
"Singer"

**Tommy Hilfiger**
485 Fifth Avenue
New York, NY 10017
"Fashion Designer"

**Anita Hill**
600 Third Avenue #200
New York, NY 10016
"Professor of Law"

**Arthur Hill**
1515 Clubview Drive
Los Angeles, CA 90024
"Actor"

**Faith Hill**
3310 West End Avenue #500
Nashville, TN 37203
"Singer"

**Grant Hill**
One Magic Place
Orlando, FL 32801
"Basketball Player"

**Lauryn Hill**
151 El Camino Drive
Beverly Hills, CA 90212
"Singer"

**Steven Hill**
18 Jill Lane
Monsey, NY 10952
"Actor"

**Terrence Hill**
3 Los Pinos Road
Santa Fe, NM 87505
"Actor"

**Virgill Hill**
117 Santa Gertudis
Bismarck, ND 58501
"Boxer"

**Sir Edmund Hillary**
278A Remuera Road
Auckland SE2 NEW ZEALAND
"Mountaineer"

**Arthur Hiller**
1218 Benedict Canyon
Beverly Hills, CA 90210
"Film Director"

**Dame Wendy Hiller**
Beaconsfield
Stratton Road
Buckinghamshire ENGLAND
"Actress"

**John Hillerman**
1110 Bade Street
Houston, TX 77055
"Actor"

**Carla Hills**
3125 Chain Bridge Road NW
Washington, DC 20018
"Ex-Government Official"

**Barron Hilton**
9336 Civic Center Drive
Beverly Hills, CA 90210
"Hotel Executive"

**John Hinckley, Jr.**
St. Elizabeth's Hospital
2700 Martin Luther King Avenue
Washington, DC 20005
"Attempted to kill Ronald Reagan"

**Gregory Hines**
4009 1/2 Ocean Front Walk
Venice, CA 90292
"Actor"

**Mimi Hines**
1605 South 11th Street
Las Vegas, NV 89109
"Actress"

**Pat Hingle**
P.O. Box 2228
Carolina Beach, NC 28428
"Actor"

**Jurgen Hingsen**
655 Circle Drive
Santa Barbara, CA 93108
"Decathlon Athlete"

**Martina Hingus**
Seidenbbaum, Truebbach
CH-9477 SWITZERLAND
"Tennis Player"

**Darby Hinton**
4138 Troost Avenue
Studio City, CA 91604
"Actor"

**James David Hinton**
2806 Oak Point Drive
Los Angeles, CA 90068
"Actor"

**S.E. Hinton**
8955 Beverly Blvd.
Los Angeles, CA 90048
"Screenwriter"

**Thora Hird**
21 Leinster Mews
Lancaster Gate
London W2 3E ENGLAND
"Actress"

**Cmdr. Kathryn P. Hire**
P.O. Box 580146
Houston, TX 77258
"NASA Astronaut"

**Hiroshima**
4346 Redwood Avenue
Marina del Rey, CA 90292
"Jazz Group"

**Elroy "Crazlegs" Hirsch**
50 Oak Creek Trail
Madison, WI 53717
"Actor"

**Judd Hirsch**
137 West 12th Street
New York, NY 10011
"Actor"

**Al Hirschfield**
122 East 95th Street
New York, NY 10028
"Caricaturist"

**Shere Hite**
P.O. Box 1037
New York, NY 10028
"Actress"

**Don Ho**
P.O. Box 90039
Honolulu, HI 96814
"Singer, Songwriter"

**Tony Hoare**
430 Edgware Road
London W2 1EH ENGLAND
"Playwright"

**Scott Hoch**
9329 Cypress Cove
Orlando, FL 33219
"Golfer"

**David Hockney**
7506 Santa Monica Blvd.
Los Angeles, CA 9046
"Artist"

**Patricia Hodge**
82 Constance Road, Twickenham
Middlesex TW2 7JA ENGLAND
"Actress"

**Stephanie Hodge**
141 El Camino Drive #205
Beverly Hills, CA 90212
"Actress"

**Joy Hodges**
P.O. Box 1252
Cathedral City, CA 92235
"Actress"

**Tyler Hoechlin**
9107 Wilshire Blvd. #500
Beverly Hills, CA 90210
"Actor"

**Syd Hoff**
P.O. Box 2463
Miami Beach, FL 33140
"Cartoonist"

**James Hoffa, Jr.**
2593 Hounds Chase Drive
Troy, MI 48096
"Union Leader"

**Alice Hoffman**
3 Hurlbut Street
Cambridge, MA 02138
"Screenwriter"

**Basil Hoffman**
4456 Cromwell
Los Angeles, CA 90027
"Actor"

**Dustin Hoffman**
11661 San Vicente Blvd. #222
Los Angeles, CA 90049
"Actor"

**Gaby Hoffmann**
8942 Wilshire Blvd.
Beverly Hills, CA 90211
"Actress"

**Philip Seymour Hoffman**
104 Lombard Street
Philadelphia, PA 19147
"Actor"

**Isabella Hoffmann**
6500 Wilshire Blvd. #2200
Los Angeles, CA 90048
"Actress"

**Terry "Hulk" Hogan**
130 Willadel Drive
Belleair, FL 34616
"Wrestler"

**Paul Hogan**
701 Santa Monica Blvd. #240
Santa Monica, CA 90401
"Actor"

**Robert Hogan**
344 West 89th Street #1B
New York, NY 10024
"Actor"

**Drake Hogestyn**
914724 Venture Blvd. #505
Sherman Oaks, CA 91403, CA
"Actor"

**Hal Holbrook**
9200 Sunset Blvd. #1130
Los Angeles, CA 90069
"Actor"

**Sue Holderness**
10 Rectory Close, Windsor
Berks. SL4 5ER ENGLAND
"Actress"

**Xaviera Hollander**
Stadionweg 17
1077 RU Amsterdam HOLLAND
"Author"

**Polly Holliday**
201 East 17th Street #23H
New York, NY 10003
"Actress"

**Earl Holliman**
P.O. Box 1969
Studio City, CA 91614
"Actor"

**Sen. Ernest F. Hollings (SC)**
125 Russell Senator Office Bldg.
Washington, DC 20510
"Politician"

**Celeste Holm**
88 Central Park West
New York, NY 10023
"Actress"

**Ian Holm**
46 Albermarle Street
London W1X 4PP ENGLAND
"Actor"

**Clint Holmes**
697 Middle Neck Road
Great Neck, NY 11023
"Actor"

**Jennifer Holmes**
P.O. Box 6303
Carmel, CA 93921
"Actress"

**Katie Holmes**
17430 Miranda Street
Encino, CA 91316
"Actress"

**Larry Holmes**
91 Larry Holmes Drive #101
Easton, PA 18042
"Ex-Boxing Champion"

**Jack Holt, Jr.**
504 Temple Drive
Harrah, OK 73045
"Actor"

**Lou Holtz**
9209 Cromwell Park Place
Orlando, FL 32827
"Ex-College Football Coach"

**Evander Holyfield**
60 East 42nd Street #464
New York, NY 10165
"Boxer"

**Honeymoon Suite**
1505 West 2nd Avenue #200
Vancuver BC V6H 3Y4 CANADA
"Rock & Roll Group"

**Benjamin J. Hooks**
200 Wagner Place #407
Memphis, TN 38103
"Ex-N.A.A.C.P. President"

**Kevin Hooks**
P.O. Box 36D58
Los Angeles, CA 90036
"Actor, Director"

**Robert Hooks**
145 North Valley Street
Burbank, CA 91505
"Actor"

**Burt Hooten**
3619 Grandby Court
San Antonio, TX 78217
"Ex-Baseball Player"

**Hootie & The Blowfish**
P.O. Box 5656
Columbia, SC 29250
"Music Group"

**William Hootkins**
16 Berners Street
London W1 ENGLAND
"Actor"

**Bob Hope**
10346 Moopark
North Hollywood, CA 91602
"Actor, Comedian"

**Dolores Hope**
10346 Moopark
North Hollywood, CA 91602
"Mrs. Bob Hope"

**Sir Anthony Hopkins**
15250 Ventura Blvd., #710
Sherman Oaks, CA 91403
"Actor"

**Bo Hopkins**
6628 Ethel Avenue
North Hollywood, CA 91606
"Actor"

**Linda Hopkins**
2005 North Ivar #21
Los Angeles, CA 90067
"Singer"

**Paul Hopkins**
101000 Santa Monica Blvd. #2500
Los Angeles, CA 90067
"Actor"

**Telma Hopkins**
4122 Don Luis Drive
Los Angeles, CA 90008
"Actress, Singer"

**Dennis Hopper**
330 Indiance
Venice, CA 90291
"Actor, Director"

**Lena Horne**
23 East 74th Street #5A
New York, NY 10021
"Singer"

**Marilyn Horne**
165 West 57th Street
New York, NY 10019
"Mezzo-Soprano"

**Paul Hornung**
325 West Main Street #1116
Louisville, KY 40202
"Ex-Football Player"

**Bruce Hornsby**
P.O. Box 3545
Williamburg, VA 23187
"Rock & Roll Group"

**David Horowitz**
P.O. Box 49915
Los Angeles, CA 90049
"TV Show Host"

**Jane Horrocks**
34-43 Russell
London WC2B 5HA ENGLAND
"Actress"

**Anna Maria Horsford**
P.O. Box 48082
Los Angeles, CA 90048
"Actress"

**Lee Horsley**
9350 East Caley Avenue #200
Englewood, CO 80111
"Actor"

**Peter Horton**
9560 Wilshire Blvd. #500
Beverly Hills, CA 90212
"Actor"

**Willie Horton**
15124 Warwick Street
Detroit, MI 48223
"Ex-Baseball Player"

**Bob Hoskins**
60-66 Wardour Street
London SW1V 4ND ENGLAND
"Actor"

**Robert Hossein**
33 rue Galilee
75116 Paris, FRANCE
"Actor"

**Richard C. Hottelet**
120 Chestnut Hill Road
Wilton, CT 06897
"News Correspondent"

**Dee Hoty**
333 West 56th Street
New York, NY 10019
"Actress"

**Charlie Hough**
2266 Shade Tree Circle
Brea, CA 92621
"Ex-Baseball Manager"

**John Hough**
5 Denmark Street
London WC2 8LP ENGLAND
"Film Director"

**Ralph Houk**
3000 Plantation Road
Winter Haven, FL 33884
"Ex-Baseball Manger"

**Djimon Hounsou**
9152 Wilshire Blvd. #350
Beverly Hills, CA 90211
"Actor"

**Jerry Houser**
8325 Skyline Drive
Los Angeles, CA 90046
"Actor"

**Cissy Houston**
60 Park Place
Newark, NJ 07102
"Singer"

**Thelma Houston**
250 West 57th Street #821
New York, NY 10107
"Singer"

**Whitney Houston**
60 Park Place
Newark, NJ 07102
"Singer"

**Clint Howard**
449 N. Florence Street
Burbank, CA 91505
"Actor"

**Ken Howard**
11718 Barrington Court #300
Los Angeles, CA 90049
"Actor"

**Rance Howard**
4286 Clybourne Avenue
Burbank, CA 91505
"Actor, Writer"

**Ron Howard**
150 S. Rodeo Drive #300
Beverly Hills, CA 90212
"Actor, Director"

**Susan Howard**
P.O. Box 1456
Boerne, TX 78006
"Actress"

**Traylor Howard**
9560 Wilshire Blvd. #516
Beverly Hills, CA 90212
"Actor"

**Gordie Howe**
1008 Glenwod Court
Bloomfield Hills, MI 48302
"Ex-Hockey Player"

**Michael Howe**
7 Floral Street
London WC2 9DH ENGLAND
"Actor, Singer, Dancer"

**C. Thomas Howell**
151 El Camino Drive
Beverly Hills, CA 90212
"Actor"

**Anne Howells**
Milestone, Broomclose
Esher, Surrey, ENGLAND
"Opera Singer"

**Sally Ann Howes**
265 Liverpool Road
London N1 1LX ENGLAND
"Actress"

**Kelly Hu**
1505 Tenth
Los Angeles, CA 900401
"Actress"

**Hubcaps**
P.O. Box 1388
Dover, DE 19003
"Rock & Roll Group"

**Season Hubley**
4185 Dixie Canyon Avenue
Sherman Oaks, CA 91423
"Actress"

**Cooper Huckabee**
1800 East Cerrito Place #34
Los Angeles, CA 90068
"Actor"

**David Huddleston**
484 West 43rd Street #27A
New York, NY 10036
"Actor"

**Bill Hudson**
6419 Tapla Drive
Malibu, CA 90265
"Singer, Actor"

**Hudson Brothers**
151 El Camino Drive
Beverly Hills, CA 90212
"Vocal Group"

**Ernie Hudson**
5711 Hoback Glen Road
Hidden Hills, CA 91302
"Actor"

**Kate Hudson**
9830 Wilshire Blvd.
Beverly Hills, CA 90212
"Actress"

**Hues Corporation**
1560 Broadway #1308
New York, NY 10036
"Vocal Trio"

**Brent Huff**
10100 Santa Monica Blvd. #2490
Los Angeles, CA 90067
"Actor"

**Ex-Rep. Michael Huffington**
3005 45th Street NW
Washington, D.C. 20016
"Politician"

**Billy Hufsey**
15415 Muskingam
Brook Park, OH 44142
"Actor"

**Daniel Hugh-Kelly**
130 West 42nd Street #2400
New York, NY 10036
"Actor"

**Barnard Hughes**
250 West 94th Street
New York, NY 10025
"Actor"

**Finola Hughes**
270 North Canon Drive #1064
Beverly Hills, CA 90210
"Actress"

**Irene Hughes**
500 N. Michigan Avenue #1039
Chicago, IL 60611
"Journalist"

**Kathleen Hughes**
8818 Rising Glen Place
Los Angeles, CA 90069
"Actress"

**Miko Hughes**
6300 Wilshire Blvd. #2100
Beverly Hills, CA 90048
"Actor"

**Wayne H. Huizenga**
One Blockbuster Plaza
Ft. Lauderdale, FL 33301
"Blockbuster Video Owner"

**Thomas Hulce**
2305 Stanley Hills
Los Angeles, CA 90046
"Actor"

**Britt Hume**
3100 "N" St. NW #9
Washington, DC 20007
"News Correspondent"

**Mary Margaret Humes**
P.O. Box 1168-714
Studio City, CA 91604
"Actress, Model"

**Englebert Humperdinck**
8942 Wilshire Blvd.
Beverly Hills, CA 90211
"Singer"

**Sammo Hung**
16530 Ventura Blvd. #228
Encino, CA 91436
"Actor"

**Leann Hunley**
1888 North Crescent Heights
Los Angeles, CA 90069
"Actress, Model"

**Gayle Hunnicutt**
174 Regents Park Road
London NW1 8XP ENGLAND
"Actress"

**Bonnie Hunt**
8500 Wilshire Blvd. #700
Beverly Hills, CA 90211
"Actress"

**Helen Hunt**
9171 Wilshire Blvd. #406
Beverly Hills, CA 90210
"Actress"

**Lamar Hunt**
1601 Elm #2800
Dallas, TX 75021
"Football Team Owner"

**Linda Hunt**
1434 North Ogden Drive
Los Angeles, CA 90046
"Actress"

**Marsha Hunt**
13131 Magnolia Blvd.
Sherman Oaks, CA 91423
"Actress"

**Holly Hunter**
23801 Calabasas Road #2004
Calabasas, CA 91302
"Actress"

**Rachel Hunter**
1122 South Robertson Blvd. #15
Los Angeles, CA 90035
"Model"

**Tab Hunter**
223 North Guadalupe Street #292
Santa Fe, NM 87501
"Actor"

**Isabelle Huppert**
20 Avenue Rapp
75007 Paris FRANCE
"Actress"

**Douglas Hurd**
5 Mitford Cottages, Westwell
Burford Oxon ENGLAND
"Government Official"

**Gale Ann Hurd**
270 North Canon Drive #1195
Beverly Hills, CA 90210
"Film Producer"

**Elizabeth Hurley**
36 Redcliff Road
London SW10 9NJ ENGLAND
"Model"

**John Hurt**
46 Albermarle Street
London W1X 4PP ENGLAND
"Actor"

**William Hurt**
132 S. Rodeo Drive 3300
Beverly Hills, CA 90212
"Actor"

**Ferlin Husky**
4540 Lake Lowry Road
Haines City, FL 33844
"Singer, Songwriter"

**Rick Husky**
13565 Lucca Dive
Pacific Palisades, CA 90272
"Actor, Writer, Producer"

**Ruth Hussey**
3361 Don Pablo Drive
Carlsbad, CA 92008
"Actress"

**Angelica Huston**
74 Market Street
Venice, CA 90291
"Actress"

**Will Hutchins**
P.O. Box 371
Glen Head, NY 11545
"Actor"

**Sen. Kay Bailey Hutchinson (TX)**
703 Hart Bldg.
Washington, DC 20510
"Politician"

**Danny Hutton**
2437 Horseshoe Canyon Road
Los Angeles, CA 90046
"Singer, Songwriter"

**Lauren Hutton**
382 Lafayette Street #6
New York, NY 10003
"Actress, Model"

**Timothy Hutton**
9465 Wilshire Blvd. #820
Beverly Hills, CA 90212
"Actor"

**Laura Huxley**
6233 Mulholland Drive
Los Angeles, CA 90068
"Author"

**Joe Hyams**
10375 Wilshire Blvd. #4D
Los Angeles, CA 90024
"Author"

**Peter Hyams**
P.O. Box 10
Basking Ridge, NJ 07929
"Writer, Producer"

**Rep. Henry J. Hyde (IL)**
Rayburn House Office Building
#2110
Washington, DC 20515
"Politicain"

**Alex Hyde-White**
2326 - 16th Street #C
Santa Monica, CA 90405
"Actor"

**Earle Hyman**
484 West 43rd Street #33E
New York, NY 10036
"Actor"

**Kenneth Hyman**
Sherwood House
Tilehouse Lane
Denham, Bucks. ENGLAND
"Film Executive"

**Joyce Hyser**
10100 Santa Monica Blvd. #2500
Los Angeles, CA 90067
"Actress"

**Lee Iacocca**
10614 Chalon  Road
Los Angeles, CA 90077
"Automobile Executive"

**Ice Cube**
(Oshea Jackson)
5420 Lindley Avenue #4
Encino, CA 91316
"Rap Singer, Actor"

**Ice Tea**
2287 Sunset Plaza Drive
Los Angeles, CA 90069
"Rap Singer, Actor"

**Eric Idle**
52/53 Poland Street
London W1F 7LX ENGLAND
"Actor, Director"

**Billy Idol**
27a Floral Street #300
Covent Garden
London W1V 3DE ENGLAND
"Singer, Songwriter"

**Iggy Pop**
307 Seventh Avenue #807
New York, NY 10001
"Singer"

**Julio Iglesias**
5 Indian Creek Drive
Miami Beach, FL 33154
"Singer"

**Rev. Ike**
4140 Broadway
New York, NY 10004
"Evangelist"

**Iman**
180-182 Tottenham Ct. Rd.
London W1P 9LE ENGLAND
"Model"

**Don Imus**
34-12  36th Street
Astoria, NY 11106
"Radio Talk Show Host"

**Indigo Girls**
751 Bridgeway #300
Sausalito, CA 94965
"Music Group"

**Marty Ingels**
4531 Noeline Way
Encino, CA 91436
"Actor"

**James Ingram**
867 Muirfield Road
Los Angeles, CA 90005
"Singer"

**John Inman**
8 King Street
London WC2E 8HN ENGLAND
"Actor"

**The Ink Spots**
5100 DuPont Blvd. #10A
Ft. Lauderdale, FL 33308
"Vocal Group"

**Laura Innes**
10100 Santa Monica Blvd. #2500
Los Angeles, CA 90067
"Actress"

**Roy Innis**
800 Riverside Drive #6E
New York, NY 10032
"Activist"

**Sen. Daniel Inouye (HI)**
Senate Hart Bldg. #722
Washington, DC 20510
"Politician"

**INXS**
8 Hayes St.
#1 Neutray Bay
NSW 20891 AUSTRALIA
"Rock & Roll Group"

**Kathy Ireland**
1122 S. Robertson Blvd. #15
Los Angeles, CA 90035
"Model"

**Donnie Iris**
807 Darlington Road
Beaver Falls, PA 15010
"Singer"

**Iron Butterfly**
P.O. Box 770850
Orlando, FL 32877
"Rock & Roll Group"

**Iron Maiden**
45-53 Sinclair Road
London W14 0NS ENGLAND
"Rock & Roll Group"

**Jeremy Irons**
9830 Wilshire Blvd.
Beverly Hills, CA 90212
"Actor"

**Michael Ironside**
3500 W. Olive Avenue #1400
Burbank, CA 91505
"Actor"

**Monte Irvin**
11 Douglas Court South
Homosassa, FL 32646
"Ex-Baseball Player"

**Amy Irving**
1180 South Beverly Drive #608
Los Angeles, CA 90035
"Actress"

**Michael Irving**
1280 S. Main Street #103
Grapevine, TX 76051
"Football Player"

**Hale Irwin**
10726 Manchester Road #212
St. Louis, MO 63124
"Golfer"

**Peter Isaacksen**
4635 Placidia Avenue
North Hollywood, CA 91602
"Actor"

**Chris Isaak**
9200 Sunset Blvd. #530
Los Angeles, CA 90069
"Singer"

**Isley Brothers**
89 Fifth Avenue #700
New York, NY 10036
"R&B Group"

**Lance A. Ito**
210 West Temple Street #M-6
Los Angeles, CA 90012
"Judge"

**Zeljko Ivanek**
145 West 45th Street #1204
New York, NY 10036
"Actor"

**Allen Iverson**
1st Union Center
3601 S. Broad Street
Philadelphia, PA 19148
"Basketball Player"

**Dana Ivey**
10100 Santa Monica Blvd. #2500
Los Angeles, CA 90067
"Actress"

**Judith Ivey**
53 West 87th Street #2
New York, NY 10024
"Actress"

**James Ivory**
250 W. 57th Street #1913-A
New York, NY 10019
"Actor"

**Ja Rule**
1100 Glendon Avenue #100
Los Angeles, CA 90024
"Rap Singer"

**Alan Jackson**
1400 - 18th Avenue South
Nashville, TN 37212
"Singer"

**Barry Jackson**
29 Rathcoole Avenue
London N8 9LY ENGLAND
"Actor"

**Bo Jackson**
P.O. Box158
Mobile, AL 36601
"Ex-Football & Baseball Player"

**Donald Jackson**
1080 Brocks
South Pickering
Ontario, CANADA

**Freddie Jackson**
250 West 57th Street #821
New York, NY 10107
"Singer"

**PM Glenda Jackson**
c/o House of Commons
Westminster
London SW1A OAA ENGLAND
"Actress"

**Janet Jackson**
9560 Wilshire Blvd. #516
Beverly Hills, CA 90212
"Singer, Songwriter"

**Jeremy Jackson**
6100 Wilshire Blvd. #400
Beverly Hills, CA 90048
"Singer"

**Jermaine Jackson**
4641 Hayvenhurst Avenue
Encino, CA 91316
"Singer, Songwriter"

**Rev. Jesse Jackson**
400 "T" Street N.W.
Washington, DC 20001
"Politician, Evangelist"

**Rep. Jesse Jackson, Jr. (IL)**
312 Cannon House Office Bldg.
Washington, DC 20515
"Son of Jesse Jackson"

**Joe Jackson**
6 Pembridge Road #200
London W11 3HL ENGLAND
"Singer, Songwriter"

**John M. Jackson**
c/o JAG
5555 Melrose Avenue
Clara Bow #204
Los Angeles, CA 90038
"Actor"

**Jonathan Jackson**
1815 Butler Avenue #120
Los Angeles, CA 90025
"Actor"

**Joshua Jackson**
151 El Camino Drive
Beverly Hills, CA 90212
"Actor"

**Kate Jackson**
P.O. Box 57593
Sherman Oaks, CA 91403
"Actress"

**LaToya Jackson**
14126 Rosecrans Avenue
Santa Fe Springs, CA 90670
"Singer, TV Show Host"

**Marlon Jackson**
4641 Hayvenhurst Avenue
Encino, CA 91316
"Singer"

**Mary Jackson**
2055 Grace Avenue
Los Angeles, CA 90068
"Actress"

**Mary Ann Jackson**
1242 Alessandro Drive
Newbury Park, CA 91320
"Actress"

**Mel Jackson**
4210 W. Sarah Street #1
Burbank, CA 91505
"Actor"

**Michael Jackson**
Neverland Ranch
Los Olivos, CA 93441
"Singer, Songwriter"

**Michael Jackson**
1420 Moraga Drive
Los Angeles, CA 90049
"Talk Show Host"

**Paul Jackson, Jr.**
40 West 57th Street
New York, NY 10019
"Actor"

**Randy Jackson**
4641 Hayvenhurst Drive
Encino, CA 91316
"Singer"

**Reggie Jackson**
305 Amador Avenue
Seaside, CA 93955
"Ex-Baseball Player"

**Richard Lee Jackson**
1815 Butler Avenue #120
Los Angeles, CA 90025
"Actor"

**Samuel L. Jackson**
9465 Wilshire Blvd. #600
Beverly Hills, CA 90212
"Actor"

**Stonewall Jackson**
6007 Cloverland Drive
Brentwood, TN 37027
"Singer, Songwriter

**Tito Jackson**
21645 Medina Estates Drive
Woodland Hills, CA 91364
"Singer"

**Victoria Jackson**
9200 Sunset Blvd. #900
Los Angeles, CA 90069
"Actress"

**Wanda Jackson**
P.O. Box 891498
Oklahoma City, OK 73189
"Singer"

**Sir Derek Jacobi**
76 Oxford Street
London W1N OAX ENGLAND
"Actor"

**Lawrence-Hilton Jacobs**
3804 Evans #2
Los Angeles, CA 90027
"Actor"

**Billy Jacoby**
P.O. Box 46324
Los Angeles, CA 90046
"Actor"

**Laura Jacoby**
P.O. Box 46324
Los Angeles, CA 90046
"Actress"

**Scott Jacoby**
P.O. Box 461100
Los Angeles, CA 90046
"Actor"

**Brian Jacques**
P.O. Box 57
Mossley Hill L18 3NZ ENGLAND
"Author"

**Henry Jaffe**
7920 Sunset Blvd. #400
Los Angeles, CA 90046
"Film Producer"

**Bianca Jagger**
530 Park Avenue #18-D
New York, NY 10021
"Actress, Model"

**Mick Jagger**
110 West 57th Street, 3rd Floor
New York, NY 10019
"Singer"

**Henry Jaglom**
609 E. Channel Road
Santa Monica, CA 90402
"Actor"

**Ahmad Jamal**
122 East 57th Street #300
New York, NY 10022
"Musician"

**Anthony James**
1801 Avenue of the Stars #1250
Los Angeles, CA 90067
"Actor"

**Clifton James**
500 West 43rd Street #26J
New York, NY 10036
"Actor"

**Etta James**
16409 Sally Lane
Riverside, CA 92504
"Singer"

**Godfrey James**
The Shack, Western Road
Pevensey Bay
East Sussex ENGLAND
"Actor"

**John James**
8827 Beverly Blvd.
Los Angeles, CA 90048
"Actor"

**Joni James**
P.O. Box 7027
Westchester, IL 60154
"Singer"

**Baroness P.D. James**
37A Goldhawk Rd.
London W12 8QQ ENGLAND
"Writer"

**Sheila James-Kuehl**
3201 Pearl Street
Santa Monica, CA 90405
"Actress"

**Sonny James**
818 - 18th Avenue
Nashville, TN 37203
"Singer, Songwriter"

**Tommy James**
Box 3074, Allwood Sta.
Clifton, NJ 07012
"Singer"

**Louise Jameson**
18-21 Jermyn Street
London, SW1Y 6HP, ENGLAND
"Actress"

**Milo Jameson**
1231 Tennyson Street
Manhattan Beach, CA 90266
"Composer"

**Paulene Jameson**
7 Warrington Gardens
London W9 2QB ENGLAND
"Actress"

**Mae Jamison**
P.O. Box 580317
Houston, TX 77258
"Astronaut"

**Jan & Dean**
221 Main Street #P
Huntington Beach, CA 92648
"Vocal Duo"

**Jane's Addiction**
9830 Wilshire Blvd.
Beverly Hills, CA 90212
"Rock & Roll Group"

**Conrad Janis**
1434 N. Genesee Avenue
Los Angeles, CA 90069
"Actor"

**Dan Jansen**
P.O. Box 567
Greendale, WI 53129
"Ice Skater"

**Famke Janssen**
9830 Wilshire Blvd.
Beverly Hills, CA 90212
"Actress"

**Don January**
14316 Hughes Lane
Dallas, TX 75240
"Golfer"

**Lois January**
P.O. Box 1233
Beverly Hills, CA 90210
"Actress"

**Lee Janzen**
7512 Dr. Phillips Blvd. #50-906
Orlando, FL 32819
"Golfer"

**Al Jardine**
P.O. Box 36
Big Sur, CA 93920
"Singer, Musician"

**Claude Jarman, Jr.**
16 Tamai Vista Lane
Kentfield, CA 94904
"Actor"

**Al Jarreau**
9830 Wilshire Blvd.
Beverly Hills, CA 90212
"Musician"

**Tom Jarrell**
77 West 66th Street
New York, NY 10023
"News Correspondent"

**Clark Jarrett**
4051 Radford Avenue #A
Studio City, CA 91604
"Actor"

**Dale Jarrett**
1510 46th Avenue Northeast
Hickory, NC 28601
"Race Car Driver"

**Gen. Wojciech Jaruzelski**
ul Klonowa 1
009909 Warsaw, POLAND
"Military, Politician"

**Graham Jarvis**
15351 Via De Las Olas
Pacific Palisades, CA 90272
"Actor"

**Lucy Jarvis**
171 West 57th Street
New York, NY 10019
"TV Executive, Producer"

**Martin Jarvis**
2-4 Noel Street
London W1V 3RB ENGLAND
"Actor"

**Jason & The Scorchers**
901 - 18th Avenue South
Nashville, TN 37212
"Rock & Roll Group"

**Harvey Jason**
1280 Sunset Plaza Drive
Los Angeles, CA 90069
"Writer"

**Sybil Jason**
P.O. Box 40024
Studio City, CA 91604
"Actress"

**Terry Jastrow**
13201 Old Oak Lane
Los Angeles, CA 90049
"Director, Producer"

**Ron Jaworski**
8 Silver Hill Lane
West Berlin, NJ 08043
"Ex-Football Player"

**Jay & The Americans**
17 Pauline Court
Rensselear, NY 12144
"Rock & Roll Group"

**Michael Jayston**
125 Gloucester Road
London SW7 4TE ENGLAND
"Actor"

**D.J. Jazzy Jeff &**
**The Fresh Prince**
298 Elizabeth Street #100
New York, NY 10012
"Rap Duo"

**Gloria Jean**
3410 Peninsula Road #125
Oxnard, CA 93035
"Actress"

**Wyclef Jean**
c/o DAS
83 Riverside Drive
New York, NY 10024
"Singer"

**Sen. James Jeffords**
728 Hart Senate Office Bldg.
Washington, DC 20510
"Politicain"

**Anne Jeffreys-Sterling**
18915 Nordhoff Street #5
Northridge, CA 91324
"Actress"

**Herb Jeffries**
44-489 Town Center Way, PMB D-492
Palm Desert, CA 92260
"Singer"

**Lionel Jeffries**
Guild House
Upper St. Martin's Lane
London WC2H 9EG ENGLAND
"Actor, Director"

**Richard Jeni**
9454 Wilshire Blvd. #405
Beverly Hills, CA 90212
"Comedian"

**Hayes Alan Jenkins**
1750 E. Boulder Street
Colorado Springs, CO 80909
"Skater"

**Bruce Jenner**
25254 El Dorado Meadow Road
Hidden Hills, CA 91302
"Athlete, Actor"

**Peter Jennings**
77 West 66th Street
New York, NY 10023
"News Anchor"

**Salome Jens**
9301 Wilshire Blvd. #300
Beverly Hills, CA 90210
"Actress"

**Michael Jeter**
8840 Wilshire Blvd.
Beverly Hills, CA 90211
"Actor"

**Jethro Tull**
2-12 Pentonville Road
London N1 9PL ENGLAND
"Rock & Roll Goup"

**Joan Jett**
636 Broadway #1218
New York, NY 10022
"Rock & Roll Group"

**Jewel**
P.O. Box 1388
Brea, CA 92822
"Singer"

**Norman Jewison**
3000 W. Olympic Blvd. #1314
Santa Monica, CA 90404
"Director, Producer"

**Ann Jillian**
P.O. Box 57739
Sherman Oaks, CA 91413
"Actress, Singer"

**Jim & Jesse**
P.O. Box 27
Gallatin, TN 37066
"C&W Group"

**Marlene Jobert**
8-10 Blvd. de Courcelles
75008 Paris, FRANCE
"Actress"

**Steve Jobs**
1001 West Cutting Blvd.
Redwood City, CA 94804
"Computer Executive"

**Billy Joel**
QBQ Entertainment
150 East 58th Street #1900
New York, NY 10155
"Singer, Songwriter"

**Roland Joffee**
10351 Santa Monica Blvd #402
Los Angeles, CA 90025
"Film Director"

**Ingemar Johansson**
Box 134
S-13054 Stockholm SWEDEN
"Boxer"

**David Johanssen**
9200 Sunset Blvd. #900
Los Angeles, CA 90069
"Actor"

**Sir Elton John**
Woodside
Crump Hill Road
Old Windsor, Berkshire ENGLAND
"Singer, Songwriter"

**Pope John Paul II**
Palazzo Apostolico Vaticano
1-00120 Citta Del Vaticano, ITALY
"Pope"

**Tommy John**
6202 Seton House Lane
Charlotte, NC 28277
"Ex-Baseball Player"

**Gordon Johncock**
931 Bedtelyon Road
West Branch, MI 48661
"Race Car Driver"

**Johnny Hates Jazz**
321 Fulham Road
London ZW10 9QL ENGLAND
"Rock & Roll Group"

**Glynis Johns**
10701 Wilshire Blvd. #2201
Beverly Hills, CA 90024
"Actress"

**Amy Jo Johnson**
1122 S. Robertson Blvd., #15
Los Angeles, CA 90035
"Actress"

**Arte Johnson**
2725 Bottlebrush Drive
Los Angeles, CA 90024
"Actor, Comedian"

**Beverly Johnson**
2711 Angelo Drive
Los Angeles, CA 90077
"Actress, Model"

**Brad Johnson**
9465 Wilshire Blvd. #212
Beverly Hills, CA 90212
"Actor"

**Don Johnson**
1122 South Robertson Blvd. #15
Los Angeles, CA 90035
"Actor"

**Dwayne Johnson** (The Rock)
1241 East Main Street
Box 3857
Stamford, CT 06905
"WWE Wrestler"

**Earvin "Magic" Johnson**
9100 Wilshire Blvd. #700
Beverly Hills, CA 90212
"Ex-Basketball Player"

**Georgann Johnson**
218 North Glenroy Place
Los Angeles, CA 90049
"Actress"

**J.J. Johnson**
648 Broadway #703
New York, NY 10012
"Trombonist, Composer"

**Jill Johnson**
43 Matheson Road
London W14 8SNENGLAND
"Actress"

**Kevin Johnson**
201 East Jefferson Street
Phoenix, AZ 85004
"Basketball Player"

**Kristin Johnson**
9830 Wilshire Blvd.
Beverly Hills, CA 90212
"Actress"

**Lamont Johnson**
900 Alameda Avenue
Monterey, CA 93940
"Director, Producer"

**Laura Johnson**
1917 Weepah Way
Los Angeles, CA 90046
"Actress"

**Mrs. Lady Bird Johnson**
LBJ Ranch
Stonewall, TX 78671
"Ex-First Lady"

**Lucie Baines Johnson**
LBJS Broadcasting
8309 North IH-35
Austin, TX 78753
"Ex-President's Daughter"

**Lynn-Holly Johnson**
178 South Victory Blvd. #205
Burbank, CA 91502
"Actress"

**Rafer Johnson**
6071 Bristol Parkway #100
Culver City, CA 90230
"Actor"

**Richard Johnson**
18-21 Jermyn Street
London SW1Y 6NB ENGLAND
"Actor"

**Russell Johnson**
P.O. Box 11198
Bainbridge Island, WA 98110
"Actor"

**Van Johnson**
405 East 54th Street
New York, NY 10022
"Actor"

**Lynn Johnston**
4520 Main St. #700
Kansas City, MO 64111
"Cartoonist"

**Tom Johnston Band**
P.O. Box 878
Sonoma, CA 95476
"Rock & Roll Group"

**Angelina Jolie**
8500 Wilshire Blvd. #700
Beverly Hills, CA 90211
"Actress"

**Chuck Jones**
P.O. Box 2319
Costa Mesa, CA 92628
"Animated Cartoon Producer"

**Davey Jones**
P.O. Box 400
Beavertown, PA 17813
"Singer, Actor"

**Dean Jones**
P.O. Box 570276
Tarzana, CA 91357
"Actor"

**Dub Jones**
223 Glendale
Rusten, LA 71270
"Actor"

**Ed "Too Tall" Jones**
1 Lost Valley Drive
Dallas, TX 75234
"Football Player"

**Gemma Jones**
Upper St. Martin Lane
London WC2H 9EG ENGLAND
"Actor"

**George Jones**
1101 - 17th Avenue South
Nashville, TN 37212
"Singer, Songwriter"

**Grace Jones**
P.O. Box 28286
London N21 3WT ENGLAND
"Singer"

**The Jones Girls**
P.O. Box 6010, #761
Sherman Oaks, CA 91413
"Vocal Group"

**Dame Gwyneth Jones**
P.O. Box 380,
8040 Zurich, Switzerland
"Soprano"

**Howard Jones**
Box 185, High Wycom.
Bucks. HP11 2E2 ENGLAND
"Singer, Songwriter"

**Jack Jones**
12747 Riverside drive #208
Valley Village, CA 91607
"Singer, Actor"

**James Earl Jones**
P.O. Box 610
Pawling, NY 12564
"Actor"

**Janet Jones**
9100 Wilshire Blvd. #1000W
Beverly Hills, CA 90212
"Actress"

**Jeffrey Jones**
8730 Sunset Blvd. #480
Los Angeles, CA 90069
"Actor"

**Jenny Jones**
P.O. Box 3333
Chicago, IL 60654
"Talk Show Host"

**Jill Marie Jones**
2050 S. Bundy Drive #200
Los Angeles, CA 90025
"Actress"

**L.Q. Jones**
2144 1/2 N. Cahuenga Blvd.
Los Angeles, CA 90068
"Actor, Director"

**Marcia Mae Jones**
4541 Hazeltine Avenue #4
Sherman Oaks, CA 91423
"Actress"

**Marilyn Jones**
357 East Price Street
Keller, TX 76248
"Actress"

**Orlando Jones**
9460 Wilshire Blvd. #700
Beverly Hills, CA 90212
"Actor"

**Parnelli Jones**
P.O. Box "W"
Torrance, CA 90507
"Race Car Driver"

**Paula Jones**
c/o Court TV
600 Third Avenue
New York, NY 10016
"Right Wing Puppet"

**Peter Jones**
11520 San Vicente Blvd. #207
Los Angeles, CA 90049
"Author"

**Quincy Jones**
1888 Century Park East #500
Los Angeles, CA 90067
"Composer, Producer"

**Rashida Jones**
1606 Rosecrans Avenue
Bldg. 4A, 3rd Floor
Manhattan Beach, CA 90266
"Actor"

**Shirley Jones**
4531 Noeline Way
Encino, CA 91436
"Actress"

**Star Jones**
1325 Avenue of the Americas
New York, NY 10019
"Television Court Reporter"

**Terry Jones**
34 Thistlewaite Road
London E5 0QQ ENGLAND
"Actor, Writer, Director"

**Tom Jones**
10100 Santa Monica Blvd. #225
Los Angeles, CA 90067
"Singer"

**Tommy Lee Jones**
5750 Wilshire Blvd. #640
Los Angeles, CA 90036
"Actor"

**Trevor Jones**
46 Avenue Road
Highgate,
London N6 5DR ENGLAND
"Actor"

**Jennifer Jones-Simon**
P.O. Box 50067
Pasadena, CA 91115
"Actress"

**Erica Jong**
P.O. Box 1434
New York, NY 10021
"Poet, Author"

**Kathryn Joosten**
1680 North vine Street #614
Hollywood, CA 90028
"Actress"

**The Jordanaires**
46-19 220th Place
Bayside, NY 11361
"Music Group"

**Lee Roy Jordan**
2425 Burbank Street
Dallas, TX 75225
"Ex-Football Player"

**Michael Jordan**
676 N. Michigan Avenue #2940
Chicago, IL 60611
"Basketball Player"

**Montel Jordan**
250 West 57th Street #821
New York, NY 10107
"Singer"

**Neil Jordan**
6 Sorrento Terrace
Dalkey County, Dublin IRELAND
"Film Director"

**Stanley Jordan**
9200 Sunset Blvd. #900
Los Angeles, CA 90069
"Guitarist"

**Vernon E. Jordan, Jr.**
c/o Lazard Freres
30 Rockefeller Plaza #400
New York, NY 10112
"Politician"

**Jeffrey Joseph**
400 S. Beverly Drive #102
Beverly Hills, CA 90212
"Actor"

**Louis Jourdan**
1139 Maybrook
Beverly Hills, CA 90210
"Actor"

**Journey**
1100 Glendon Avenue #200
Los Angeles, CA 90024
"Rock & Roll Group"

**Milla Jovovich**
8942 Wilshire Blvd.
Beverly Hills, CA 90211
"Model, Actress"

**Brenda Joyce**
947 Shearer Street
Roseville, CA 95678
"Author"

**Elaine Joyce**
10745 Chalon Road
Los Angeles, CA 90077
"Actress"

**Jackie Joyner-Kersee**
1034 S. Brentwood Blvd. #1530
St. Louis, MO 63117
"Track & Field Athlete"

**Wally Joyner**
856 Hawks Rest Drive
Mapleton, UT 84664
"Ex-Baseball Player"

**Judas Priest**
17 East 76th Street
New York, NY 10021
"Music Group"

**Ashley Judd**
P.O. Box 1569
Franklin, TN 37065
"Actress"

**Naomi Judd**
1142 Canal Avenue
Nashville, TN 37206
"Singer"

**Gordon Jump**
P.O. Box 80093
Rancho Santa
Margarita, CA 92788
"Actor, Director"

**Nathan Juran**
623 Via Horquilla
Palos Verdes, CA 90274
"Writer & Producer"

**Martin Jurow**
5833 Berkshire Lane
Dallas, TX 75209
"Film Producer"

**Charlie Justice**
315 E. Main Street
Cherryville, NC 28021
"Violinist"

**David Justice**
4173 Tattershall Drive
Decatur, GA 30034
"Baseball Player"

**K.C. & The Sunshine Band**
7530 Loch Ness Drive
Miami Lakes, FL 33014
"Rock & Roll Group"

**Jim Kaat**
P.O. Box 1130
Port Salerno, FL 34992
"Ex-Baseball Player"

**Jane Kaczmarek**
5761 Valley Oak Drive
Los Angeles, CA 90068
"Actress"

**David Kagen**
6457 Firmament Avenue
Van Nuys, CA 91406
"Actor"

**Marvin Kalb**
79 John F. Kennedy Street
Cambridge, MA 01238
"Journalist"

**Patricia Kalember**
1505 10th Street
Santa Monica, CA 90401
"Actress"

**Al Kaline**
945 Timberlake Drive
Bloomfield Hills, MI 48013
"Ex-Baseball Player"

**Herbert Kalmbach**
1056 Santiago Drive
Newport Beach, CA 92660
"Watergate Participant"

**Stanley Kamel**
9360 Wilshire Blvd. #300
Beverly Hills, CA 90210
"Actor"

**Steven Kanaly**
4663 Grand Avenue
Ojai, CA 93023
"Actor"

**Big Daddy Kane**
151 El Camino Drive
Beverly Hills, CA 90212
"Rap Singer"

**Carol Kane**
8205 Santa Monica Blvd. #1426
Los Angeles, CA 90046
"Actress"

**Fay Kanin**
653 Ocean Front
Santa Monica, CA 90402
"Screenwriter"

**Stan Kann**
570 North Rossmore Avenue
Los Angeles, CA 90004
"Actor"

**Hal Kanter**
15941 Woodvale Road
Encino, CA 91316
"Writer, Producer"

**Mickey Kanter**
5019 Klingle Street NW
Washington, DC 20016
"Government Official"

**Archie Kao**
3500 W. Olive Avenue #1400
Burbank, CA 91505
"Actor"

**Gabriel Kaplan**
9551 Hidden Valley Road
Beverly Hills, CA 90210
"Comedian, Actor"

**Jonathan Kaplan**
2413 Canyon Oak Dr.
Los Angeles, CA 90069
"Director"

**Marvin Kaplan**
P.O. Box 1522
Burbank, CA 91505
"Actor"

**Kimmi Kappenberg**
2794 Ocean Avenue
Ronkonoma, NY 11779
"Survivor Show Contestant"

**Valerie Kapriski**
20 Avenue, Rapp
F-75007 Paris FRANCE
"Actress"

**Mitzi Kapture**
3605 Sandy Plaines Road #40-116
Marietta, GA 30066
"Actress"

**Donna Karan**
550-7th Avenue #1500
New York, NY 10018
"Fashion Designer"

**Kym Karath**
2267 Roscomare Road
Los Angeles, CA 90077
"Actress"

**Robert Kardashian**
18056 Lake Drive
Encino, CA 91316
"Attorney"

**James Karen**
4455 Los Feliz Blvd. #807
Los Angeles, CA 90027
"Actor"

**John Karlen**
P.O. Box 1195
Santa Monica, CA 90406
"Actor"

**Fred Karlin**
1187 Coast Village Road #1-339
Montecito, CA 93108
"Composer, Conductor"

**Phil Karlson**
3094 Patricia Avenue
Los Angeles, CA 90064
"Director"

**Richard Karn**
345 North Maple Drive #302
Beverly Hills, CA 90210
"Actor"

**Anatoly Karpov**
Luzhnetskaya 8
Moscow 119270 RUSSIA
"Chess Champion"

**Alex Karras**
7943 Woodrow Wilson Drive
Los Angeles, CA 90046
"Ex-Football Player, Actor"

**Lawrence Kasdan**
10345 West Olympic Blvd.
Los Angeles, CA 90064
"Director, Producer"

**Casey Kasem**
138 North Mapleton Drive
Los Angeles, CA 90077
"Radio-TV Personality"

**Jean Kasem**
138 North Mapleton Drive
Los Angeles, CA 90077
"Radio-TV Personality"

**John Kassir**
8436 West 3rd Street #740
Los Angeles, CA 90048
"Comedian"

**Dr. Irene Kassorla**
908 North Roxbury Drive
Beverly Hills, CA 90210
"Psychologist, Author"

**Andreas Katsulas**
1505 - 10th Street
Santa Monica, CA 90401
"Actor"

**William Katt**
23508 Canzonet Street
Woodland Hills, CA 91367
"Actor"

**Julie Kavner**
25154 Malibu Road #2
Malibu, CA 90265
"Actress"

**Charles Kay**
18 Epple Road
London SW6 ENGLAND
"Actor"

**Dianne Kay**
1559 Palisades Drive
Pacific Palisades, CA 90272
"Actress"

**Lila Kaye**
47 Courtfield Road #9
London SW7 4DB ENGLAND
"Actress"

**Melvina Kaye**
P.O. Box 6085
Burbank, CA 90510
"Singer"

**Lainie Kazan**
9903 Santa Monica Blvd #283
Beverly Hills, CA 90212
"Singer, Actress"

**James Keach**
612 Lighthouse Avenue #220
Pacific Grove, CA 93951
"Actor"

**Stacy Keach, Jr.**
27525 Winding Way
Malibu, CA 90265
"Actor"

**Jane Kean**
28128 West Pacific Coast Highway
Malibu, CA 90265
"Actress"

**Staci Keanan**
4526 Wilshire Blvd.
Los Angeles, CA 90010
"Actress"

**Bill Keane**
5815 East Joshua Tree Lane
Paradise Valley, AZ 85253
"Cartoonist"

**Diane Keane**
23 Primrose Hill
Charleton Mackrell
Summerset ENGLAND
"Actress"

**James Keane**
612 Lighthouse Avenue #220
Pacific Grove, CA 93951
"Actor"

**Michael Kearns**
4305 Gateway Avenue #25
Los Angeles, CA 90029
"Actor"

**Diane Keaton**
151 El Camino Drive
Beverly Hills, CA 90212
"Actress, Director"

**Michael Keaton**
11901 Santa Monica Blvd. #547
Los Angeles, CA 90025
"Actor"

**Don Keefer**
4146 Allot Avenue
Sherman Oaks, CA 91423
"Actor"

**Howard Keel**
394 Red River Road
Palm Desert, CA 92211
"Actor, Singer"

**William Keene**
435 29th Street
Manhattan Beach, CA 90266
"Actor"

**Catherine Keener**
3859 Cardiff Avenue #200
Culver City, CA 90232
"Actress"

**Bob Keeshan**
(Capt. Kangaroo)
P.O. Box 1243
Norwich, VT 05055
"TV Show Host"

**Garrison Keillor**
45 E. 7th Street
St. Paul, MN 55101
"Author, Radio Personality"

**Betty Lou Keim**
10642 Arnel Place
Chatsworth, CA 91311
"Actress"

**Harvey Keitel**
9560 Wilshire Blvd., 10th Floor
Beverly Hills, CA 90212
"Actor"

**David Keith**
8383 Wilshire Blvd. #550
Beverly Hills, CA 90211
"Actor"

**Penelope Keith**
66 Berkeley House
Hay Hill
London SW3 ENGLAND
"Actress"

**Toby Keith**
9 Music Square #130
Nashville, TN 37203
"Singer"

**Robert Kelker-Kelly**
3500 West Olive Avenue #300
Burbank, CA 91505
"Actor"

**George Kell**
P.O. Box 70
Swifton, AR 72471
"Ex-Baseball Player"

**Marthe Keller**
5 rue St. Dominique
75007 Paris, FRANCE
"Actress"

**Mary Page Keller**
151 El Camino Drive
Beverly Hills, CA 90212
"Actress"

**Sally Kellerman**
7944 Woodrow Wilson Drive
Los Angeles, CA 90046
"Actress"

**Daniel Hugh Kelley**
130 West 42nd Street #2400
New York, NY 10036
"Actor"

**Kitty Kelley**
1228 Eton Court NW
Washington, DC 20007
"Author"

**Sheila Kelley**
8730 Sunset Blvd. #490
Los Angeles, CA 90069
"Actress"

**Barbara Kelly**
5 Kidderpore Avenue
London NW3 7SX ENGLAND
"Actress"

**David E. Kelley**
535 King Steet #219
The Plaza
London SW10 OSZ ENGLAND
"Actor"

**Moira Kelly**
P.O. Box 5617
Beverly Hills, CA 90210
"Actress"

**R. Kelly**
165-167 High Road Willesden
London, NW10 2SG, ENGLAND
"R&B Singer"

**Roz Kelly**
5161 Riverton Avenue #105
North Hollywood, CA 91601
"Actress"

**Tommy Kelly**
1643 Carrie Street
Maplewood, MN 55119
"Singer"

**Linda Kelsey**
400 South Beverly Drive #101
Beverly Hills, CA 90212
"Actress"

**Jack Kemp**
7904 Greentree Road
Bethesda, MD 20817
"Ex-Football Player & Politician"

**Jeremy Kemp**
12/13 Poland Street
London W1F 8QB ENGLAND
"Actor"

**Rhonda Ross Kendrick**
10100 Santa Monica Blvd. #2490
Los Angeles, CA 90067
"Actress"

**Justice Anthony Kennedy**
1-1st Street N.E.
Washington, DC 20543
"Supreme Court Justice"

**Caroline Kennedy-Schlosseberg**
888 Park Avenue
New York, NY 10021
"Ex-President's Daughter"

**Sen. Edward Kennedy (MA)**
315 Russell office Bldg.
Washington, DC 20510
"Politician"

**Jamie Kennedy**
9465 Wilshire Blvd., #212
Beverly Hills, CA 90212
"Actor"

**Rep. Joseph Kennedy II (MA)**
530 Atlantic Avenue #500
Boston, MA 02210
"Politician"

**Kathleen Kennedy**
100 Universal City Plaza
Bung 477
Universal City, CA 91608
"Politicain"

**Leon Isaac Kennedy**
859 N. Hollywood Way #385
Burbank, CA 91505
"Actor, Producer"

**Maxwell Taylor Kennedy**
Boston College
437 Higgins Hall
Chestnet Hill, MA 02467
"Author"

**Nigel Kennedy**
9A Penzance Place
London W11 4PE ENGLAND
"Violinist"

**Rep. Patrick Kennedy (RI)**
Longworth House Office Building
#1505
Washington, DC 20515
"Politicain"

**Robert F. Kennedy, Jr.**
78 North Broadway
White Plains, NY 10603
"Robert Kennedy's Son"

**Rory Kennedy**
Moxie Firecracker Films
180 Varick Street, 12th Floor
New York, NY 10014
"Documentary Filmmaker"

**Mr. Kenneth**
19 East 54th Street
New York, NY 10022
"Hairstylist"

**Patsy Kensit**
14 Lambton Place, Nottinghill
London W11 2SH ENGLAND
"Actress"

**Arthur Kent**
2184 Torringford Street
Torrington, CT 06790
"News Correspondent"

**Jean Kent**
2-4 Noel Street
London W1V 3RB ENGLAND
"Actress"

**Louis Philip Kentner**
1 Mallord Street
London SW3 6DT ENGLAND
"Musician"

**Kentucky Headhunters**
212 - 3rd Avenue North
Nashville, TN 37201
"Music Group"

**Ken Kercheval**
P.O. Box 4844
Louisville, KY 40204
"Actor"

**Joanna Kerns**
P.O. Box 49216
Los Angeles, CA 90049
"Actress"

**Sandra Kerns**
620 Resolano Drive
Pacific Palisades, CA 90272
"Actress"

**Dagney Kerr**
1801 Avenue of the Stars #902
Los Angeles, CA 90072
"Actress"

**Deborah Kerr**
Wyhergut, 7250 Klosters
Grisons SWITZERLAND
"Actress"

**Edward Kerr**
100 South Hayworth Avenue #106
Los Angeles, CA 90048
"Actor"

**John Kerr**
16130 Ventura Blvd. #650
Encino, CA 10538
"Actor"

**ex-Sen. Robert "Bob" Kerrey**
7602 Pacific Street
Omaha, NE 78114
"Politician"

**Nancy Kerrigan**
40 Salem Street #101
Lynnfield, MA 01940
"Ice Skater"

**Sen. John Kerry (MA)**
10 Park Plaza #3220
Boston, MA 02116
"Politician"

**Doug Kershaw**
Route 1, Box 34285
Weld Country Road 47
Eaton, CO 80615
"Fiddler"

**Sammy Kershaw**
473 Lickton Place
White Creek, TN 37189
"Singer"

**Brian Kerwin**
200 West 57th Street #900
New York, NY 10019
"Actor"

**Dave Ketchum**
2318 Waterby Street
Westlake Village, CA 91361
"Writer, Producer"

**Dr. Jack Kevorkian #284797**
Oaks Correctional Facility
1500 Caberfae Highway
P.O. Box 38
Eastlake, MI 49626
"Assisted Suicide Advocate"

**Ted Key**
1694 Glenhardie Road
Wayne, PA 19087
"Cartoonist"

**Dr. Alan Keyes**
c/o MSNBC
2200 Fletcher Drive
Ft. Lee, NJ 07024
"Talk Show Host"

**Evelyn Keyes**
999 North Doheny Drive #509
Los Angeles, CA 90069
"Actress"

**Chaka Khan**
12431 Oxnard Street #B
North Hollywood, CA 91606
"Singer"

**Princess Yasmin Khan**
146 Central Park West
New York, NY 10023
"Royalty"

**Adnan Khashoggi**
La Baraka
Marbella, SPAIN
"Arms Dealer"

**Sidney Kibrick**
10490 Wilshire Blvd. #1901
Los Angeles, CA 90024
"Actor"

**Jason Kidd**
New Jersey Nets
390 Murray Hill Parkway
E. Rutherford, NJ 07073
"Basketball Player"

**Michael Kidd**
1614 Old Oak Road
Los Angeles, CA 90049
"Actor, Dancer"

**Margot Kidder**
315 West Lewis Street
Livingston, MT 59047
"Actress"

**Nicole Kidman**
9830 Wilshire Blvd.
Beverly Hills, CA 90212
"Actress"

**Richard Kiel**
42805 Ranger Circle Drive
Coarsegold, CA 93614
"Actor"

**Merle Kilgore**
P.O. Box 850
Paris, TN 38242
"Singer, Songwriter"

**Harmon Killebrew**
P.O. Box 14550
Scottsdale, AZ 85267
"Ex-Baseball Player"

**Billy Kilmer**
111 South Saint Joseph Street
South Bend, IN 46601
"Ex-Football Player"

**Jean-Claude Killey**
13 Chemin Bellefontaine
1223 Cologny GE SWITZERLAND
"Skier"

**Val Kilmer**
9830 Wilshire Blvd.
Beverly Hills, CA 90212
"Actor"

**Eric Kilpatrick**
6330 Simpson Avenue #3
North Hollywood, CA 91606
"Actor"

**Lincoln Kilpatrick**
1710 Garth Avenue
Los Angeles, CA 90035
"Actor"

**Daniel Dae Kim**
145 West 45th Street #1204
New York, NY 10036
"Actor"

**Bruce Kimmel**
12230 Otsego Street
North Hollywood, CA 91607
"Writer, Director"

**Richard Kind**
142 East 35th Street #200
New York, NY 10016
"Actor"

**Roslyn Kind**
13701 Riverside Drive #201
Burbank, CA 91521
"Actress"

**Alan King**
404 Park Avenue South #1000
New York, NY 10016
"Comedian, Actor"

**Andrea King**
1225 Sunset Plaza Drive #3
Los Angeles, CA 90069
"Actress"

**B.B. King**
P.O. Box 268867
Las Vegas, NV 89126
"Singer, Guitarist"

**Ben E. King**
P.O. Box 1097
Teaneck, NJ 07666
"Singer, Songwriter"

**Billie Jean King**
1130 East 9th Street #100
Cleveland, OH 44114
"Tennis Player"

**Cammie Conlon King**
13775-A Mono Way #220
Sonora, CA 95370
"Actress"

**Carole King**
509 Hartnell Street
Monterey, CA 93940
"Singer, Songwriter"

**Coretta Scott King**
234 Sunset Avenue N.W.
Atlanta, GA 30314
"Mrs. Martin Luther King, Jr."

**Don King**
501 Fairway Drive
Deerfield Beach, FL 33441

"Fight Promoter"

**Evelyn "Champagne" King**
1560 Broadway #1306
New York, NY 10036
"Singer"

**Larry King**
13607 Hatteras Street
Vally Glen, CA 91401
"TV Talk Show Host"

**Perry King**
3500 West Olive Avenue #1400
Burbank, CA 91505
"Actor"

**Regina King**
8271 Melrose Avenue, #110
Los Angeles, CA 90046
"Actress"

**Rodney King**
9100 Wilshire Blvd. #250-W
Beverly Hills, CA 90212
"Beaten Motorist"

**Stephen King**
49 Florida Avenue
Bangor, ME 04401
"Novelist"

**Zalman King**
308 Alta Drive
Santa Monica, CA 90402
"Writer"

**Roger Kingdom**
322 Mall Blvd. #303
Monroeville, PA 15146
"Track & Field Athlete"

**Ben Kingsley**
Pabworth House
Stratford-on-Avon
Warwickshire CU37 8XQ EN-
GLAND
"Actor"

**The Kingsmen**
1720 North Ross Avenue
Santa Ana, CA 92706
"Rock & Roll Group"

**Alex Kingston**
3400 Floyd Terrace
Los Angeles, CA 90068
"Actress"

**The Kingston Trio**
9410 South 46th Street
Phoenix, AZ 85044
"Vocal Trio"

**Kathleen Kinmont**
11364 Ventura Blvd. #100
Box 7403
Studio City, CA 91604
"Actress"

**The Kinks**
29 Rushton Mews
London W11 1RB ENGLAND
"Rock & Roll Group"

**Greg Kinnear**
9150 Wilshire Blvd. #350
Beverly Hills, CA 90212
"Actor"

**Kathy Kinney**
10061 Riverside Drive #777
North Hollywood, CA 91602
"Actress"

**Michael Kinsley**
5602 Lakeview Drive #J
Kirkland, WA 98033
"Political Commentator"

**Nastassja Kinski**
1000 Bel Air Place
Los Angeles, CA 90077
"Actress, Model"

**Bruce Kirby**
629 N .Oakland Avenue #3
Los Angeles, CA 90048
"Actor"

**Phyllis Kirk**
321-M South Beverly Drive
Beverly Hills, CA 90212
"Actress"

**Clare Kirkconnell**
P.O. Box 63
Rutherford, CA 94573
"Actress"

**Gelsey Kirkland**
191 Silver Moss Drive
Vero Beach, FL 32963
"Dancer"

**Sally Kirkland**
11300 West Olympic Blvd.
Los Angeles, CA 90064
"Actress"

**Terry Kiser**
10th Street
Santa Monica, CA 90401
"Actor, Comedian"

**KISS**
8730 Sunset Blvd. #200
West Hollywood, CA 90069
"Rock & Roll Group"

**Dr. Henry Kissinger**
350 Park Avenue, 26th Floor
New York, NY 10022
"Politician"

**Tawny Kitaen**
6300 Wilshire Blvd. #900
Los Angeles, CA 90048
"Actress"

**Michael Kitchen**
4 Windmill Street
London W1P 1HF ENGLAND
"Actor"

**Eartha Kitt**
P.O. Box 36
Scarsdale, NY 10583
"Singer, Actress"

**Franz Klammer**
Mooswald 22
A-9712 Friesach, AUSTRIA
"Skier"

**Calvin Klein**
205 West 39th Street
New York, NY 10018
"Fashion Designer"

**Robert Klein**
67 Ridge Crest Road
Briarcliff, NY 10510
"Comedian, Actor"

**Randal Kleiser**
3050 Runyan Canyon
Los Angeles, CA 90046
"Film Writer & Director"

**Kevin Kline**
1636 3rd Avenue #309
New York, NY 10128
"Actor"

**Richard Kline**
P.O. Box 261003
Encino, CA 91426
"Actor"

**Patricia Klous**
2539 Benedict Canyon Drive
Beverly Hills, CA 90210
"Actress"

**Jack Klugman**
22548 Pacific Coast Highway
Malibu, CA 90265
"Actor, Writer"

**Evel Knievel**
2375 East Tropicana Avenue #178
Las Vegas, CA 89119
"Daredevil"

**Bobby Knight**
c/o Texas Tech Athletic Dept.
Lubbock, TX 79409
"Basketball Coach"

**Gladys Knight**
3221 La Mirada Avenue
Las Vegas, NV 89120
"Singer"

**Jonathan Knight**
90 Apple Street
Essex, MA 01929
"Singer"

**Jordan Knight**
1501 Broadway #1301
New York, NY 10036
"Singer"

**Marlon "Suge" Knight**
4727 Wilshire Blvd. #335
Los Angeles, CA 90010
"Rap Music Executive"

**Michael E. Knight**
1344 Lexington Avenue
New York, NY 10120
"Actor"

**Shirley Knight**
19528 Ventura Blvd. #559
Tarzana, CA 91356
"Actress"

**Mark Knopfler**
16 Lamberton Place
London W11 2SH ENGLAND
"Rock Musician"

**Don Knotts**
13701 Riverside Drive #201
Sherman Oaks, CA 91423
"Actor"

**Chuck Knox**
11220 N.E. 53rd Street
Kirkland, WA 98033
"ex-Football Coach"

**Jeff Kober**
11365 Ventura Blvd. #100
Sherman Oaks, CA 91423
"Actor"

**Walter Koenig**
P.O. Box 4395
North Hollywood, CA 91607
"Actor, Writer"

**Helmut Kohl**
CDU/CSU
Maurerstr. 85
D-10117 Berlin GERMANY
"Politician"

**Mayor Teddy Kollek**
22 Jaffa Road
Jerusalem, ISRAEL
"Politician"

**Dorothy Konrad**
10650 Missouri Avenue #2
Los Angeles, CA 90025
"Actress"

**Kool & The Gang**
50 Church Street, #L-11
Montclair, NJ 07042
"R&B Group""

**Kool Moe Dee**
151 El Camino Drive
Beverly Hills, CA 90212
"Rap Singer"

**Dean R. Koontz**
P.O. Box 9529
Newport Beach, CA 92658
"Writer"

**Dr. C. Everett Koop**
3 Ivy Pointe Way
Hanover, NH 03755
"Ex-Surgeon General"

**Bernie Kopel**
P.O. Box 571582
Tarzana, CA 91357
"Actor, Writer"

**Arnold Kopelson**
901 N. Roxbury Drive
Beverly Hills, CA 90210
"Film Producer"

**Karen Kopins**
145 S. Fairfax Avenue #310
Los Angeles, CA 90036
"Actress"

**Ted Koppel**
1717 DeSales Street NW #300
Washington, DC 20036
"TV Show Host"

**Michael Korda**
1230 Avenue of the Americas
New York, NY 10019
"Writer"

**Harvey Korman**
1136 Stradella
Los Angeles, CA 90077
"Actor, Director"

**Bernie Kosar**
6969 Ron Park Place
Youngstown, OH 44512
"Football Player"

**Lauren Koslow**
13576 Cheltenham Drive
Sherman Oaks, CA 91423
"Actress"

**David Kossoff**
45 Roe Green Close
College Lane
Hatfield, Herts. ENGLAND
"Actor, Writer"

**Irwin Kostal**
3149 Dona Susana Drive
Studio City, CA 91604
"Conductor"

**Leo Kottke**
1658 York Street
Denver, CO 80206
"Actor"

**Yaphet Kotto**
4526 Wilshire Blvd.
Los Angeles, CA 90010
"Actor"

**Sandy Koufax**
10 Weston Avenue #430
Quincy, MA 02107
"Baseball Player"

**Anna Kournikova**
300 S. Pointe Drive
Miami Beach, FL 33139
"Tennis Player"

**Nancy Kovack**
27 Oakmont Drive
Los Angeles, CA 90049
"Actress"

**Martin Kove**
5419 Ben Avenue
North Hollywood, CA 91607
"Actor"

**Harley Jane Kozak**
21338 Colins Drive
Topanga, CA 90290
"Actor"

**Linda Kozlowski**
701 Santa Monica Blvd. #240
Santa Monica, CA 90401
"Actress"

**Jeroen Krabbe**
107 Van Eeghenstraat
1071 EZ Amsterdam, HOLLAND
"Actor"

**Ken Kragen**
1112 North Sherbourne Drive
Los Angeles, CA 90069
"Talent Agent"

**Jane Krakoroski**
12250 Addison Street
Valley Village, CA 91607
"Actress"

**Jack Kramer**
231 North Glenroy Place
Los Angeles, CA 90049
"Tennis Player"

**Joey Kramer**
P.O. Box 882494
San Fransisco, CA 94188
"Drummer"

**Stephanie Kramer**
8271 Melrose Avenue #110
Los Angeles, CA 90046
"Actress, Director"

**Steve Kramer**
1126 Hollywood Way #203-A
Burbank, CA 91505
"Actor"

**Judith Krantz**
166 Groverton Place
Los Angeles, CA 90077
"Author"

**Peter Kraus**
Kaiserplatz 7
D-80803 Munich GERMANY
"Actor"

**Brian Krause**
6043 Weeping Banyan Lane
Woodland Hills, CA 91367
"Actor"

**Alison Krauss**
P.O. Box 121711
Nashville, TN 37203
"Singer"

**Lenny Kravitz**
338 N. Foothill Road
Beverly Hills, CA 90210
"Singer"

**Paul Kreppel**
14300 Killion Street
Van Nuys, CA 91401
"Actor"

**Kreskin**
P.O. Box 1383
West Caldwell, NJ 07006
"Psychic"

**Robbie Krieger**
69 Broad Street #C
Red Bank, NJ 07701
"Actress'

**Alice Krige**
9107 Wilshire Blvd. #321
Beverly Hills, CA 90210
"Actress'

**Kris Kross**
7436 SW 117th Street #209
Miami, FL 33183
"R&B Duo"

**Kris Kristofferson**
P.O. Box 2147
Malibu, CA 90265
"Singer, Actor, Writer"

**William Kristol**
6625 Jill Court
McLean, VA 22101
"Political Conservative"

**Joan Kroc**
8939 Villa La Jolla Drive #201
La Jolla, CA 92037
"Ray Kroc's Widow"

**Marty Krofft**
7710 Woodrow Wilson Drive
Los Angeles, CA 90046
"Puppeteer, Producer"

**Sid Krofft**
7710 Woodrow Wilson Drive
Los Angeles, CA 90046
"Puppeteer, Producer"

**Steve Kroft**
51 West 52nd Street
New York, NY 10019
"News Journalist"

**Hardy Kruger**
P.O. Box 726
Crestline, CA 92325
"Actor"

**Mike Krzyzewski**
Duke University Basketball
Durham, NC 27706
"Basketball Coach"

**Lisa Kudrow**
1122 S. Robertson Blvd. #15
Los Angeles, CA 90035
"Actress"

**Mitch Kupchak**
156 N. Gunston Drive
Los Angeles, CA 90049
"Ex-Basketball Player"

**Swoosie Kurtz**
320 Central Park West
New York, NY 10025
"Actress"

**Michelle Kwan**
3955 Orchard Hill Place #150
Novi, MI 48375
"Ice Skater"

**Nancy Kwan**
1317 - 5th Street #200
Santa Monica, CA 90401
"Actress"

**Burt Kwouk**
2-4 Noel Street
London W1V 3RB ENGLAND
"Actor"

**Patti LaBelle**
947 N. La Cienega Blvd. #G
Los Angeles, CA 90069
"Singer, Actress

**Terry Labonte**
P.O. Box 9
Harrisburg, NC 28075
"Race Car Driver"

**Patrick Laborteaux**
8916 Ashcroft Avenue
Los Angeles, CA 90048
"Actor"

**Elizabeth Lackey**
2201 - 11th Avenue #300
Regina Sask
S4P OJB CANADA
"Actress"

**Jerry Lacy**
145 S. Fairfax Avenue #310
Los Angeles, CA 90036
"Actor, Writer, Director"

**Alan Ladd, Jr.**
1005 Benedict Canyon Drive
Beverly Hills, CA 90210
"Film Executive"

**Alana Ladd**
1420 Moraga Drive
Los Angeles, CA 90049
"Actress"

**Diane Ladd**
14945 Ventura Blvd. #228
Sherman Oaks, CA 31403
"Actress"

**Margaret Ladd**
444-21st Street
Santa Monica, CA 90402
"Actress"

**Dr. Arthur Laffer**
5375 Executive Square #330
La Jolla, CA 92037
"Economist"

**Perry Lafferty**
335 South Bristol Avenue
Los Angeles, CA 90049
"TV Executive"

**Guy LaFleur**
9050 Blvd. del Acadie
Montreal PQ H4N 2S5 CANADA
"Hockey Player"

**Christine Lahti**
1122 S. Robertson Blvd. #15
Los Angeles, CA 90035
"Actress"

**Francis Lai**
23 rue Franklin, F-75116
Paris, FRANCE
"Composer"

**Cleo Laine**
Wavendon (Old Rectory)
Milton Keynes
MK17 8LT ENGLAND
"Singer"

**Frankie Laine**
P.O. Box 6910
San Diego, CA 92166
"Singer, Actor"

**Melvin Laird**
1730 Rhode Island Avenue
Washington, DC 20036
"Ex-Government Official"

**Ricki Lake**
226 West 26th Street #400
New York, NY 10001
"TV Show Host"

**Sanoe Lake**
2160 Avenida de la Playa
La Jolla, CA 92037
"Actress"

**Sir Freddie Laker**
138 Cheapside
London EC2V 6BL ENGLAND
"Business Executive"

**Donny Lalonde**
2554 Lincoln Blvd. #729
Venice, CA 90291
"Boxer"

**Lorenzo Lamas**
14945 Ventura Blvd. #228
Sherman Oaks, CA 91403
"Actor"

**Christopher Lambert**
9 av. Trembley C/Lui
CH-1209 Geneva SWITLAND
"Actor"

**Jack Lambert**
RR#2. Box 101A
Worthington, PA 16262
"Ex-Football Player"

**Jerry Lambert**
P.O. Box 25371
Charlotte, NC 28212
"Singer"

**L.W. Lambert**
Route #1
Olin, NC 28860
"C&W Singer"

**Ex-Gov. Richard Lamm**
University of Denver
Center for Public Policy
Denver, CO 80208
"Politician"

**Robert Lamm**
1113 Sutton Way
Beverly Hills, CA 90210
"Musician, Songwriter"

**Jake Lamotta**
400 East 57th Street
New York, NY 10022
"Boxer"

**Zohra Lampert**
100 West 57th Street
New York, NY 10019
"Actress"

**Bert Lance**
P.O. Box 637
Calhoun, GA 30701
"Politician"

**Juliet Landau**
2154 North Vine Street
Los Angeles, CA 90068
"Actress"

**Martin Landau**
7455 Palo Vista Drive
Los Angeles, CA 90046
"Actor"

**David L. Lander**
5819 Saint Laurent Drive
Agoura Hills, CA 91301
"Actor, Writer"

**Audrey Landers**
4048 Las Palmas Drive
Sarasota, FL 34238
"Actress, Singer"

**Judy Landers**
3933 Losillas Drive
Sarasota, FL 34238
"Actress, Model"

**John Landis**
11688 San Ysidro Drive
Beverly Hills, CA 90210
"Film Writer, Director"

**Joe Lando**
70 Sabra Avenue
Oak Park, CA 91377
"Actor"

**Paul Landres**
5343 Amestoy Avenue
Encino, CA 91316
"TV Director"

**Sen. Mary Landrieu (LA)**
702 Hart Office Bldg.
Washington, DC 20110
"Politician"

**Moon Landrieu**
4301 South Prieur
New Orleans, LA 70125
"Ex-Mayor"

**Valerie Landsburg**
22745 Chamera Lane
Topanga, CA 90290
"Actress"

**Andre Landzaat**
7500 Devista Drive
Los Angeles, CA 90046
"Actor"

**Abby Lane**
444 North Faring Road
Los Angeles, CA 90077
"Actress, Singer"

**Charles Lane**
321 Gretna Green Way
Los Angeles, CA 90049
"Actor"

**Diane Lane**
25 Sea Colony Drive
Santa Monica, CA 90405
"Actress"

**Nathan Lane**
P.O. Box 1249
White River Junction, VT 05001
"Actor"

**Eric Laneuville**
5138 W. Slauson Avenue
Los Angeles, CA 90056
"Actor"

**June Lang-Morgan**
12756 Kahlenberg Lane
North Hollywood, CA 91607
"Actress"

**Katherine Kelly Lang**
7800 Beverly Blvd. #3371
Los Angeles, CA 90036
"Actress"

**K.D. Lang**
947 La Cienega Blvd. #G
Los Angeles, CA 90036
"Singer"

**Robert Lang**
68 St. James's Street
London SW1A 1PH ENGLAND
"Actor"

**Stephen Lang**
Pure Arts
8840 Wilshire Blvd.
Beverly Hills, CA 90211
"Actor"

**Harry Langdon**
181 N. McCadden Place
Los Angeles, CA 90004
"Photographer"

**Hope Lange**
1801 Avenue of the Stars
Los Angeles, CA 90067
"Actress"

**Ted Lange**
6950 McLennan Avenue
Van Nuys, CA 91406
"Actor, Writer, Director"

**Frank Langella**
151 El Camino Drive
Beverly Hills, CA 90212
"Actor"

**Heather Langenkamp**
156 "F" Street SW
Washington, DC 20003
"Actress"

**Bernhard Langer**
1120 S.W. 21st Lane
Boca Raton, FL 33486
"Golfer"

**Frances Langford**
P.O. Box 96
Jensen Beach, FL 33457
"Singer"

**Wallace Langham**
10264 Rochester Avenue
Los Angeles, CA 90024
"Actor"

**Murray Langston**
P.O. Box 5734
Santa Rosa, CA 95402
"Comedian, Actor"

**Lester Lanin**
901 Winding River Road
Vero Beach, FL 32963
"Band Leader"

**Kim Lankford**
400 S. Beverly drive #101
Beverly Hills, CA 90212
"Actress"

**Angela Lansbury**
635 Bonhill Road
Los Angeles, CA 90049
"Actress"

**Sherry Lansing**
10451 Bellagio Road
Los Angeles, CA 90077
"Film Executive"

**Anthony LaPaglia**
955 S. Carrillo Drive #300
Los Angeles, CA 90048
"Actor"

**Guy LaPointe**
Hockey Hall of Fame
BCE Place, 30 Yonge Street
Toronto, Ontario M5E 1X8
CANADA
"Hockey Player"

**John Larch**
4506 Varna Avenue
Sherman Oaks, CA 91403
"Actor"

**Vincent Lardo**
c/o Berkeley Publishing
375 Hudson Street
New York, NY 10022
"Author"

**Rep. Steve Largent (OK)**
Cannon House Office Bldg. #410
Washington, DC 20515
"Politician"

**Barry Larkin**
5410 Osprey Isle Lane
Orlando, FL 32819
"Baseball Player"

**Julius LaRosa**
67 Sycamore Lane
Irvington, NY 10533
"Actor, Singer"

**Lyndon LaRouche**
15820 Round Top Lane
Round Hill, VA 20141
"Politician"

**John Larroquette**
8942 Wilshire Blvd.
Beverly Hills, CA 90211
"Actor"

**Don Larsen**
P.O. Box 2863
Hayden Lake, ID 83835
"Ex-Baseball Player"

**Jack Larson**
449 Skyewiay Road North
Los Angeles, CA 90049
"Actor"

**Wolf Larson**
10600 Holman Avenue, #1
Los Angeles, CA 90024
"Actor"

**Eva La Rue-Callahan**
11661 San Vicente Blvd. #307
Los Angeles, CA 90049
"Actress"

**Florence La Rue**
4300 Louis Avenue
Encino, CA 91316
"Singer"

**Tony LaRussa**
338 Golden Meadow Place
Alamo, CA 945071
"Baseball Manager"

**Vincent LaRusso**
419 Park Avenue So.#1009
New York, NY 10016
"Actor"

**Tommy Lasorda**
1473 West Maxzim Avenue
Fullerton, CA 92633
"Baseball Manager"

**Louise Lasser**
200 East 71st Street #20C
New York, NY 10021
"Actor, Writer"

**Sydney Lassick**
2734 Bellevue
Los Angeles, CA 90026
"Actor"

**Louise Latham**
9229 Sunset Blvd. #311
Los Angeles, CA 90069
"Actress"

**Queen Latifah**
155 Morgan Street
Jersey City, NJ 07302
"Rap Singer"

**Kenny Lattimore**
151 El Camino Drive
Beverly Hills, CA 90212
"Singer"

**Niki Lauda**
San Costa de Baix
Santa Eucalia IBIZA
SPAIN
"Race Car Driver, Author"

**Andrew Lauer**
9150 Wilshire Blvd. #350
Beverly Hills, CA 90212
"Actor"

**Estee Lauder**
767 Fifth Avenue
New York, NY 10153
"Fashion Designer"

**Matt Lauer**
30 Rockefeller Plaza #701
New York, NY 10112
"TV Show Host"

**John Laughlin**
11815 Magnolia Blvd., #2
North Hollywood, CA 91607
"Actor"

**Tom Laughlin**
P.O. Box 840
Moorpark, CA 93020
"Actor, Producer"

**Cyndi Lauper**
2211 Broadway #10F
New York, NY 10024
"Singer, Songwriter"

**Matthew Laurance**
1951 Hillcrest Road
Los Angeles, CA 90068
"Actor"

**Ralph Lauren**
1107 - 5th Avenue
New York, NY 10128
"Fashion Designer"

**Tammy Lauren**
14724 Ventura Blvd. #515
Sherman Oaks, CA 91403
"Child Actress"

**Arthur Laurents**
P.O. Box 582
Quoque, NY 11959
"Writer"

**Dan Lauria**
12712 Moorpark Street #205
Studio City, CA 91604
"Actor"

**Piper Laurie**
2118 Wilshire Blvd., PMB 931
Los Angeles, CA 90403
"Actress"

**Rod Laver**
P.O. Box 4798
Hilton Head, SC 29928
"Tennis Player"

**Avril Lavigne**
Nettwert Mgnt.
345 - 7th Avenue, 24th Floor
New York, NY 10001
"Singer"

**Linda Lavin**
321 Front Street
Wilmington, NC 28401
"Actress, Director"

**John Phillip Law**
1339 Miller Drive
Los Angeles, CA 90069
"Actor"

**Jude Law**
46 Albermarle Street
London W1X 4PP ENGLAND
"Actor"

**Patricia Kennedy Lawford**
1 Sutton Place South
New York, NY 10021
"Widow of Peter Lawford"

**Lucy Lawless**
9701 Wilshire Blvd., 10th Floor
Beverly Hills, CA 90212
"Actress"

**Carol Lawrence**
12337 Ridge Circle
Los Angeles, CA 90049
"Actress, Singer"

**Joey Lawrence**
151 El Camino Drive
Beverly Hills, CA 90212
"Actor"

**Linda Lawrence**
4926 Commonwealth
La Canada, CA 91011
"Actress"

**Martin Lawrence**
P.O. Box 7304, Suite #440
North Hollywood, CA 91603
"Actor"

**Patricia Lawrence**
33 St. Luke's Street
London SW3 ENGLAND
"Actress"

**Sharon Lawrence**
P.O. Box 462048
Los Angeles, CA 90046
"Actress"

**Steve Lawrence**
944 Pine hurst Drive
Las Vegas, NV 89109
"Singer"

**Tracy Lawrence**
1100 - 17th Avenue South
Nashville, TN 37212
"Singer"

**Vicki Lawrence-Schultz**
6000 Lido Avenue
Long Beach, CA 90803
"Actress, Singer"

**Hubert Laws**
1078 South Ogden Drive
Los Angeles, CA 90019
"Flutist"

**Leigh Lawson**
162-170 Wardour Street
London W1V 3AT ENGLAND
"Actress"

**Paul Laxalt**
801 Pennsylvania Avenue NW #750
Washington, DC 20004
"Ex-Senator"

**Kenneth Lay**
1302 West Gray Street
Houston, TX 77019
"Ex-Enron Official"

**Barbara Lazaroff**
805 N. Sierra Drive
Beverly Hills, CA 90210
"Designer"

**Buddy Lazier**
8135 West Crawfordsville
Indianapolis, IN 46224
"Race Car Driver"

**Rep. Jim Leach (IA)**
Rayburn House Office Bldg. #2186
Washington, DC 20515
"Politician"

**Rosemary Leach**
1 Stratton Street,
London, W1X 5FD, ENGLAND
"Actress"

**Cloris Leachman**
410 S. Barrington Avenue #307
Los Angeles, CA 90049
"Actress"

**Sen. Patrick J. Leahy (VT)**
Senate Russell Bldg. #433
Washington, DC 20510
"Politician"

**Norman Lear**
1911 Westridge Road
Los Angeles, CA 90049
"TV Writer, Producer"

**Michael Learned**
1600 N. Beverly Drive
Beverly Hills, CA 90210
"Actress"

**Denis Leary**
9171 Wilshire Blvd. #406
Beverly Hills, CA 90210
"Commedian"

**Eddie LeBaron**
7524 Pineridge Lane
Fair Oaks, CA 95628
"Football Player"

**Sabrina Le Beauf**
1613 Maltman Avenue
Los Angeles, CA 90026
"Actress"

**Matt LeBlanc**
1122 S. Robertson Blvd. #15
Los Angeles, CA 90035
"Actor"

**Jean LeClerc**
RD #2 Freborn Street
St. Albans, VT 05478
"Actor"

**Henri Leconte**
2 Avenue Gordon Benett,
Paris, F-75016 FRANCE
"Tennis Player"

**Led Zeppelin**
46 Kensington Court Street
London, W8 5DP, ENGLAND
"R & B Group"

**Heath Ledger**
8455 Beverly Blvd. #410
Los Angeles, CA 90048
"Actor"

**Chris Ledoux**
P.O. Box 253
Sumner, IA 50674
"Singer, Songwriter"

**Ang Lee**
417 Canal Street, #400
New York, NY 10013
"Artist"

**Anna Lee**
1240 N. Doheny Drive
Los Angeles, CA 90069
"Actress"

**Brenda Lee**
P.O. Box 101188
Nashville, TN 37210
"Singer"

**Christopher Lee**
2/4 Noel Street
London W1V 3RB ENGLAND
"Actor"

**Dickey Lee**
27 L'Ambiaca Court
New York, NY 10954
"Singer"

**Jason Scott Lee**
P.O. Box 1083
Pearl City, HI 96782
"Actor"

**Johnny Lee**
P.O. Box 1644
Dickinson, TX 77539
"Singer, Songwriter"

**Kathy Lee**
204 River Edge Lane
Seiverville, TN 37862
"Singer"

**Michelle Lee**
830 Birchwood
Los Angeles, CA 90024
"Actress, Singer"

**Ruta Lee**
2623 Laurel Canyon Road
Los Angeles, CA 90046
"Actress"

**Dr. Sammy Lee**
16537 Harbour Lane
Huntington Beach, CA 92649
"Physician, Athlete"

**Sheryl Lee**
151 El Camino Drive
Beverly Hills, CA 90212
"Actress"

**Spike Lee**
40 Acres & A Mule Film Works
124 De Kalb Avenue #2
Brooklyn, NY 11217
"Actor, Film Director"

**Beverly Leech**
9150 Wilshire Blvd. #175
Beverly Hills, CA 90212
"Actress"

**Richard Leech**
27 Clayland's Road
London SW8 1NX ENGLAND
"Actor"

**Jane Leeves**
4918 Norwich Avenue
Sherman Oaks, CA 91403
"Actress"

**Michel Legrand**
157 W. 57th Street
New York, NY 10019
"Pianist, Composer"

**John Leguizamo**
3859 Cardiff Avenue #2
Culver City, CA 90232
"Actor"

**Edie Lehman**
24844 Malibu Road
Malibu, CA 90265
"Singer"

**Jim Lehrer**
3556 Macomb Street NW
Washington, DC 20016
"Broadcast Journalist"

**Ron Leibman**
27 W. 87th Street #2
New York, NY 10024
"Actor, Writer"

**Janet Leigh**
1625 Summitridge Drive
Beverly Hills, CA 90210
"Actress"

**Jennifer Jason Leigh**
2400 Whitman Place
Los Angeles, CA 90068
"Actress"

**Mike Leigh**
8 Earlham Grove
London N22 ENGLAND
"Film Writer, Director"

**David Leisure**
8428-C Melrose Place
Los Angeles, CA 90069
"Actor"

**Donovan Leitch**
8794 Lookout Mountain Avenue
Los Angeles, CA 90046
"Actor"

**Claude LeLouch**
15 Avenue Foch
F-7516 Paris, FRANCE
"Director, Producer"

**Michael Lembeck**
23852 Pacific Coast Hwy. #355
Malibu, CA 90265
"Actor"

**Mario Lemieux**
630 Academy Street
Sewickley, PA 15143
"Hockey Player"

**Christopher Lemmon**
80 Murray Drive
South Glastonbury, CT 06073
"Actor"

**Meadowlark Lemon**
13610 N. Scottsdale Road #1026
Scottsdale, AZ 85254
"Ex-Basketball Player"

**Greg Lemond**
15500 Wayzata Blvd. #604-262
Wayzata, MN 55391
"Bicyclist"

**Ivan Lendl**
400 - 5 1/2 Mile Road
Goshen, CT 05756
"Tennis Player"

**Julian Lennon**
30 Ives Street
London SW3 2ND ENGLAND
"Singer, Composer"

**Sean Lennon**
27a Floral Street #300
London SC2E 9DQ ENGLAND
"Singer, Composer"

**Lennon Sisters**
1984 State Highway 165
Branson, MO 65616
"Vocal Group"

**Annie Lennox**
35 - 37 Park Gate Road
Unit #2 Ransome's Dock
London SW1 4NP ENGLAND
"Singer"

**Jay Leno**
P.O. Box 7885
Burbank, CA 91510
"TV Show Host, Comedian"

**Kay Lenz**
5719 Allot Avenue
Van Nuys, CA 91401
"Actress"

**Rick Lenz**
12955 Calvert Street
Van Nuys, CA 91401
"Actor"

**Melissa Leo**
485 Madison Avenue #1300
New York, NY 10022
"Actress"

**Elmore Leonard**
2192 Yarmouth Road
Bloomfield Village, MI 48301
"Author, Screenwriter"

**Justin Leonard**
3304 Dartmouth Avenue
Dallas, TX 75205
"Golfer"

**Lu Leonard**
8525 S.W. Pfaffle Street #5
Tigard, OR 97223
"Actress"

**Robert Sean Leonard**
14 Bergen Avenue
Waldwick, NJ 07463
"Actor"

**Sugar Ray Leonard**
4401 East-West Highway #206-B
Bethsesda, MD 20814
"Boxer"

**Tea Leoni**
2300 W. Victory Blvd.
Burbank, CA 91506
"Actress"

**Michael Lerner**
1980 Coldwater Canyon Drive
Beverly Hills, CA 90210
"Actress"

**Gloria LeRoy**
13775-A Mono Way #220
Sonora, CA 95370
"Actress"

**Aleen Leslie**
1700 Lexington Road
Beverly Hills, CA 90210
"Writer"

**Joan Leslie**
2228 North Catilina Avenue
Los Angeles, CA 90027
"Actress"

**Lenn Lesser**
934 N. Evergreen St.
Burbank, CA 91505
"Actor"

**Ketty Lester**
5931 Comey Avenue
Los Angeles, CA 90034
"Actress"

**Mark Lester**
1 Carlton Street
Cheltenham
Gloustershire ENGLAND
"Singer, Actor"

**Richard Lester**
River Land
Petersham Surrey, ENGLAND
"Film Director, Composer"

**Terry Lester**
2401 Main Street
Santa Monica, CA 90405
"Actor"

**Jared Leto**
9100 Wilshire Blvd. #600
Beverly Hills, CA 90212
"Actor"

**David Letterman**
1597 Broadway
New York, NY 10019
"TV Show Host"

**The Lettermen**
9255 Sunset Blvd. #407
Los Angeles, CA 90069
"Music Group"

**Shelby Leverington**
1801 Avenue of the Stars #1250
Los Angeles, CA 90067
"Actress"

**Sen. Carl Levin (MI)**
Senate Russell Bldg. #459
Washington, DC 20510
"Politician"

**Ira Levin**
1172 Park Avenue
New York, NY 10128
"Author"

**Michael Levine**
10333 Ashton Avenue
Los Angeles, CA 90024
"Media Expert"

**Rep. Sandy Levine (MI)**
House Rayburn Bldg. #2909
Washington, DC 20515
"Politician"

**Ted Levine**
1505 10th Street
Santa Monica, CA 90401
"Actor"

**Barry Levinson**
9830 Wilshire Blvd.
Beverly Hills, CA 90212
"Film Writer, Director"

**Jonathan Levitt**
2934 Beverly Glen Circle #107
Los Angeles, CA 90077
"Actor"

**Monica Lewinsky**
660 Greewich Street
New York, NY 10014
"Ex-White House Intern"

**Al Lewis**
13775-A Mono Way #220
Sonora, CA 95370
"Actor"

**Ananda Lewis**
1515 Broadway
New York, NY 10036
"Actress"

**Carl Lewis**
1 Olympic Plaza
Colorado Springs, CO 80909
"Track & Field Athlete"

**Clea Lewis**
1122 S. Roxbury Drive
Los Angeles, CA 90035
"Actress"

**Damian Lewis**
P.O. Box 681736
West Hollywood, CA 90069
"Actor"

**Dawnn Lewis**
P.O. Box 56718
Sherman Oaks, CA 91413
"Actress"

**Eddie Lewis**
1801 S. Prairie Avenue
Chicago, IL 60616
"Composer"

**Gary Lewis**
27 L'Ambiance Court
Bardonia, NY 10954
"Singer, Drummer"

**Geoffrey Lewis**
5750 Wilshire Blvd. #580
Los Angeles, CA 90036
"Actor"

**Hedgemon Lewis**
1516 north Main Street, Box 130
Las Vegas, NV 89101
"Boxer"

**Huey Lewis**
P.O. Box 819
Mill Valley, CA 94942
"Singer"

**Jerry Lewis**
3160 West Sahara Avenue
Las Vegas, NV 89102
"Comedian, Actor"

**Jerry Lee Lewis**
P.O. Box 348
Nesbit, MS 38651
"Singer, Composer"

**Rep. John Lewis (GA)**
Cannon House Office Bldg. #229
Washington, DC 20515
"Politician"

**Juliette Lewis**
151 El Camino Drive
Beverly Hills, CA 90212
"Actress"

**Lennox Lewis**
Shelana House
Eastcastle Street #100
London, W1N 8NL ENGLAND
"Boxer"

**Marcia Lewis**
700 New Hampshire Avenue NW
Washington, D.C. 20037
"Monica Lewinsky's Mother"

**Ramsey Lewis**
1022 Rt. 376
Wappingers Falls, NY 12590
"Pianist, Composer"

**Richard Lewis**
9260 Cordell Road
Los Angeles, CA 90069
"Actor"

**John Leyton**
53 Keyes House, Dophin Sq.
London SW1V 3NA ENGLAND
"Actor"

**Richard Libertini**
2313 McKinley Avenue
Venice, CA 90291
"Actor"

**Jeremy Licht**
4355 Clybourn Avenue
Toluca Lake, CA 91602
"Actor"

**G. Gordon Liddy**
9112 Riverside Drive
Ft. Washington, MD 20744
"Talk Show Host"

**Sen. Joseph I Lieberman (CT)**
706 Senate Hart Office Bldg.
Washington, DC 20510
"Politician"

**Jennifer Lien**
195 South Beverly Hill Drive #400
Beverly Hills, CA 90212
"Actress"

**Tina Lifford**
8436 West 3rd Street, #740
Los Angeles, CA 90048
"Actress"

**Judith Light**
1475 Sierra Vista Drive
Aspen, CO 81611
"Actress"

**Gordon Lightfoot**
1365 Yonge Street #207
Toronto, Ontario
M4T 2P7 CANADA
"Singer, Songwriter"

**Leonard Lightfoot**
446 South Orchard Drive
Burbank, CA 91506
"Actor"

**Tom Ligon**
227 Waverly Place
New York, NY 10014
"Actor"

**Rush Limbaugh**
P.O. Box 2182
Palm Beach, FL 33480
"Radio & TV Talk Show Host"

**Cho-Laing Lin**
473 West End Avenue #15A
New York, NY 10024
"Violinist"

**Abbey Lincoln**
122 East 57th Street, #400
New York, NY 10022
"Singer"

**Chad Lindberg**
5750 Wilshire Blvd. #640
Los Angeles, CA 90036
"Actor"

**Erik Lindbergh**
722-A Spirit of st. Louis Blvd.
Chesterfield, MO 63005
"Grandson of Charles Lindbergh"

**Reeve Lindbergh**
839 Tripp Lane
St. Johnsbury, VT 05819
"Daughter of Charles Lindbergh"

**DeDe Lind**
P.O. Box 1712
Boca Raton, FL 33429
"Model"

**Hal Linden**
8436 West 3rd Street #740
Los Angeles, CA 90048
"Actor, Director"

**Kate Linden**
9111 Wonderland Avenue
Los Angeles, CA 90046
"Actress"

**Delroy Lindo**
151 El Camino Drive
Beverly Hills, CA 90212
"Actor"

**Eric Lindros**
1 Pattison Place
Philadelphia, PA 19148
"Hockey Player"

**Mark Lindsay**
P.O. Box 1269
Haiku, HI 96708
"Singer, Composer"

**Mort Lindsey**
6970 Fernhill Drive
Malibu, CA 90265
"Composer, Conductor"

**Robert Lindsay**
1 Robert Street
London WC2N 6BH ENGLAND
"Actor"

**Jon Lindstrom**
10100 Santa Monica Blvd. #2490
Los Angeles, CA 90067
"Actor"

**Linkin Park**
8484 Wilshire Blvd. #425
Beverly Hills, CA 90211
"Singer"

**Art Linkletter**
8484 Wilshire Blvd. #205
Beverly Hills, CA 90211
"TV Personality"

**Terri Ann Linn**
145 South Fairfax Avenue #310
Los Angeles, CA 90036
"Actress"

**Mark Linn-Baker**
27702 Fairweather Street
Canyon Country, CA 91351
"Actor"

**Laura Linney**
9465 Wilshire Blvd. #600
Beverly Hills, CA 90211
"Actress"

**Ray Liotta**
16829 Monte Hermosa Drive
Pacific Palisades, CA 90272
"Actor"

**Tara Lipinski**
P.O. Box 472288
Charlotte, NC 28247
"Ice Skater"

**Peggy Lipton**
1505 - 10th Street
Santa monica, CA 90401
"Actress"

**Robert Lipton**
9300 Wilshire Blvd. #410
Beverly Hills, CA 90212
"Actor"

**Lisa Lisa**
1560 Broadway #1308
New York, NY 10036
"R&B Group"

Via Gluseppe Pisanelli 2
I-00196 Rome ITALY
"Actress"

**Stephen Liska**
15050 Sherman Way #167
Van Nuys, CA 91405
"Actor"

**John Lithgow**
1319 Warnall Avenue
Los Angeles, CA 90024
"Actor"

**Little River Band**
9850 Sandalfoot Blvd. #458
Boca Raton, FL 33428
"Rock & Roll Group"

**Rich Little**
13849 Riverside Drive
Sherman Oaks, CA 91423
"Actor, Comedian"

**Little Richard**
Hyatt Sunset Hotel
8401 Sunset Blvd.
Los Angeles, CA 90069
"Singer, Songwriter"

**Tawny Little**
5515 Melrose Avenue
Los Angeles, CA 90038
"TV Show Host"

**Big Tiny Little**
West 3985 Taft Drive
Spokane, WA 98208
"Singer, Songwriter"

**Warren Littlefield**
815 Brooktree Road
Pacific Palisades, CA 90272
"Television Executive"

**Gene Littler**
P.O. Box 1949
Rancho Santa Fe, CA 92067
"Golfer"

**Robin Lively**
151 El Camino Drive
Beverly Hills, CA 90212
"Actress"

**Barry Livingston**
8271 Melrose Avenue #202
Los Angeles, CA 90046
"Actor"

**Stanley Livingston**
P.O. Box 1782
Studio City, CA 91604
"Actor"

**Keri Lizer**
15260 Ventura Blvd. #1040
Sherman Oaks, CA 91403
"Actress"

**LL Cool J**
c/o Island Def Jam Music
835 - 8th Avenue, 27th Floor
New York, NY 10019
"Rap Singer & Actor"

**Doug Llewelyn**
8075 West Third Street #303
Los Angeles, CA 90048
"Actor"

**Emily Lloyd**
9560 Wilshire Blvd. #516
Beverly Hills, CA 90212
"Actress"

**Kathleen Lloyd**
116 Rosehedge Lane
Agoura, CA 91301
"Actress"

**Norman Lloyd**
1813 Old Ranch Road
Los Angeles, CA 90049
"Actor, Director"

**Dick Locher**
435 N. Michigan Avenue
Chicago, IL 60611
"Cartoonist"

**Sondra Locke**
6955 La Presa Drive
Los Angeles, CA 90068
"Actress"

**Brad Lockerman**
300 South Raymond Avenue #11
Pasadena, CA 91105
"Actor"

**Anne Lockhart**
191 Upper Lake Road
Thousand Oaks, CA 91361
"Actress"

**June Lockhart**
P.O. Box 3207
Santa Monica, CA 90403
"Actress"

**Heather Locklear**
1836 Counrtney Terrace
Los Angeles, CA 90046
"Actress, Model"

**Hank Locklin**
P.O. Box 117
Brewton, AL 36427
"C & W Singer"

**Gary Lockwood**
3083 1/2 Rambla Pacifica
Malibu, CA 90265
"Actor"

**David Lodge**
8 Sydney Road
Richmond, Surrey, ENGLAND
"Actor"

**Phyllis Logan**
47 Courtfield Road #9
London SW7 4DB ENGLAND
"Actress"

**Robert Loggia**
544 Bellagio Terrace
Los Angeles, CA 90049
"Actor, Director"

**Kenny Loggins**
1187 Coast Village Road #1-499
Santa Barbara, CA 93108
"Singer, Songwriter"

**Donal Logue**
1964 Westwood Blvd #400
Los Angeles, CA 90025
"Actor"

**Gina Lollobrigida**
Via Appino Antica 223
I-00178 Rome, ITALY
"Actress"

**Herbert Lom**
2-4 Noel Street
London W1F 8GB ENGLAND
"Actor"

**Louise Lombard**
9 Newburgh Street
London WIV 11H ENGLAND
"Actress"

**Jeremy London**
P.O. Box 5617
Beverly Hills, CA 90210
"Actor"

**John Lone**
1740 Broadway, 22nd Floor
New York, NY 10019
"Actor"

**Howie Long**
8942 Wilshire Blvd.
Beverly Hills, CA 90211
"Ex-Football Player"

**Shelley Long**
15237 Sunset Blvd.
Pacific Palisades, CA 90272
"Actress"

**Johnny Longdon**
5401 Palmer Drive
Banning, CA 92220
"Actor"

**Tony Longo**
24 Westwind Street
Marina del Rey, CA 90292
"Actor"

**Mike Lookinland**
3481 South 2700 East
Salt Lake City, UT 84109
"Actor"

**Rod Loomis**
5114 Vineland Avenue
North Hollywood, CA 91601
"Actor"

**Al Lopez**
3601 Beach Street
Tampa, FL 33609
"Ex-Baseball Player"

**George Lopez**
240 - 26th Street #3
Santa Monica, CA 90402
"Comedian"

**Jennifer Lopez**
5810 North Bay Drive
Miami Beach, FL 34140
"Actress"

**Mario Lopez**
4526 Wilshire Blvd.
Beverly Hills, CA 90210
"Actor"

**Nancy Lopez**
2308 Tara Drive
Albany, GA 31707
"Golfer"

**Trini Lopez**
1139 Abrigo Road
Palm Springs, CA 92262
"Singer, Actress"

**John Loprieno**
10647 Wilkinds Avenue, #306
Los Angeles, CA 90024
"Actor"

**Stefan Lorant**
215 West Mountain Road
Lenox, MA 01240
"Photojournalist, Author"

**Marjorie Lord**
1110 Maytor Place
Beverly Hills, CA 90210
"Actress"

**Traci Lords**
1505 - 10th Street
Santa Monica, CA 90401
"Actress"

**Donna Loren**
64-1040 Mamalahoa Hwy.
Kamuela, HI 96743
"Actress & Singer"

**Sophia Loren**
6 Rue Charles Bonnet
CH-1206 Geneva SWITZERLAND
"Actress"

**Gloria Loring**
P.O. Box 1243
Cedar Glen, CA 92321
"Singer, Actress"

**Joan Lorring**
233 East 69th Street #15H
New York, NY 10021
"Actress"

**Ronnie Lott**
11342 Canyon View Circle
Cupertino, CA 95014
"Ex-Football Player"

**Sen. Trent Lott (MS)**
Senate Russell Bldg. #487
Washington, DC 20510
"Politician"

**Dorothy Loudon**
101 Central Park West
New York, NY 10023
"Actress"

**Greg Louganis**
P.O. Box 4130
Malibu, CA 90264
"Diver"

**Lori Loughlin**
1122 S. Robertson Blvd. #15
Los Angeles, CA 90035
"Actress"

**Julia Louis-Dreyfus**
535 Alma Real Drive
Pacific Palisades, CA 90272
"Actress"

**Tina Louise**
310 East 46th Street #18T
New York, NY 10017
"Actress"

**Col. Jack R. Lousma**
2722 Roseland Street
Ann Arbor, MI 48103
"Astronaut"

**Charlie Louvin**
2825 Blue Brick Drive
Nashville, TN 37115
"Singer"

**Courtney Love**
P.O. Box 880790
San Francisco, CA 94188
"Singer"

**Mike Love**
24563 Ebelden Avenue
Santa Clarita, CA 91321
"Singer, Songwriter"

**Love & Rockets**
4, The Lakes
Bushey, Hertsfordshire
WD2 1HS ENGLAND
"Rock & Roll Group"

**Patty Loveless**
P.O. Box 1423
White House, TN 37188
"Singer"

**James Lovell**
5725 East River Road
Chicago, IL 60611
"Astronaut"

**Loverboy**
1505 West 2nd Street #200
Vancouver B.C. V6H 3Y4
 CANADA
"Rock & Roll Group"

**Lyle Lovett**
c/o General Delivery
Klein, TX 77391
"Singer"

**Candy Loving**
2112 Broadway
Santa Monica, CA 90404
"Model"

**Jon Lovitz**
4774 Park Encino  Lane #305
Encino, CA 91436
"Actor"

**Dale Lowdermilk**
P.O. Box 5743
Montecito, CA 93150
"Actor"

**Barry Lowe**
31 South Audley Street
London W1 ENGLAND
"Actor"

**Chad Lowe**
1180 South Beverly Drive #608
Los Angeles, CA 90035
"Actor"

**Rob Lowe**
15030 Ventura Blvd. #710
Sherman Oaks, CA 91403
"Actor"

**Carey Lowell**
8942 Wilshire Blvd.
Beverly Hills, CA 90211
"Model, Actress"

**George Lucas**
P.O. Box 2459
San Rafael, CA 94912
"Writer, Producer, Director"

**Jerry Lucas**
P.O. Box 728
Templeton, CA 93465
"Ex-Basketball Player"

**Susan Lucci**
P.O. Box 621
Quogue, NY 11959
"Actress"

**Laurance Luckenbill**
P.O. Box 636
Cross River, NY 10518
"Actor"

**Lorna Luft**
1401 University Drive #602
Coral Gables, FL 33071
"Actress"

**Sen. Richard Lugar (IN)**
306 Hart Office Bldg.
Washington, DC 20510
"Politician"

**James Luisi**
22562 Seaver Court
Santa Clarita, CA 91350
"Actor"

**Johnny Lujack**
6321 Crow Valley Drive
Bettendorf, IA 52722
"Ex-Football Player"

**Derek Luke**
651 N. Kilkea Drive
Los Angeles, CA 90048
"Actor"

**Lulu**
Box 22, Sunbury-On-Thames
Middlesex TW16 5RT
ENGLAND
"Singer, Actress"

**Carl Lumbly**
8721 Sunset Blvd. #205
Los Angeles, CA 90069
"Actor"

**Sidney Lumet**
1 West 81st Street
New York, NY 10024
"Film Writer, Director"

**Joanna Lumley**
18-21 Jermyn Street #300
London SW1Y 6NB ENGLAND
"Actress"

**Barbara Luna**
18026 Rodarte Way
Encino, CA 91316
"Actress"

**Deanna Lund**
545 Howard Street
Salem, VA 24153
"Actress"

**Joan Lunden**
235 East 45th Street
New York, NY 10017
"TV Show Host"

**Dolph Lundgren**
8942 Wilshire Blvd.
Beverly Hills, CA 90211
"Bodybuilder, Actor"

**Jessica Lundy**
151 El Camindo Drive
Beverly Hills, CA 90212
"Actress"

**Patti LuPone**
8942 Wilshire Blvd.
Beverly Hills, CA 90211
"Singer"

**Peter Lupus**
11375 Dona Lisa Drive
Studio City, CA 91604
"Actor"

**Nellie Lutcher**
1524 La Baig Avenue
Los Angeles, CA 90028
"Pianist, Vocalist"

**Frank Luz**
606 North Larchmont Blvd. #309
Los Angeles, CA 90004
"Actor"

**Greg Luzinski**
25100 Ridge Oak Drive
Bonita Springs, FL 34134
"Baseball Player"

**Jimmy Lydon**
3538 Lomacitas Lane
Bonita, CA 91902
"Actor"

**A.C. Lyles**
2115 Linda Flora
Los Angeles, CA 90024
"Writer, Producer"

**Dorothy Lyman**
1604 Vista Del Mar
Hollywood, CA 90028
"Actress"

**Dawn Lyn**
P.O. Box 1527
Avalon, CA 90704
"Actress"

**David Lynch**
7017 Sanalda Road
Los Angeles, CA 90068
"TV Writer

**Kelly Lynch**
8942 Wilshire Blvd.
Beverly Hills, CA 90211
"Actress"

**Adrian Lyne**
9876 Beverly Grove Drive
Beverly Hills, CA 90210
"Film Director"

**Carol Lynley**
13775-A Mono Way #220
Sonora, CA 95370
"Actress"

**Betty Lynn**
10424 Tennessee Avenue
Los Angeles, CA 90064
"Actress"

**Johnathan Lynn**
8942 Wilshire Blvd.
Beverley Hills, CA 90211
"Actor, Writer"

**Loretta Lynn**
c/o General Delivery
Hurricane Mills, TN 37078
"Singer"

**Dame Vera Lynn**
Ditchling
Sussex ENGLAND
"Singer, Actress"

**Shelby Lynne**
751 Bridgeway #300
Sausalito, CA 94965
"Actress"

**Lynyrd Skynyrd**
1607 - 17th Avenue South
Nashville, TN 37212
"Music Group"

**Sue Lyon**
2019 N. Bronson Avenue
Los Angeles, CA 90068
"Actress"

**Jeffrey Lyons**
205 W. 57th Street
New York, NY 10019
"Film Critic"

**Robert F. Lyons**
4605 Lankershim Blvd. #305
North Hollywood, CA 91602
"Actor"

**Andrea McArdle**
38 Cambridge Street
Souderton, PA 18964
"Actress"

**Alex McArthur**
10435 Wheatland Avenue
Sunland, CA 91040
"Actor"

**Diane McBain**
13317 Ventura Blvd. #1
Sherman Oaks, CA 91423
"Actress"

**Chi McBride**
9560 Briarcrest Court
Las Vegas, NV 89120
"Actor"

**Jeff McBride**
3960 Briarcrest Court
Las Vegas, NV 89120
"Comedian"

**Ken McBride**
3446 Cypress Circle
Westlake, OH 44145
"Baseball Player"

**Martina McBride**
P.O. Box 291627
Nashville, TN 37229
"Singer"

**Amanda McBroom**
167 Fairview Road
Ojai, CA 93023
"Singer, Songwriter"

**Sen. John McCain (AZ)**
Senate Russell Bldg. #241
Washington, DC 20510
"Politician"

**Mitzi McCall**
3635 Wrightwood Drive
Studio City, CA 91604
"Actress"

**Lon McCallister**
P.O. Box 6030
Stateline, NV 89449
"Actor"

**David McCallum**
68 Old Brompton Road
London SW7 3LQ ENGLAND
"Actor"

**Napoleon McCallum**
1320 Harbor Bay Parkway
Alameda, CA 94502
"ex-Football Player"

**Mercedes McCambridge**
156 Fifth Avenue #820
New York, NY 10010
"Actress"

**Chuck McCann**
2941 Briar Knoll Drive
Los Angeles, CA 90046
"Actor, Comedian"

**Les McCann**
4031 Panama Court
Piedmont, CA 94611
"Musician, Composer"

**Chris McCarron**
P.O. Box 861
Sierra Madre, CA 91025
"Jockey"

**Andrew McCarthy**
10345 West Olympic Blvd. #300
Los Angeles, CA 90064
"Actor"

**Eugene McCarthy**
271 Hawlin Road
Woodville, VA 22749
"Ex-Senator"

**Jenny McCarthy**
8424A Santa Monica Blvd. #804
West Hollywood, CA 90069
"MTV Host/Model"

**Julianna McCarthy**
8436 West 3rd Street #740
Los Angeles, CA 90048
"Actress"

**Kevin McCarthy**
14854 Sutton Street
Sherman Oaks, CA 91403
"Actor"

**Sir Paul McCartney**
1 Soho Square
London W1 ENGLAND
"Singer, Composer"

**Kelli McCarty**
P.O 491328
Los Angeles, CA 90049
"Actress"

**Tim McCarver**
118 County Line Road
Bryn Mawr, PA 19010
"Ex-Baseball Player"

**Chris McCarty**
9105 Carmelita Avenue #101
Beverly Hills, CA 90210
"Singer, Songwriter"

**McCaughey Septuplets**
615 N. First
Carlisle, IA 50047
"Muti-Birth Babies"

**Peggy McCay**
8811 Wonderland Avenue
Los Angeles, CA 90046
"Actress"

**Charly McClain**
P.O. Box 198888
Nashville, TN 37219
"Singer"

**Rue McClanahan**
10474 Santa Monica Blvd. #380
Los Angeles, CA 90025
"Actress"

**Reily McClendon**
706 Trail Rock Court
Simi Valley, CA 93065
"Actor & Musician"

**Sarah McClendon**
3133 Connecticut Avenue NW #215
Washington, DC 20008
"News Correspondent"

**Leigh McCloskey**
6032 Philip Avenue
Malibu, CA 90265
"Actor"

**Paul McCloskey**
580 Mountain Home Road
Woodside, CA 94062
"Ex-Congressman"

**Marc McClure**
1420 Beaudry Blvd.
Glendale, CA 91208
"Actor"

**Edie McClurg**
9229 Sunset Blvd. #315
Los Angeles, CA 90069
"Actress"

**Heather McComb**
9615 Brighton Way #300
Beverly Hills, CA 90212
"Actress"

**Matthew McConaughey**
8436 West Third Street #650
Los Angeles, CA 90048
"Actor"

**Marilyn McCoo-Davis**
2639 Lavery Court #5
Newbury Park, CA 91320
"Singer"

**John McCook**
7800 Beverly Blvd. #3371
Los Angeles, CA 90036
"Actor, Writer, Director"

**Kent McCord**
6767 Forest Lawn Dr. #115
Los Angeles, CA 90068
"Actor"

**Mary McCormack**
8500 Wilshire Blvd. #700
Beverly Hills, CA 90211
"Actress"

**Patty McCormack**
4360 Tujunga Avenue
Studio, CA 91604
"Actress"

**Carolyn McCormick**
11500 W. Olympic Blvd. #510
Los Angeles, CA 90064
"Actress"

**Maureen McCormick**
22817 Pera Road
Woodland Hills, CA 91364
"Actress"

**Pat McCormick**
23388 Mulholland Drive
Woodland Hills, CA 91364
"Comedian"

**Pat McCormick**
P.O. Box 250
Seal Beach, CA 90740
"Swimmer"

**Willie McCovey**
P.O. Box 590
Cooperstown, NY 13326
"Baseball Player"

**Alec McCowen**
3 Goodwins Court
St. Martin's Lane
London WG2 ENGLAND
"Actor"

**Charlie McCoy**
1300 Division Street #304
Nashville, TN 37203
"Singer, Guitarist"

**Mark McCoy**
7120 Hawthorne #18
Los Angeles, CA 90046
"Actor"

**Paul McCrane**
5670 Wilshire Blvd. #820
Los Angeles, CA 90048
"Actor"

**Jody McCrea**
Country Road 395
P.O. Box 195
Hondo, NM 89336
"Actor"

**Mindy McCready**
3310 West End Avenue #500
Nashville, TN 37203
"Singer"

**David McCullough**
c/o Janklow & Nesbitt
445 Park Avenue, 13th Floor
New York, NY 10022
"Author"

**Shanna McCullough**
7920 Alabama Avenue
Canoga Park, CA 91304
"Actress"

**Lawrence McCutcheon**
19981 Weems Lane
Huntington Beach, CA 92646
"Ex-Football Player"

**James McDaniel**
8730 Sunset Blvd., #480
Los Angeles, CA 90069
"Actor"

**Brian McDermott**
27 Upper Berkeley Street
London W1 ENGLAND
"Actor"

**Dylan McDermott**
201 S. Rockingham Avenue
Los Angeles, CA 90048
"Actor"

**James McDivitt**
3520 East Calle Puerta de Acero
Tucson, AZ 85718
"Astrouaut"

**Christopher McDonald**
151 El Camino Drive
Beverly Hills, CA 90212
"Actor"

**"Country" Joe McDonald**
17337 Ventura Blvd. #208
Encino, CA 91316
"Singer"

**Michael McDonald**
P.O. Box 442
Franklin, TN 37064
"Singer, Songwriter"

**Mary McDonough**
1964 Westwood Blvd. #400
Los Angeles, CA 90025
"Actress"

**Neal McDonough**
1180 South Beverly Drive #608
Los Angeles, CA 90035
"Actor"

**Frances McDormand**
9701 Wlishire Blvd., 10th Floor
Beverly Hills, CA 90212
"Actress"

**Susan McDougal**
350 South Grand Avenue #3900
Los Angeles, CA 90071
"Defied Ken Starr Prosecution"

**Malcolm McDowell**
4 Windmill Street
London W1P 1HF ENGLAND
"Actor"

**Ronnie McDowell**
20 Music Square West #200
Nashville, TN 37203
"Singer"

**Peter McEnery**
9 Cork Street
London W1 ENGLAND
"Actor"

**Natasha McElhone**
67 Codolphin Road
London W12 8JN ENGLAND
"Actress"

**John McEnroe**
23712 Malibu Colony Road
Malibu, CA 90265
"Tennis Player"

**Reba McEntire**
40 Music Spuare W.
Nashville, TN 37203
"Singer"

**Geraldine McEwan**
308 Regent Street
London W1 ENGLAND
"Actress"

**Robert C. McFarlane**
3414 Prospect Street N.W.
Washington, DC 20007
"Ex-Government Official"

**Bobby McFerrin**
826 Broadway #400
New York, NY 10003
"Singer"

**Paul McGann**
12-13 Poland Street
London W1F 8QB ENGLAND
"Actor"

**Darren McGavin**
P.O. Box 2939
Beverly Hills, CA 90213
"Actor"

**Henry McGee**
19 Sydney Mews
London SW3 6HL ENGLAND
"Actor"

**Kirk McGee**
P.O Box 626
Franklin, TN 37064
"Singer"

**Vonetta McGee**
1801 Avenue of the Stars #902
Los Angeles, CA 90067
"Actress"

**Howard McGinnin**
200 West 57th Street #900
New York, NY 10019
"Actor, Singer"

**Kelly McGillis**
303 Whitehead Street
Key West, FL 33040
"Actress"

**Ted McGinley**
1505 10th Street
Santa Monica, CA 90401
"Actor"

**Patrick McGoohan**
16808 Bollinger Drive
Pacific Palisades, CA 90272
"Actor, Writer, Producer"

**Elizabeth McGovern**
17319 Magnolia Blvd.
Encino, CA 91316
"Actress"

**Maureen McGovern**
10101 Galaxy Way, Bldg 1, #104
Los Angeles, CA 90067
"Singer"

**Rose McGowan**
17530 Ventura Blvd. #201
Encino, CA 91316
"Actress"

**Tim McGraw**
P.O. Box 128138
Nashville, TN 37212
"Singer"

**Tug McGraw**
6 Rose Hill Road
Media, PA 19063
"Ex-Baseball Player"

**Ewan McGregor**
34-43 Russell
London WC2B 5HA ENGLAND
"Actor"

**Aaron McGrudy**
c/o Universal Press Syndicate
4520 Main Street
Kansas City MO 6411
"Cartoonist

**Roger McGuinn**
59 Pearson Street
West Newton, MA 02165
"Singer, Songwriter"

**William Biff McGuire**
1443 Pandora Avenue
Los Angeles, CA 90024
"Actor"

**McGuire Sisters**
6420 SW River Road
Hillsboro, OR 97123
"Vocal Group"

**Mark McGwire**
16631 Carousel Lane
Huntington Beach, CA 92649
"Baseball Player"

**Stephen McHattie**
505 West 2nd Street #200
Vancouver BC V6H 3YA CANADA
"Actor"

**Gardner McKay**
252 Lumahai Place
Honolulu, HI 96825
"Actor"

**Jim McKay**
2805 Sheppard Road
Monkton, MD 21111
"Sportscaster"

**Peggy McKay**
8811 Wonderland Avenue
Los Angeles, CA 90046
"Actress"

**Michael McKean**
833 Thornhill Road
Calabasas, CA 91302
"Actor"

**Todd McKee**
32362 Lake Pleasant Drive
Westlake Village, CA 91361
"Actor"

**Danica McKellar**
10635 Santa Monica Blvd. #130
Los Angeles, CA 90025
"Actress"

**Sir Ian McKellen**
25 Earl's Terrace
London W8 ENGLAND
"Actor"

**Virginia McKenna**
8 Buckfast Court, Runcorn
Cheshire, WA7 1QJ ENGLAND
"Actress"

**Julia McKenzie**
Richmond Park
Kingston Surrey, ENGLAND
"Actress"

**Doug McKeon**
818-6th Street #202
Santa Monica, CA 90403
"Actor"

**Nancy McKeon**
P.O. Box 6778
Burbank, CA 91510
"Actress"

**Les McKeown**
27 Preston Grange
Preston Pans
E. Lothian SCOTLAND
"Singer"

**Leo McKern**
29 Roehampton Gate
London SW15 5JR ENGLAND
"Actor"

**Tamara McKinney**
4935 Parkers Mill Road
Lexington, KY 40502
"Skier"

**Brian McKnight**
151 El Camino Drive
Beverly Hills, CA 90212
"Singer"

**Rod McKuen**
P.O. Box G
Beverly Hills, CA 90213
"Singer, Poet"

**Andrew McLaglen**
P.O. Box 1056
Friday Harbor, WA 98250
"Film Director"

**Denny McLain**
11994 Hyne Road
Brighton, MI 48116
"Ex-Baseball Player"

**John McLaughlin**
1211 Connecticut Avenue N.W.
Washington, DC 20036
"News Correspondent"

**Don McLean**
1711 Lawrence Road #101
Nashville, TN 37069
"Singer, Songwriter"

**Allyn Ann McLerie**
3344 Campanil Drive
Santa Barbara, CA 93109
"Actress"

**Rachel McLish**
P.O. Box 1699
Rancho Mirage, CA 92270
"Actress"

**Ed McMahon**
12000 Crest Court
Beverly Hills, CA 90210
"TV Show Host"

**Jenna McMahon**
435 Palisades Ave.
Santa Monica, CA 90402
"Writer, Producer"

**Jim McMahon**
9520 Viking Drive
Eden Prarie, MN 55344
"Football Player"

**John McMartin**
250 West 57th Street #703
New York, NY 10107
"Actor"

**Terry McMillan**
P.O. Box 2408
Danville, CA 94526
"Novelist"

**Sam McMurray**
11500 W. Olympic Blvd. #510
Los Angeles, CA 90064
"Actor"

**Larry McMurtry**
P.O. Box 552
Archer City, TX 76351
"Screenwriter"

**Barbara McNair**
13701 Riverside Drive #201
Sherman Oaks, CA 91423
"Singer & Actress"

**Steve McNair**
The Coliseum
One Titans Way
Nashville, TN 37213
"Football Player"

**Terrence McNally**
218 West 10th Street
New York, NY 10014
"Dramatist"

**Brian McNamara**
11730 National Blvd. #19
Los Angeles, CA 90064
"Actor"

**Robert McNamara**
1350 "I" Street #500
Washington, DC 20005
"Banker, Government"

**William McNamara**
P.O. Box 25148
Farmington, NY 14425
"Actor"

**Kate McNeil**
6500 Wilshire Blvd. #2200
Los Angeles, CA 90048
"Actress"

**Robert Duncan McNeill**
861 Burrell Street
Marina del Rey, CA 90292
"Actor"

**Chad McQueen**
8306 Wilshire Blvd. #438
Beverly Hills, CA 90211
"Actor"

**Neile McQueen**
2323 Bowmont Drive
Beverly Hills, CA 90210
"Actress"

**Gerald McRaney**
3633 Lankershim Blvd.
Los Angeles, CA 90069
"Actor, Director"

**Jesse McReynolds**
P.O. Box 304
Gallatin, TN 37066
"Singer, Guitarist"

**Ian McShane**
11620 Wilshire Blvd. #700
Los Angeles, CA 90025
"Actor"

**Christie McVie**
29 Spirit Lane
Owings Mills, MD 21117
"Singer, Songwriter"

**John McVie**
21650 Oxnard Street #1925
Woodland Hills, CA 91367
"Singer, Songwriter"

**Jillian McWhirter**
P.O. Box 6308
Beverly Hills, CA 90212
"Actress"

**Bernie Mac**
1995 Broadway #501
New York, NY 10023
"Comedian"

**James MacArthur**
74092 Covered Wagon Trail
Palm Desert, CA 92260
"Actor"

**Ralph Macchio**
15030 Ventura Blvd. #1-710
Sherman Oaks, CA 91403
"Actor"

**Simon MacCorkindale**
520 Washington Blvd. #187
Marina del Rey, CA 90292
"Actor"

**Dr. Jeffrey MacDonald**
#00131-177
Federal Correctional Institute
27072 Ballston
Sheridan, OR 97378
"Accused of Killing His Family"

**Norm MacDonald**
9150 Wilshire Blvd., #350
Beverly Hills, CA 90212
"Singer"

**Andie MacDowell**
939 8th Avenue #400
New York, NY 10019
"Actress"

**Jeff MacGregor**
151 El Camino Drive
Beverly Hills, CA 90212
"TV Personality"

**Mario Machado**
5750 Briarcliff Road
Los Angeles, CA 90068
"Actor"

**Stephen Macht**
248 South Rodeo Drive
Beverly Hills, CA 90212
"Actor"

**ex-Sen. Connie Mack (FL)**
627 26th Street
South Arlington, VA 22202
"Politician"

**Warner Mack**
1136 Sunnymeade Drive
Nashville, TN 37216
"Singer, Guitarist"

**Patch MacKenzie**
3500 West Olive Avenue #1400
Burbank, CA 91505
"Actress"

**John Mackey**
1198 Pacific Coast Hwy. #506
Seal Beach, CA 90740
"Composer"

**David Macklin**
5410 Wilshire Blvd. #227
Los Angeles, CA 90036
"Actor"

**Janet MacLachlan**
1919 North Taft Avenue
Los Angeles, CA 90068
"Actress"

**Kyle MacLachlan**
955 S Carrillo Drive #300
Los Angeles, CA 90048
"Actor"

**Shirley MacLaine**
25200 Old Malibu Road
Malibu, CA 90265
"Actress"

**Gavin MacLeod**
1025 Fifth Avenue
New York, NY 10028
"Actor"

**Patrick Macnee**
P.O. Box 1683
Rancho Mirage, CA 92270
"Actor"

**Robert Macneil**
356 West 58th Street
New York, NY 10019
"News Correspondent"

**William MacNamara**
P.O. Box 25158
Farmington, NY 14425
"Ex-Government Official"

**Elle MacPherson**
414 East 52nd Street PH-B
New York, NY 10022
"Model"

**Bill Macy**
10130 Angelo Circle
Beverly Hills, CA 90210
"Actor"

**William H. Macy**
9100 Wilshire Blvd., W. Tower #600
Beverly Hills, CA 90212
"Actor"

**John Madden**
5095 Soho Square
London W1V 5DG ENGLAND
"Film Director"

**John Madden**
5955 Coronado Blvd.
Pleasanton, CA 94588
"Sportscaster"

**Lester Maddox**
3155 Johnson Ferry Road N.E.
Marietta, GA 30062
"Ex-Governor"

**Greg Maddux**
8124 Desert Jewel Circle
Las Vegas, NV 89128
"Ex-Baseball Player"

**Amy Madigan**
151 El Camino Drive
Beverly Hills, CA 90212
"Actress"

**Madonna**
8491 Sunset Blvd. #485
West Hollywood, CA 90069
"Singer, Actress"

**Michael Madsen**
8899 Beverly Blvd. #919
Los Angeles, CA 90048
"Actor"

**Debra Sue Maffett**
1525 McGavock Street
Nashville, TN 37203
"Actress, Model"

**Brandon Maggart**
8730 Sunset Blvd. #480
Los Angeles, CA 90069
"Actor"

**Ann Magnuson**
1317 Maltman Avenue
Los Angeles, CA 90026
"Proformance Artist"

**Tobey Maguire**
1122 S. Robertson Blvd. #15
Los Angeles, CA 90035
"Actress"

**Volerio Mahaffey**
121 North San Vicente Blvd.
Beverly Hills, CA 90211
"Actress"

**Taj Mahal**
P.O. Box 429094
San Fransisco, CA 94142
"Singer"

**George Maharis**
13150 Mulholland Drive
Beverly Hills, CA 90210
"Actor"

**Bill Maher**
240 - 26th Street #3
Santa Monica, CA 90402
"Actor"

**Robert Maheu**
3523 Cochise Lane
Las Vegas, NV 89109
"Actor"

**John Mahoney**
40 West 57th Street
New York, NY 10019
"Actor"

**Cardinal Roger Mahony**
1531 West 9th Street
Los Angeles, CA 90012
"Clergy"

**Phil Mahre**
70 Roza View Drive
Yakima, WA 98901
"Skier"

**Steve Mahre**
2408 North 52nd Avenue
Yakima, WA 98908
"Skier"

**Norman Mailer**
142 Columbia Heights
Brooklyn, NY 11201
"Author"

**Robert Mailhouse**
4470 Sunset Blvd. #462
Los Angeles, CA 90027
"Actor"

**Kathy Maisnik**
260 South Beverly Drive #308
Beverly Hills, CA 90212
"Actress"

**Beth Maitland**
280 S. Beverly Drive #400
Beverly Hills, CA 90212
"Actress"

**Austin Majors**
3940 Laurel Canyon Blvd. #177
Studio City, CA 91604
"Actor"

**John Major**
8 Stuckley Road
Huntingdon
Cambs, ENGLAND
"Ex-Prime Minister"

**Lee Majors**
3000 Holiday Drive, PH #1
Ft. Lauderdale, FL 33316
"Actor"

**Tommy Makem**
2 Longmeadow Road
Dover, NH 03820
"Singer"

**Wendy Makkena**
6100 Wilshire Blvd. #310
Los Angeles, CA 90048
"Actress"

**Mako**
6477 Pepper Tree Lane
Somis, CA 93066
"Actor"

**Kristina Malandro**
P.O. Box 491035
Los Angeles, CA 90049
"Actress"

**Karl Malden**
1845 Mandeville Canyon
Los Angeles, CA 90049
"Actor"

**Wendy Malick**
1505 10th Street
Santa Monica, CA 90401
"Actress"

**Terrence Malick**
7920 Sunset Blvd.
Los Angeles, CA 90067
"Writer"

**Art Malik**
19 Sydney Mews
London SW3 6HL ENGLAND
"Actor"

**Ross Malinger**
6212 Banner Aveune
Los Angeles, CA 90038
"Actor"

**John Malkovich**
P.O. Box 5106
Westport, CT 06881
"Actor"

**Carole Mallory**
2300-5th Avenue
New York, NY 10037
"Model, Actress, Author"

**Bruce Malmuth**
9981 Robin Drive
Beverly Hills, CA 90210
"Screenwriter, Director"

**Dorothy Malone**
P.O. Box 7287
Dallas, TX 75209
"Actress"

**Karl Malone**
111 S Figeuroa Street
Los Angeles, CA 90015
"Basketball Player"

**Nancy Malone**
8857 West Olympic Blvd. #201
Beverly Hills, CA 90211
"Actress"

**Janel Maloney**
8436 West Third Street #650
Los Angeles, CA 90048
"Actress"

**Moses Malone**
1001 N. 4th Street
Milwaukee, WI 53203
"Ex-Basketball Player"

**Patty Maloney**
6767 Forest Lawn Drive #101
Los Angeles, CA 90068
"Actress"

**Leonard Maltin**
10424 Whipple Street
Toluca Lake, CA 91602
"Film Critic, Author"

**The Mamas & The Papas**
P.O. Box 1821
Ojai, CA 93024
"Rock & Roll Group"

**David Mamet**
P.O. Box 381589
Cambridge, MA 02238
"Writer"

**Charles T. Manatt**
4814 Woodway Lane N.W.
Washington, DC 20016
"Politician"

**Melissa Manchester**
5440 Corbin Avenue
Tarzana, CA 91356
"Singer, Songwriter"

**William Manchester**
P.O. Box 329 Wesleyan Station
Middletown, CT 06457
"Author"

**Ray "Boom Boom" Mancini**
12524 Indianapolis Street
Los Angeles, CA 90066
"Boxer"

**Nick Mancuso**
9229 Sunset Blvd. #900
Los Angeles, CA 90069
"Actor"

**Robert Mandan**
9229 Sunset Blvd. #310
Los Angeles, CA 90069
"Actor"

**Howie Mandel**
23679 Calabasas Road #334
Calabasas, CA 91302
"Actor, Comedian"

**Johnny Mandel**
28946 Cliffside Drive
Malibu, CA 90265
"Composer, Conductor"

**Loring Mandel**
555 West 57th Street #1230
New York, NY 10019
"Screenwriter"

**Nelson Mandela**
51 Plain Street
Johannesburg 2001
SOUTH AFRICA
"Social Activist, Politician"

**Winnie Mandela**
Orlando West, Soweto
Johannesburg SOUTH AFRICA
"Social Activist"

**Barbara Mandrell**
P.O. Box 620
Hendersonville, TN 37077
"Singer, Singwriter"

**Erline Mandrell**
544 Nashvillle Pike #244
Gallatin, TN 37077
"Actress, Drummer"

**Louise Mandrell**
2046 Parkway
Pigeon Forge, TN 37863
"Singer, Musician"

**Costas Mandylor**
6100 Wilshire Blvd. #1170
Los Angeles, CA 90048
"Actor"

**Louis Mandylor**
275 S. Beverly Drive #215
Beverly Hills, CA 90212
"Actor"

**Larry Maneti**
4615 Winnetka
Woodland Hills, CA 91364
"Actor"

**Chuck Mangione**
23 West 73rd Street #915
New York, NY 10023
"Musician"

**Camryn Manheim**
9057 Nemo Street #C
West Hollywood, CA 90069
"Actor"

**Barry Manilow**
151 El Camino Drive
Beverly Hills, CA 90212
"Singer, Composer"

**Tom Mankiewicz**
1609 Magnetic Terrace
Los Angeles, CA 90069
"Writer, Producer"

**Abby Mann**
8383 Wilshire Blvd. #550
Beverly Hills, CA 90211
"Writer, Producer"

**Delbert Mann**
401 South Burnside Avenue
Suite #11D
Los Angeles, CA 90036
"Director, Producer"

**Johnny Mann**
78516 Gorham Lane
Indio, CA 92203
"Composer, Conductor"

**Michael Mann**
13746 Sunset Blvd.
Pacific Palisades, CA 90272
"Writer, Producer"

**Miss Manners**
1651 Harvard Street N.W.
Washington, DC 20009
"Etiquette Expert"

**Irene Manning**
3165 La Mesa Drive
Santa Carlos, CA 94070
"Actress, Singer, Author"

**Marilyn Manson**
25935 Detroit Road
Westlake, OH 44145
"Singer"

**Paul Mantee**
9057A Nemo Street
West Hollywood, CA 90069
"Actor"

**Joe Mantegna**
P.O. Box 7304 #103
North Hollywood, CA 91603
"Actor"

**Jerri Manthey**
9899 Santa Monica Blvd., PBM
2002
Beverly Hills, CA 90212
"CBS Survivor Show Contestant"

**John Mantley**
4121 Longridge Avenue
Sherman Oaks, CA 91423
"Screenwriter"

**Randolph Mantooth**
2735 Hollyridge Drive
Los Angeles, CA 90068
"Actor"

**Martin Manulis**
242 Copa de Oro Road
Los Angeles, CA 90077
"TV Producer"

**Ralph Manza**
550 Hygeia Avenue
Leucadia, CA 92024
"Actor"

**Adela Mara**
1928 Mandeville Canyon
Los Angeles, CA 90049
"Dancer, Actress"

**Diego Maradona**
Brandsen 805
1161 Capital Federal ARGENTINA
"Soccer Player"

**Sophie Marceau**
20 Avenue Rapp
F-75007 Paris FRANCE
"Actress"

**Marcel Marceau**
1418 N. Highland Avenue, #102
Los Angeles, CA 90028
"Mime"

**Mario Marcelino**
1418 North Highland Avenue #102
Los Angeles, CA 90028
"Actress, Writer"

**Barbara March**
606 North Larchmont Blvd., #309
Los Angeles, CA 90004
"Actress"

**Jane March**
BBC Centre
Wood Lane
London W12 7RJ ENGLAND
"Actress"

**Guy Marchand**
40 rue Francois ler
F-75008 Paris, FRANCE
"Actor"

**Bruce Marchiano**
11333 Moorpark Street #171
Studio City, CA 91604
"Actor"

**Vanessa Marcil**
P.O. Box 691736
Los Angeles, CA 90069
"Actress"

**Imelda Marcos**
Leyte Providencia Dept.
Tolosa, Leyte PHILIPPINES
"Politician"

**Adrea Marcovicci**
3761 Reklaw Drive
Studio City, CA 91604
"Actress, Singer"

**Stuart Margolin**
Box 489, STM Ganges
Salt Spring Island
BC V8K2W1 CANADA
"Actor, Director"

**Miriam Margolyes**
121 North San Vicente Blvd.
Beverly Hills, CA 90211
"Actress"

**Julianna Margulies**
9465 Wilshire Blvd. West Tower
#212
Beverly Hills, CA 90212
"Actress"

**Cesare Mariago**
19 788 Ciadel Drive #120
Pt. Coquitiam, BC V3C 6G
CANADA
"Hockey Player"

**Robert Mariano**
1154 Angela Street
Canton, MA 02021
"CBS Survivor Show Contestant"

**Juan Marichal**
9458 NW 54 Doral Circle Lane
Miami, FL 33128
"Ex-Baseball Player"

**Lisa Marie**
151 El Camino Drive
Beverly Hills, CA 90212
"Actress"

**Teena Marie**
1000 Laguna Road
Pasadena, CA 91105
"Actress"

**Marilyn**
33-34 Cleveland Street
London W1 ENGLAND
"Singer"

**Richard Marin**
(Cheech & Chong)
224 Sea Cliff Avenue
San Francisco, CA 94124
"Actor, Comedian"

**Ed Marinaro**
151 El Camino Drive
Beverly Hills, CA 90212
"Ex-Football Player, Actor"

**Dan Marino**
300 SW 1st Avenue
Ft. Lauderdale, FL 33301
"Football Player"

**Monte Markhan**
P.O. Box 607
Malibu, CA 90265
"Actor"

**Marky Mark**
63 Pilgrim Road
Braintree, MA 02184
"Rap Singer"

**Ziggy Marley**
Jack's Hill
Kingston, JAMAICA
"Raggae Singer"

**Jean Marlow**
32 Exeter Road
London NW2 ENGLAND
"Actress"

**Gabriel Garcia Marques**
Fuego 144
Pedregal de San Angel
Mexico DF MEXICO
"Author"

**Raul Marquez**
14611 Maisemore
Houston, TX 77015
"Boxer"

**Evan Marriott** (Joe Millionaire)
24331 San Juan Capistrano #1014
San Juan Capistrano, CA 92675
"Joe Millionaire"

**Kenneth Mars**
8942 Wilshire Blvd. #219
Beverly Hills, CA 90211
"Actor"

**Wynton Marsalis**
33 West 60th Street
New York, NY 10023
"Trumpeter"

**James Marsden**
10635 Santa Monica Blvd. #140
Los Angeles, CA 90025
"Actor"

**Marian Marsh**
P.O. Box 1
Palm Desert, CA 92260
"Actress"

**Marshall Tucker Band**
100 West Putnam
Greenwich, CT 06830
"Music Group"

**Garry Marshall**
4252 West Riverside Drive
Burbank, CA 91505
"Writer, Producer"

**James Marshall**
30710 Monte Lado Drive
Malibu, CA 90265
"Author"

**Ken Marshall**
345 N. Maple Drive #302
Beverly Hills, CA 90210
"Actor"

**Mike Marshall**
4436 Plum Street
Zephryhille, FL 33541
"Actor"

**Paula Marshall**
c/o IA
1505 10th Street
Santa Monica, CA 90401
"Actress"

**Penny Marshall**
9465 Wilshire Blvd. #419
Beverly Hills, CA 90212
"Actress"

**Peter Marshall**
16714 Oakview Drive
Encino, CA 91316
"Actor, TV Show Host"

**Trudy Marshall**
1852 Marcheeta Place
Los Angeles, CA 90069
"Actress"

**William Marshall**
P.O. Box 331212
Pacoima, CA 91331
"Actor"

**Donna Martell**
P.O. Box 3335
Granada Hills, CA 91394
"Actress"

**Martika**
8995 Elevado Avenue
Los Angeles, CA 90069
"Actress"

**Benito Martinez**
8447 Wilshire Blvd. #206
Beverly Hills, CA 90211
"Actor"

**Andrea Martin**
130 West 42nd Street #1804
New York, NY 10036
"Actress"

**Barney Martin**
12838 Milbank Street
Studio City, CA 91604
"Actor"

**Casey Martin**
P.O. Box 109601
Palm Beach Gardens, FL 33410
"Golfer"

**Dewey Martin**
1371 E. Avenue De Los Arboles
Thousand Oaks, CA 91360
"Actor"

**Dick Martin**
30765 Pacifc Coast Highway #10
Malibu, CA 90265
"Actor, Writer, Comedian"

**Eric Martin Band**
P.O. Box 5952
San Francisco, CA 94101
"Rock & Roll Group"

**Kellie Martin**
P.O. Box 5617
Beverly Hills, CA 90210
"Actress"

**Lynn Martin**
180 North Stetson
Chicago, IL 60601
"Ex-Government Official"

**Millicent Martin**
P.O. Box 101
Redding, CT 06875
"Singer, Actresss"

**Nan Martin**
33604 Pacific Coast Hwy.
Malibu, CA 90265
"Actress"

**Pamela Sue Martin**
13775-A Mono Way @220
Sonora, CA 95370
"Actress, Producer"

**Ricky Martin**
5030 North Bay Road
Miami, FL 33140
"Singer"

**Steve Martin**
P.O. Box 929
Beverly Hills, CA 90213
"Actor"

**Todd Martin**
1751 Pinnacle Dr. #1500
McLean, VA 22102
"Actor"

**Tony Martin**
10724 Wilshire Blvd. #1406
Los Angeles, CA 90024
"Actor, Singer"

**Wink Martindale**
5744 Newcastle
Calabasas, CA 91302
"Game Show Host"

**A. Martinez**
P.O. Box 6387
Malibu, CA 90264
"Actor"

**Al Martino**
927 North Rexford Drive
Beverly Hills, CA 90210
"Singer'

**Leslie Martinson**
2288 Coldwater Canyon
Beverly Hills, CA 90210
"TV Director"

**Elizabeth Marvel**
12636 Beatrice Street
Los Angeles, CA 90066
"Actress"

**The Marvelettes**
141 Dunbar Avenue
Fords, NJ 08863
"R & B Group"

**Richard Marx**
QBQ
150 East 58th Street #1900
New York, NY 10155
"Conductor"

**Ron Masak**
5440 Shirley Avenue
Tarzana, CA 91356
"Actor"

**Joseph Mascolo**
CBS/B&B
7800 Beverly Blvd. #3371
Los Angeles, CA 90036
"Actor"

**Hugh Masekela**
230 Park Avenue #1512
New York, NY 10169
"Trumpeter"

**Jackie Mason**
146 West 57th Street
New York, NY 10019
"Comedian"

**Marlyn Mason**
27 Glen Oak
Medford, OR 97504
"Actress, Singer"

**Marsha Mason**
528 Don Gaspar Avenue
Sante Fe, NM 87505
"Actress"

**Osa Massen**
10501 Wilshire Blvd. #704
Los Angeles, CA 90024
"Actress"

**Andrew Masset**
11635 Huston
No. Hollywood, CA 91607
"Actor"

**Master P**
151 El Camino Drive
Beverly Hills, CA 90212
"Rap Singer"

**Ben Masters**
8730 Sunset Blvd. #480
Los Angeles, CA 90069
"Actor"

**Danny Masterson**
6277 Holly Mont Drive
Los Angeles, CA 90068

**Mary Stuart Masterson**
P.O. Box 1249
White River Junction, VT 05001
"Actress"

**Mary Elizabeth Mastrantonio**
34-43 Russell Street
London WC2B 5HA ENGALND
"Actress"

**Richard Masur**
121 North San Vicente Blvd.
Beverly Hills, CA 90211
"Actor, Writer"

**Jerry Mathers**
30290 Rancho Vljeo Road #122
San Juan Capistrano, CA 92675
"Actor"

**Don Matheson**
10275 1/2 Missouri Ave.
Los Angeles, CA 90025
"Actor"

**Richard Matheson**
P.O. Box 81
Woodland Hills, CA 91364
"Writer"

**Tim Matheson**
1187 Coast Village Road #1-504
Santa Barbara, CA 93108
"Actor"

**Kerwin Mathews**
67-A Buena Vista Terrace
San Francisco, CA 94117
"Actor"

**Bob Mathias**
7469 East Pine Avenue
Fresno, CA 93727
"Athlete, Actor"

**Mirielle Mathieu**
12 rue du Boise de Blulogne
F-92200 Neuilly FRANCE
"Singer"

**Buster Mathis, Jr.**
4409 Carol SW
Wyoming, MI 49509
"Boxer"

**Judge Greg Mathis**
3500 West Olive Avenue #305
Burbank, CA 91506
"TV Show Judge"

**Johnny Mathis**
1612 West Olive Avenue #305
Burbank, CA 91506
"Singer"

**Samantha Mathis**
7536 Sunnywood Lane
Los Angeles, CA 90046
"Orchestra Leader"

**Melissa Mathison**
655 MacCulloch Drive
Los Angeles, CA 90049
"Screenwriter"

**Marlee Matlin**
8942 Wilshire Blvd.
Beverly Hills, CA 90211
"Actress"

**Kathy Mattea**
P.O. Box 1776
Orem, UT 84059
"Singer"

**Roland Matthes**
Storkower Street 118
D-10407 Berlin GERMANY
"Swimmer"

**Chris Matthews**
2200 Fletcher Avenue
Fort Lee, NJ 07024
"News Reporter"

**Dave Matthews Band**
509 Hartnell Street
Monterey, CA 93940
"Music Group"

**Delane Mathews**
6500 Wilshire Blvd. #2200
Los Angeles, CA 90048
"Actress"

**Don Mattingly**
7624 Sly's Drive
Evansville, IN 47712
"ex-Baseball Player"

**Robin Mattson**
P.O. Box 450085
Atlanta, GA 31145
"Professional Chef & Actress"

**Billy Mauch**
538-C W. Northwest Highway
Palatine, IL 60067
"Actor"

**Bobby Mauch**
538-C W. Northwest Highway
Palatine, IL 60067
"Actor"

**Gene Mauch**
71 Princeton
Rancho Mirage, CA 92270
"Baseball Manager"

**Bill Mauldin**
c/o Gordon Dillow
Orange County Register
625 N. Grand Avenue
Santa Ana, CA 92701
"Cartoonist

**Brad Maule**
4136 Dixie Canyon
Sherman Oaks, CA 91423
"Actor"

**Nicole Maurey**
21 Chemin Vauillons
78160 Marly-le-roi FRANCE
"Actress"

**Claire Maurier**
11 rue de la Montague-le-Breuil
91360 Epinay sur Orge, FRANCE
"Actress"

**Max Maven**
7095 Hollywood Blvd. #382
Hollywood, CA 90028
"Mind Reader"

**The Mavericks**
209 Tenth Avenue South #322
Nashville, TN 37203
"Music Group"

**Peter Max**
118 Riverside Drive
New York, NY 10024
"Artist, Designer"

**Maxwell**
9465 Wilshire Blvd. #517
Beverly Hills, CA 90212
"R & B Singer"

**Frank Maxwell**
447 San Vicente Blvd. #301
Santa Monica, CA 90401
"Actor"

**Lois Maxwell**
76 Oxford Street
London W1N OAX ENGLAND
"Actress"

**Billy May**
8730 Sunset Blvd., 3rd Floor West
Los Angeles, CA 90069
"Composer"

**Bob May**
420 Grand Augusta Lane
Las Vegas, NV 89114
"Golfer"

**Brian May**
The Old Bakehouse
16A Barnes High Street
London SW13 9LW ENGLAND
"Composer"

**Deborah May**
14200 Chandler Blvd.
Sherman Oaks, CA 91401
"Actress"

**Donald May**
733 N. Seward Street, PH
Los Angeles, CA 90038
"Actor"

**Elaine May**
145 Central Park West
New York, NY 10023
"Actress, Writer, Director"

**John Mayall**
200 West Superior #202
Chicago, IL 60610
"Singer"

**Wendell Mayes**
1504 Bel Air Road
Los Angeles, CA 90077
"Screen writer"

**Don Maynard**
6545 Butterfield Drive
El Paso, TX 79932
"Ex-Football Player"

**Virginia Mayo**
109 East Avenue De Los Arboles
Thousand Oaks, CA 91360
"Actress"

**Melanie Mayron**
7510 Sunset Blvd.
Los Angeles, CA 90046
"Actress, Writer"

**Willie Mays**
P.O. Box 2410
Menlo Park, CA 94026
"Ex-Baseball Player"

**Debi Mazar**
9560 Wilshire Blvd. #516
Beverly Hills, CA 90212
"Actress"

**Bill Mazeroski**
RR 6, Box 130
Greensburg, PA 15601
"Ex-Baseball Player"

**Julia Meade**
1010 Fifth Avenue
New York, NY 10021
"Actress"

**Kristen Meadows**
13576 Cheltenham Drive
Sherman Oaks, CA 91423
"Actress"

**Jayne Meadows-Allen**
15201 Burbank Blvd.
Van Nuys, CA 91411
"Actress"

**Colm Meaney**
9560 Wilshire Blvd. #516
Beverly Hills, CA 90212
"Actor"

**Anne Meara**
118 Riverside Drive #A
New York, NY 10011
"Actress, Comedienne"

**Rick Mears**
204 Spyglass Lane
Jupiter, FL 33477
"Race Car Driver"

**Meatloaf**
252 Regent Street #100
London W1B 3BP ENGLAND
"Singer, Composer"

**Eddie Mecca**
129 West Wilson Street #202
Costa Mesa, CA 92627
"Actor"

**Peter Medak**
1712 Stanley Avenue
Los Angeles, CA 90046
"Film Director"

**Mike Medavoy**
7920 Sunset Blvd. #401
Los Angeles, CA 90046
"Film Executive"

**Thomas Meehan**
Brook House
Obtuse Road
Newtown, CT 06470
"Screenwriter"

**Edwin Meese**
1075 Springhill Road
McLean, VA 22102
"Ex-Government Official"

**Zubin Mehta**
27 Oakmont Drive
Los Angeles, CA 90049
"Violinist"

**Randy Meisner**
4766 Park Granada Blvd. #104
Calabasas, CA 91303
"Singer, Songwriter"

**Eddie Mekka**
3518 Cahuenga Blvd. W. #216
Los Angeles, CA 90068
"Actor"

**Melanie**
1906 Chet Atkins Place #502
Nashville, TN 37212
"Singer"

**Ib Melchoir**
8228 Marmont Lane
Los Angeles, CA 90069
"Writer, Producer"

**Tracy Lindsey Melchior**
13576 Cheltenham Drive
Sherman Oaks, CA 91423
"Actress"

**Bill Melendez**
13400 Riverside Drive #201
Sherman Oaks, CA 91421
"Animation Director"

**John Mellencamp**
P.O. Box 6677
Bloomington, IN 47408
"Singer, Songwriter"

**Sid Melton**
5347 Cedros Avenue
Van Nuys, CA 91410
"Actor"

**Allen Melvin**
271 North Bowling Green Way
Los Angeles, CA 90049
"Actor"

**Donnie Melvin**
45 Overlook Terrace
New York, NY 10033
"Singer"

**Murray Melvin**
535 Kings Road
19 Plaza #2
London SW10 OSZ ENGLAND
"Actor"

**Men At Work**
Box 124, Round Corner
NSW 2158 AUSTRALIA
"Rock & Roll Group"

**Erik Menedez #1878449**
CSP-Sac
P.O. Box 290066
Represa, CA 95671
"Charged for Killing Parents"

**Lyle Menedez #1887106**
California Correctional Institution
P.O. Box 1031
Tehachapi, CA 93581
"Charged for Killing Parents"

**John Mengatti**
8322 Beverly Blvd. #200
Los Angeles, CA 90048
"Actor"

**Gian Carlo Menotti**
Gilford Haddington
East Lothian
EH41 4JF SCOTLAND
"Composer"

**Menudo**
2895 Biscayne Blvd. #455
Miami, FL 33137
"Rock & Roll Group"

**Heather Menzies**
P.O. Box 5973-10006
Sherman Oaks, CA 91403
"Actress"

**Marian Mercer**
25901 Piuma
Calabasas, CA 91302
"Actress"

**Natalie Merchant**
9830 Wilshire Blvd.
Beverly Hills, CA 90212
"Singer"

**Paul Mercurio**
53-55 Brisbane Street
Surryhills, Sydney
NSW 2010 AUSTRALIA
"Actor"

**Don Meredith**
P.O. Box 597
Santa Fe, NM 87504
"Ex-Football Player"

**James Meredith**
929 Meadowbrook Road
Jackson, MS 39206
"First Black to Attend U of MS"

**Lee Ann Meriwether**
2555 East Colorado Blvd.
Pasadena, CA 91107
"Actress"

**Jan Merlin**
347 N. California Street
Burbank, CA 91505
"Actor, Director"

**Dawn Merrick**
8281 Melrose Avenue #200
Los Angeles, CA 90046
"Actress"

**Dina Merrill**
405 East 54th Street #12A
New York, NY 10022
"Actress"

**Ryan Merryman**
606 North Larchmont Blvd. #309
Los Angeles, CA 90004
"Actor"

**Dale Messick**
435 N. Michigan Avenue #1417
Chicago, IL 60611
"Cartoonist"

**Jim Messina**
P.O. Box 770850
Orlando, FL 32877
"Singer, Songwriter"

**Debra Messing**
1122 South Robertson Blvd. #15
Los Angeles, CA 90035
"Actress"

**Reinhold Messner**
St. Magdalena 52
I-39040 Villnoss ITALY
"Mountaineer, Author"

**Metallica**
727 - 7th Avenue #1400
New York, NY 10019
"Rock & Roll Group"

**Laurie Metcalf**
11845 Kling Street
North Hollywood, CA 91607
"Actress"

**Burt Metcalfe**
11800 Brookdale Lane
Studio City, CA 91604
"TV Writer, Producer"

**Pat Metheny**
c/o Insight
1222 - 16th Avenue, 3rd Floor
Nashville, TN 37212
"Guitarist"

**Art Metrano**
9460 Wilshire Blvd. #300
Beverly Hills, CA 90212
"Actor"

**Howard Metzenbaum**
8477 Broadview Road
Cleveland, OH 44147
"Ex-Senator"

**Jim Metzler**
5670 Wilshire Blvd. #820
Los Angeles, CA 90048
"Actor"

**Bess Meyer**
P.O. Box 5617
Beverly Hills, CA 90210
"Actress"

**Russ Meyer**
3121 Arrowhead Drive
Los Angeles, CA 90068
"Film Writer, Producer"

**Ari Meyers**
c/o Tarom Enterprises
17 East 96th Street
New York, NY 10128
"Actress"

**Kweisi Mfume**
3000 Druld Park Drive
Baltimore, MD 21215
"N.A.A.C.P. Director"

**Miami Sound Machine**
420 Jefferson Avenue
Miami, FL 33139
"Rock & Roll Group"

**Bob Michael**
1029 N. Glenwood Street
Peoria, IL 61606
"Former Congressman"

**George Michael**
21 Pond Square
London N6 6BA ENGLAND
"Singer, Composer"

**Prince Michael of Kent**
Kensington Palace
London W8 5AF ENGLAND
"Royalty"

**Princess Michael of Kent**
Kensington Palace
London W8 5AFENGLAND
"Royalty"

**Al Michaels**
c/o ABC Sports
47 West 66th Street
New York, NY 10023
"Sports Announcer"

**Lorne Michaels**
88 Central Park West
New York, NY 10023
"TV Writer, Producer"

**Marilyn Michaels**
185 West End Avenue
New York, NY 10023
"Comedienne"

**Keith Michell**
130 West 57th Street #10-A
New York, NY 10019
"Actor"

**Guy Michelmore**
72 Goldsmith Avenue
London W3 6HN ENGLAND
"Actor"

**Phil Mickelson**
14646 N. Kierland Blvd. #230
Scottsdale, AZ 85254
"Golfer"

**Dale Midkiff**
3950 Sunswept Drive
Studio City, CA 91604
"Actor"

**Bette Midler**
1222 16th Avenue South #300
Nashville, TN 37212
"Singer, Actress, Comedienne"

**Mike & The Mechanics**
252 - 260 Regent Street
London W1B 3BX ENGLAND
"Rock & Roll Group

**George Mikell**
23 Shuttleworth Road
London SW11 ENGLAND
"Actor"

**Sen. Barbara A. Mikulski (MD)**
Senate Hart Bldg. #709
Washington, DC 20510
"Politician"

**Alyssa Milano**
20 Ocean Park Blvd. #25
Santa Monica, CA 90405
"Actress"

**Joanna Miles**
2062 North Vine Street
Los Angeles, CA 90068
"Actress"

**Sarah Miles**
Chithurst Manor
Trotton, nr. Petersfield
Hampshire GU31 5EU ENGLAND
"Actor, Singer"

**Sylvia Miles**
240 Central Park South #191
New York, NY 10019
"Actress"

**Vera Miles**
P.O. Box 1599
Palm Desert, CA 92261
"Actress"

**Tomas Milian**
2 Fifth Avenue #3A
New York, NY 10011
"Actor"

**Michael Milken**
4543 Tara Drive
Encino, CA 91436
"Finance Expert"

**Ann Miller**
618 North Alta Drive
Beverly Hills, CA 90210
"Actress, Dancer"

**Arthur Miller**
Box 320 RR #1 Tophet Road
Roxbury, CT 06783
"Author, Dramatist"

**Cheryl Miller**
3206 Ellington Drive
Los Angeles, CA 90068
"Basketball Coach"

**Christa Miller**
1212 Avenue of the Americas #3
New York, NY 10003
"Actress"

**Denny Miller**
1214 Daly Road
Ojai, CA 92023
"Actor"

**George Miller**
30 Orwell Steet Kings Cross
Sydney, 2011, Australia
"Film Director"

**Jeremy Miller**
5255 Vesper Avenure
Van Nuys, CA 91411
"Actor"

**Jody Miller**
Rt. #3
Blanchard, OK 73010
"Singer"

**Johnny Miller**
P.O. Box 2260
Napa, CA 94558
"Golfer"

**Johnny Lee Miller**
8730 Sunset Blvd. #490
Los Angeles, CA 90069
"Actor"

**Jonathan Miller**
63 Gloucester Crescent
London NW1 ENGLAND
"Film Director"

**Larry Miller**
11845 West Olympic Blvd. #1125
Los Angeles, CA 90064
"Writer"

**Linda G. Miller**
242 Conway Avenue
Los Angeles, CA 90024
"Actress"

**Mitch Miller**
345 West 58th Street
New York, NY 10019
"Musician, Composer"

**Reggie Miller**
11116 Catamaran Court
Indianapolis, IN 46236
"Basketball Player"

**Shannon Miller**
2415 Newbridge Court
Pearland, TX 77584
"Gymnast"

**Sidney Miller**
2724 Bottlebrush Drive
Los Angeles, CA 90077
"Actor, Director"

**Alley Mills**
444 Carol Canal
Venice, CA 90291
"Actress"

**Donna Mills**
253 - 26th Street #259
Santa Monica, CA 90402
"Actress, Model"

**Eddie Mills**
9200 Sunset Blvd., #1130
Los Angeles, CA 90069
"Actor"

**Hayley Mills**
123a Kings Road
London SW3 4PL ENGLAND
"Actress"

**Sir John Mills**
Hill House
Denham Village
Buckinghamshire ENGLAND
"Actor"

**Judson Mills**
9200 Sunset Blvd #1130
Los Angeles, CA 90069
"Actor"

**Juliet Mills**
5252 Lennox Avenue
Sherman Oaks, CA 91401
"Actress"

**Stephanie Mills**
9255 Sunset Blvd. #200
Los Angeles, CA 90069
"Singer"

**Martin Milner**
3106 Azahar Street
Carlsbad, CA 92009
"Actor"

**Ronnie Milsap**
P.O. Box 40665
Nashville, TN 37204
"Singer, Songwriter"

**Yvette Mimieux**
9626 Oak Park Road
Beverly Hills, CA 90210
"Actress, Writer"

**Jan Miner**
P.O. Box 293
Southbury, CT 06488
"Actress"

**Anthony Minghella**
151 El Camino Drive
Beverly Hills, CA 90212
"Actor"

**Charles Mingus**
484 W. 43rd Street #43-S
New York, NY 10036
"Bassist"

**Rep. Patsy Mink (HI)**
P.O. Box 50144
Honolulu, HI 96850
"Politician"

**Liza Minnelli**
150 East 69th Street #21G
New York, NY 10021
"Actress, Singer"

**Kylie Minogue**
P.O. Box 13196
London SW6 2WAENGLAND
"Singer"

**Michael Minor**
280 S. Beverly Drive #400
Beverly Hills, CA 90212
"Actor"

**Minnie Minoso**
324 West 35th Street
Bradenton, FL 34205
"Ex-Baseball Player"

**Miou-Miou**
20 Avenue Rapp
75007 Paris FRANCE
"Actress"

**Walter Mirisch**
647 Warner Avenue
Los Angeles, CA 90024
"Film Executive, Producer"

**Helen Mirren**
91 Regent Street
London W1R 7TB ENGLAND
"Actress"

**Missing Persons**
11935 Laurel Hills Road
Studio City, CA 91604
"Rock & Roll Group"

**Andrea Mitchell**
2710 Chain Bridge Road, NW
Washington, D.C. 20016
"News Journalist"

**Capt. Edgar Mitchell**
P.O. Box 540037
Lake Worth, FL 34454
"Astronuat"

**James Mitchell**
320 West 66th Street
New York, NY 10023
"Actor"

**Joni Mitchell**
1505 W. 2nd Avenue #200
Vancouver BC V6H 3Y4
CANADA
"Singer, Songwriter"

**Kim Mitchell**
41 Britain Street #305
Toronto, Ont. M5A 1R7 CANADA
"Singer, Guitarist"

**Sasha Mitchell**
9057 A Nemo Street
W. Hollywood, CA 90069
"Actress"

**Shirley Mitchell**
10635 Santa Monica Blvd. #130
Los Angeles, CA 90025
"Actress"

**Warren Mitchell**
28 Sheldon Avenue
London N6 ENGLAND
"Actor"

**Marvin Mitchelson**
2500 Apollo Drive
Los Angeles, CA 90046
"Talent Agent"

**Carrie Mitchum**
3500 W. Olive Avenue #1400
Burbank, CA 91505
"Actress"

**Rosi Mittermaier**
Winkelmoosalm
D-83242 Reit im Winkel
GERMANY
"Skier"

**Kim Miyori**
121 North San Vicente Blvd.
Beverly Hills, CA 90211
"Actress"

**Issac Mizrahi**
133 S. Swall Drive
Beverly Hills, CA 90211
"Clothes Designer"

**Mo'nique**
11800 Wilshire Blvd.
Los Angeles, CA 90025
"Comedienne & Actress"

**Mary Ann Mobley**
2751 Hutton Drive
Beverly Hills, CA 90210
"Actress"

**The Modernaires**
11761 E. Speedway Blvd.
Tucson, AZ 85748
"Vocal Group"

**Matthew Modine**
8942 Wilshire Blvd.
Beverly Hills, CA 90211
"Actor"

**Donald Moffat**
151 El Camino Drive
Beverly Hills, CA 90212
"Actor"

**John Moffatt**
59A Warrington Street
London W9 ENGLAND
"Actor"

**Katy Moffatt**
P.O. Box 334
O'Fallon, IL 62269
"Singer, Songwriter"

**D.W. Moffett**
9460 Wilshire Blvd. #700
Los Angeles, CA 90048
"Actor"

**Jay Mohr**
1776 Broadway #2001
New York, NY 10019
"Actor"

**Gretchen Mol**
1964 Westwood Blvd. #400
Los Angeles, CA 90025

**Alfred Molina**
20 Ocean Park Blvd. #25
Santa Monica, CA 90405
"Actor"

**Richard Moll**
c/o GML
3500 West Olive Ave. #1400
Burbank, CA 91505
"Actor"

**Thomas L. Monaghan**
3001 Earhart
Ann Arbor, MI 48106
"Domino Pizza Owner"

**Paul Monash**
912 Alto Cedro Drive
Beverly Hills, CA 90210
"Writer, Producer"

**Eleanor Mondale**
282 Edge of Woods Road
South Hampton, NY 11968
"Actress"

**Walter Mondale**
50 South 6th Street #1500
Minneapolis, MN 55402
"Ambassador"

**Rick Monday**
811 Gayfeather Lane
Vero Beach, FL 32967
"EX-Baseball Player"

**Eddie Money**
8942 Wilshire Blvd.
Beverly Hills, CA 90211
"Singer"

**Monica**
c/o WMA
1325 Avenue of the Americas
New York, NY 10019
"Singer"

**Thelonious Monk, Jr.**
5225 Wisconsin Avenue #605
Washington, DC 20015
"Musician"

**The Monkees**
c/o Evolution Talent
1776 Broadway, 15th Floor
New York, NY 10019
"Rock & Roll Group"

**Bob Monkhouse**
235 Regent Street
London W1R 8AX ENGLAND
"Actor, Writer"

**Earl Monroe**
1150 West Columbus Avenue
Springfield, MA 01105
"Ex-Basketball Player"

**Joe Montagna**
10415 Sarah Street
Toluca Lake, CA 91602
"Actor"

**Lee Montague**
5 Keats Close
London NW3 2RP ENGLAND
"Actor"

**Ricardo Montalban**
13701 Riverside Drive #500
Sherman Oaks, CA 91423
"Actor, Director"

**Joe Montana**
3455 State Highway 128
Calistoga, CA 94515
"Ex-Football Player"

**Kelly Monteith**
P.O. Box 11669
Knoxville, TN 37939
"Comedian, Writer"

**Liliane Montevecchi**
24 W. 40th St. #1700
New York, NY 10011
"Singer"

**Belinda Montgomery**
280 S. Beverly Drive #400
Beverly Hills, CA 90212
"Actress"

**John Michael Montgomery**
124 - 12th Avenue #410
Nashville, TN 37203
"Singer"

**Moody Blues**
53-55 High Street, Cobham
Surrey KT11 3DP ENGLAND
"Rock & Roll Group"

**Ron Moody**
Ingleside
41 The Green, Southgate
London N14 ENGLAND
"Actor"

**Rev. Donn Moomaw**
3124 Corda Drive
Los Angeles, CA 90049
"Clergy"

**Rev. Sun Myung Moon**
4 West 43rd Street
New York, NY 10010
"Cult Leader"

**Warren Moon**
1 Lakeside Estate Drive
Missouri City, TX 77459
"Football Player"

**Chante Moore**
685 Lambert Drive Northeast
Atlanta, GA 30324
"Singer"

**Constance Moore**
10450 Wilshire Blvd. #1-B
Los Angeles, CA 90024
"Actress"

**Demi Moore**
8500 Wilshire Blvd. #700
Beverly Hills, CA 90211
"Actress"

**Dickie Moore**
150 West End Avenue #26C
New York, NY 10023
"Actor"

**Julianne Moore**
8500 Wilshire Blvd. #700
Beverly Hills, CA 90211
"Actress"

**Mandy Moore**
7280 Melrose Avenue #2
Los Angeles, CA 90046
"Singer"

**Mary Tyler Moore**
c/o MTM
1133 Avenue of the Americas
New York, NY 10022
"Actress"

**Melba Moore**
1017 "O" Street NW #B
Washington, DC 20001
"Singer"

**Michael Moorer**
811 Totowa
Paterson, NJ 07512

**Roger Moore**
2-4 Noel Street
London W1V 3RB ENGLAND
"Actor"

**Terry Moore**
10366 Wilshire Blvd. #5
Los Angeles, CA 90024
"Actress"

**Shemar Moore**
4424 Moorpark Way #1
Toluca Lake, CA 91602
"Actress"

**Esai Morales**
Chelsea Piers, Pier 62
West 23rd & 12th Avenue
New York, NY 10011
"Actor"

**Erin Moran**
P.O. Box 3261
Quartz Hill, CA 93586
"Actress"

**Tony Mordente**
4541 Comber
Encino, CA 91316
"Film Director"

**Jeanne Moreau**
201 rue de Faubourgh-St. Honore
F-75008 Paris, FRANCE
"Actress"

**Rita Moreno**
160 Gravatt Drive
Berkeley, CA 94705
"Actress"

**Cindy Morgan**
280 South Beverly Drive #400
Beverly Hills, CA 90212
"Actress"

**Debi Morgan**
8675 W. Washington Blvd. #200
Culver City, CA 90232
"Actress"

**Elaine Morgan**
24 Aberfford Road
Mountain Ash
Glamorgan ENGLAND
"Playwright"

**Harry Morgan**
13172 Boca De Canon Lane
Los Angeles, CA 90049
"Actor, Director"

**Jane Morgan**
27740 Pacific Coast Highway
Malibu, CA 90265
"Actress"

**Jaye P. Morgan**
1185 La Grange Avenue
Newbury Park, CA 91320
"Actress"

**Joe Morgan**
3239 Danvill Blvd. #A
Alamo, CA 94507
"Ex-Baseball Player"

**Lorrie Morgan**
38 Music Square #300
Nashville, TN 37293
"Singer"

**Michelle Morgan**
5 rue Jacques Dulud
92200 Neuily, FRANCE
"Actress"

**Cathy Moriarity**
15300 Ventura Blvd. #315
Sherman Oaks, CA 91403
"Actress"

**Michael Moriarty**
200 West 58th Street #3B
New York, NY 10019
"Actor"

**Patricia Morison**
400 South Hauser Blvd. #9L
Los Angeles, CA 90036
"Actress, Singer"

**Alanis Morissette**
9200 Sunset Blvd. #1000
Los Angeles, CA 90069
"Singer"

**Noriyuki "Pat" Morita**
6399 Wilshire Blvd. #414
Los Angeles, CA 90048
"Actor, Comedian"

**Louisa Moritz**
405 Cliffwood Avenue
Los Angeles, CA 90049
"Actress, Model"

**Karen Morley**
1007 Montana Avenue #540
Santa Monica, CA 90403
"Actress"

**Alonzo Morning**
701 Areana Blvd.
Miami, FL 33136
"Basketball Player"

**Giorgio Moroder**
1880 Century Park East #900
Los Angeles, CA 90067
"Composer, Conductor"

**David Morphet**
101 Honor Oak Road
London SE23 3LB ENGLAND
"Writer, Producer"

**Dr. Desmond Morris**
78 Danbury Road
Oxford, ENGLAND
"Zoologist, Author"

**Dick Morris**
20 Beeholm Road
West Redding, CT 06896
"Political Consultant"

**Garret Morris**
8436 West Third Street #740
Los Angeles, CA 90048
"Actor"

**Howard Morris**
11645 Picturesque Drive
Studio City, CA 91604
"Actor, Director"

**Phil Morris**
704 Strand
Manhattan Beach, CA 90266
"Actor"

**Mark Morrison**
28 Kensington Church St.
London W8 4EP ENGLAND
"Singer"

**Toni Morrison**
185 Nassau Street
Princeton, NJ 08544
"Writer"

**Van Morrison**
314 Albion Ct., Hammersmith
London W5 OQT ENGLAND
"Singer, Songwriter"

**Rob Morrow**
9465 Wilshire Blvd. #820
Beverly Hills, CA 90212
"Actor"

**Barry Morse**
71 Charles Street East #506
Toronto M4Y 2T3 CANADA
"Actor"

**David Morse**
9701 Wilshire Blvd. 10th Floor
Beverly Hills, CA 90212
"Actor"

**Robert Morse**
13830 Davana Terrace
Sherman Oaks, CA 91403
"Actor"

**Viggo Mortenson**
3933 Patrick Henry Place
Agoura Hills, CA 91301
"Actor"

**Joe Morton**
606 North Larchmont Blvd.
Suite #309
Los Angeles, CA 90004
"Actor"

**John Moschitta, Jr.**
11601 Dunston Way #206
Los Angeles, CA 90049
"Actor"

**Tad Mosel**
149 Eastside Dr., Box 249 #26-B
Concord, NH 03301
"Playwright"

**Mark Moseley**
16001 Berkeley Drive
Haymarket, VA 22079
"Ex-Football Player"

**Albert Moses**
15 Overstone Road
Harpenden, Herts.
AL5 5PN ENGLAND
"Actor"

**Billy Moses**
409 N. Camden Drive #202
Beverly Hills, CA 90210
"Actor"

**Edwin Moses**
One Hoosier Dome
Indianapolis, IN 46225
"Track & Field Athlete"

**Kate Moss**
5 Jubilee Place #100
London SW3 3TD ENGLAND
"Model"

**Ronn Moss**
7800 Beverly Blvd. #3371
Los Angeles, CA 90036
"Actor"

**Randy Moss**
c/o Minnesota Vikings
500 11th Avenue South
Minneapolis, MN 55415
"Football Player"

**Sterling Moss**
46 Shepherd Street, Mayfair
London W1Y 8JN ENGLAND
"Actor"

**Donny Most**
280 South Beverly Drive #400
Beverly Hills, CA 90212
"Actor"

**Mark Mothersbaugh**
2164 Sunset Plaza Drive
Los Angeles, CA 90069
"Writer"

**Stewart Mott**
515 Madison Avenue
New York, NY 10022
"Philanthropist"

**Mickey Mouse Club**
P.O. Box 10200
Lake Buena Vista, FL 32830
"Fan Club"

**Movita**
2766 Motor Avenue
Los Angeles, CA 90064
"Actress"

**Tia & Tamera Mowry**
1122 S. Robertson Blvd. #15
Los Angeles, CA 90035
"Actress"

**Bill Moyers**
151 Central Park West
New York, NY 10023
"News Correspondent"

**Pres. Hosni Mubarak**
Royal Palace
Cairo, EGYPT
"President of Egypt"

**Roger Mudd**
7167 Old Dominion Drive
McLean, VA 22101
"News Correspondent"

**Armin Mueller-Stahl**
c/o ZBF
Ordensmeisterstr. 15-1
D12099 Berlin GERMANY
"Actor"

**Diana Muldaur**
259 Quadro Vecchio Drive
Pacific Palisades, CA 90272
"Actress"

**Maria Muldaur**
P.O. Box 680006
Charlotte, NC 28216
"Singer, Songwriter"

**Patrick Muldoon**
11030 Venturaq Blvd #3
Studio City, CA 91604
"Actor"

**Shirley Muldowney**
79559 North Avenue
Armada, MI 48005
"Race Car Driver"

**Kate Mulgrew**
c/o IA
1505 - 10th Avenue
Santa Moncia, CA 90401
"Actress"

**Chris Mulkey**
918 Zenizia Avenue
Venice, CA 90291
"Actor"

**Martin Mull**
338 Chadbourne Avenue
Los Angeles, CA 90049
"Actor, Comedian, Writer"

**Greg Mullavey**
1818 Thayer Avenue #303
Los Angeles, CA 90025
"Actor"

**Lillian Muller**
3940 Laura Canyon Blvd. #269
Studio City, CA 91604
"Actress, Model"

**Gardner Mulloy**
1 Fisher Island Drive
Miami, FL 33109
"Tennis Player"

**Dermot Mulroney**
5200 Linwood Drive
Los Angeles, CA 90027
"Actor"

**The Muppets**
P.O. Box 20750
New York, NY 10023
"Puppets"

**Bobby Murcer**
P.O. Box 75089
Oklahoma City, OK 73147
"Ex-Baseball Player"

**George Murdock**
5733 Sunfield Avenue
Lakewood, CA 90712
"Actor"

**Rupert Murdoch**
News Corporation
1211 Avenue of Americas, 8th Floor
New York, NY 10036
"Publisher"

**Ben Murphy**
3601 Vista Pacifica #17
Malibu, CA 90265
"Actor"

**Dale Murphy**
P.O. Box 4064
Atlanta, GA 30302
"Ex-Baseball Player"

**Donna Murphy**
250 West 57th Street #2303
New York, NY 10107
"Actress"

**Eddie Murphy**
P.O. Box 1028
Englewood Cliffs, NJ 07632
"Actor, Comedian"

**John Cullen Murphy**
14 Mead Avenue
Cos Cob, CT 06805
"Illustrator"

**Michael Murphy**
9830 Wilshire Blvd.
Beverly Hills, CA 90212
"Actor"

**Michael Martin Murphy**
4077 State Highway 68
Rancho de Taos, NM 87557
"Singer, Guitarist"

**Rosemary Murphy**
220 East 73rd Street
New York, NY 10021
"Actress"

**Anne Murray**
12 St. Clair Ave. E., PMB 69030
Toronto, Ont. M4T 1KO CANADA
"Singer"

**Bill Murray**
24228 Malibu Road
Malibu, CA 90265
"Actor"

**Jan Murray**
1157 Calle Vista
Beverly Hills, CA 90210
"Actor, Comedian"

**Sean Murray**
8436 West Third Street #740
Los Angeles, CA 90048
"Composer"

**Kate Murtagh**
15146 Moorpark Street
Sherman Oaks, CA 91403
"Actress"

**Tony Musante**
4605 Lankershim Blvd. #305
North Hollywood, CA 91602
"Actor, Writer"

**Brent Musburger**
47 West 66th Street
New York, NY 10023
"Sportscaster"

**President Perveg Musharref**
Chief Executive's Secretariat
Islamabad PAKISTAN
"Politician"

**Stan Musial**
1655 Des Peres Rd. #125
St. Louis, MO 63131
"Ex-Baseball Player, Manager"

**Marjorie Ann Mutchie**
1169 Mary Circle
La Verne, CA 91750
"Actress"

**Dikembe Mutombo**
P.O. Box 25040
Philadelphia, PA 19147
"Basketball Player"

**Dee Dee Myers**
c/o Vanity Fair
6300 Wilshire Blvd.
Los Angeles, CA 90048
"Ex-Press Secretary"

**Bess Myerson**
3 East 71st Street
New York, NY 10021
"Columnist"

**The Mystics**
88 Anador Street
Staten Island, NY 10303
"Vocal Group"

**N Sync**
7680 Universal Blvd. #500
Orlando, FL 32819
"Music Group"

**John Naber**
P.O. Box 50107
Pasadena, CA 91105
"Swimmer"

**Jim Nabors**
151 El Camino Drive
Beverly HIlls, CA 90212
"Actor, Singer"

**Ralph Nader**
1600-20th Street, NW
Washington, DC 20009
"Consumer Advocate"

**Stu Nahan**
11274 Canton Drive
Studio City, CA 91604
"Sportscaster"

**Kathy Najimy**
120 W. 45th Street #3601
New York, NY 10036
"Actress"

**Joe Namath**
300 East 51st Street #11A
New York, NY 10022
"Ex-Football Player"

**Nantucket**
250 N. Kepler Road
Deland, FL 33724
"Rock & Roll Group"

**Charles Napier**
Star Rt. Box 60-H
Caliente, CA 93518
"Actor"

**Hugo Napier**
2207 N. Beachwood Drive
Los Angeles, CA 90068
"Actor"

**Jack Narz**
1906 Beverly Place
Beverly Hills, CA 90210
"TV Show Host"

**Graham Nash**
709 East Colorado Blvd. #220
Pasadena, CA 91101
"Singer, Songwriter"

**Ille Nastase**
Calea Plevnei 14
Bucharest ROMANIA
"Tennis Player"

**Marie-Jose Nat**
10 rue Royale
75008 Paris, FRANCE
"Actress"

**Kitten Natividad**
5917 Oak Avenue, #148
Temple City, CA 91780
"Actress, Model"

**David Naughton**
11774-B Moorpark Street
Studio City, CA 91604
"Actor, Singer"

**Naughty by Nature**
1501 Broadway #1301
New York, NY 10036
"Music Group"

**Martina Navratilova**
133 - 1st Street NE
St. Petersburg, FL 33701
"Tennis Player"

**Patricia Neal**
45 East End Avenue #4C
New York, NY 10028
"Actress"

**Christopher Neame**
8300 Wilshire Blvd. #900
Los Angeles, CA 90048
"Producer, Screenwriter, Actor"

**Ronald Neame**
2317 Kimridge Drive
Beverly Hills, CA 90210
"Film Director"

**Holly Near**
P.O. Box 236
Ukiah, CA 95482
"Singer"

**Connie Needham**
19721 Castlebar Drive
Rowland Heights, CA 91748
"Actress"

**Hal Needham**
P.O. Box 46609
Los Angeles, CA 90046
"Writer, Producer"

**Tracey Needham**
9229 Sunset Blvd. #311
Los Angeles, CA 90069
"Actress"

**Liam Neeson**
4 Great Portland Street
London W1W 8PA ENGLAND
"Actor"

**Neilly (Cornell Hayes, Jr.)**
T-Luv Mangement
3018 Gary Drive
St. Louis, MO 63121
"Rap Singer

**LeRoy Neiman**
1 West 67th Street
New York, NY 10023
"Artist"

**Stacey Nelkin**
2770 Hutton Drive
Beverly Hills, CA 90210
"Actress"

**Kate Nelligan**
1505 - 10th Street
Santa Monica, CA 90401
"Actress"

**Barry Nelson**
134 West 58th Street
New York, NY 10019
"Actor"

**Byron Nelson**
Rt. 2, Box 5
Litsey Road
Roanoke, TX 76262
"Golfer"

**Craig Richard Nelson**
12250 Addison Street
Valley Village, CA 91607
"Actor"

**Craig T. Nelson**
9701 Wilshire Blvd., 10th Floor
Beverly Hills, CA 90212
"Actor, Writer"

**David Nelson**
8544 Sunset Blvd.
Los Angeles, CA 90046
"Actor, Director"

**Ed Nelson**
1038 Marina Drive
Slidell, LA 70458
"Actor"

**John Allen Nelson**
10100 Santa Monica Blvd.
25th Floor
Los Angeles, CA 90067
"Actor"

**Judd Nelson**
9206 Cordell Drive
Los Angeles, CA 90069
"Actor"

**Willie Nelson**
Rt. #1
Briarcliff TT
Spicewood, TX 78669
"Singer, Songwriter"

**Franco Nero**
Lungotevere Mellini 17
1-00193 Rome ITALY
"Actor"

**Peter Nero**
11761 East Speedway Blvd.
Tucson, AZ 85748
"Pianist"

**Mike Nesmith**
8 Harris Court #C-1
Monterey, CA 93940
"Singer"

**Benjamin Netanyahue**
3 Kaplan Street #187
91919 Jerusalem ISRAEL
"Ex-Prime Minister"

**Graig Nettles**
1758 Burgundy Road
Encinitas, CA 92024
"Ex-Baseball Player"

**Lois Nettleton**
11762-G Moorpark Street
Studio City, CA 91604
"Actress"

**Bebe Neuwirth**
144 Prospect Avenue
Princeton, NJ 08540
"Actress"

**Aaron Neville**
360 - 17th Street #200
Oakland, CA 94612
"Singer"

**Claudette Nevins**
3500 W. Olive Avenue #1400
Burbank, CA 91505
"Actress"

**Nancy Nevinson**
23 Mill Close, Fishbourne
Chichester ENGLAND
"Actress"

**George Newburn**
9171 Wilshire Blvd. #406
Beverly Hills, CA 90210
"Actor"

**New Christy Minstrels**
2112 Casitas Way
Palm Springs, CA 92264
"Vocal Group"

**Don Newcombe**
4042 West 226th Street
Torrance, CA 90505
"Tennis Player"

**New Editon**
8942 Wilshire Blvd. #219
Beverly Hills, CA 90211
"R&B Group"

**New Grass Revival**
P.O. Box 128037
Nashville, TN 37212
"C&W Group"

**Bob Newhart**
6847 Truxton
Dallas, TX 75231
"Actor, Comedian"

**Samuel I. Newhouse, Jr.**
950 Fingerboard Road
Staten Island, NY 10305
"Publishing Executive"

**Edwin Newman**
870 United Nations Plaza #16D
New York, NY 10017
"Newscaster"

**Laraine Newman**
10480 Ashton Avenue
Los Angeles, CA 90024
"Actress"

**Nanette Newman**
Seven Pines, Wentworth
Surrey GU25 4QP ENGLAND
"Actress"

**Paul Newman**
1120 Fifth Avenue #1C
New York, NY 10128
"Actor"

**Phyllis Newman**
315 West 57th Street #4H
New York, NY 10019
"Actress"

**Randy Newman**
1610 San Remo Drive
Pacific Palisades, CA 90272
"Singer, Songwriter"

**Julie Newmar**
204 South Carmelina Avenue
Los Angeles, CA 90049
"Actress, Model"

**New Order**
The Plaza
535 Kings Road
London SW10 OSZ ENGLAND
"Rock & Roll Group"

**New Kids On The Block**
27 Dudley Street
Roxbury, MA 02132
"Music Group"

**New Riders of the Purple Sage**
P.O. Box 3773
San Rafael, CA 94912
"Rock & Roll Group"

**David Newsom**
8840 Wilshire Blvd.
Beverly Hills, CA 90211
"Actor"

**Tommy Newson**
19315 Wells Drive
Tarzana, CA 91356
"Conductor"

**Juice Newton**
P.O. Box 3035
Rancho Santa Fe, CA 92067
"Singer"

**Wayne Newton**
3422 Happy Lane
Las Vegas, NV 89120
"Singer, Actor"

**Olivia Newton-John**
P.O. Box 2710
Malibu, CA 90265
"Singer, Actress"

**Richard Ney**
800 South San Rafael Avenue
Pasadena, CA 91105
"Actor"

**Dustin Nguyen**
9150 Wilshire Blvd. #350
Beverly Hills, CA 90212
"Actor"

**Michelle Nicastro**
1800 Avenue of the Stars, #400
Los Angeles, CA 90067
"Actress"

**Denise Nicholas**
932 Longwood Avenue
Los Angeles, CA 90019
"Actress, Singer"

**Fayard Nicholas**
10153 1/2 Riverside Drive #219
Toluca Lake, CA 91602
"Dancer"

**Thomas Ian Nicholas**
4343 Lankershim Blvd. #100
Universal City, CA 91602
"Actor"

**Bobby Nichols**
8681 Glenlyon Coourt
Fort Meyers, FL 33912
"Golfer"

**Mike Nichols**
9830 Wilshire Blvd.
Beverly Hills, CA 90212
"Film Writer, Director"

**Nichelle Nichols**
22647 Ventura Blvd. #121
Woodland Hills, CA 91364
"Actress"

**Stephen Nichols**
11664 National Blvd. #116
Los Angeles, CA 90064
"Actor"

**Jack Nicholson**
11500 West Olympic Blvd. #510
Los Angeles, CA 90064
"Actor"

**Jack Nicklaus**
11397 Old Harbor Road
North Palm Beach, FL 33405
"Golfer"

**Julia Nickson**
1206 S. Hudson Avenue
Los Angeles, CA 90019
"Actress"

**Joe Niekro**
2707 Fairway Drive S.
Plant City, FL 33567
"Ex-Baseball Player"

**Phil Niekro**
P.O. Box 590
Cooperstown, NY 13326
"Baseball Player"

**Brigitte Nielsen**
P.O. Box 57593
Sherman Oaks, CA 91403
"Actress"

**Leslie Nielsen**
1622 Viewmont Drive
Los Angeles, CA 90069
"Actor"

**Birgit Nilsson**
P.O. Box 527
S-10130 Stockholm, SWEDEN
"Soprano"

**Leonard Nimoy**
501 South Beverly Drive
Beverly Hills, CA 90212
"Actor, Writer, Director"

**Yvette Nipar**
9460 Wilshire Blvd. #300
Beverly Hills, CA 90212
"Actress"

**Nitty Gritty Dirt Band**
1607 -17th Avenue South
Nashville, TN 37212
"Music Group"

**Paul Nitze**
1619 Massachusetts Ave. N.W.
Suite #811
Washington, DC 20036
"Statesman"

**Barbara Niven**
1680 North Vine Street #614
Hollywood, CA 90028
"Actress"

**Mrs. Hjordis Niven**
CH-1837 Chateau D'Oex
SWITZERLAND
"David Niven's Widower"

**David Niven, Jr.**
1457 Blue Jay Way
Los Angeles, CA 90069
"Son of David Niven"

**Agnes Nixon**
774 Conestoga Road
Rosemont, PA 19010
"TV Writer, Producer"

**Julia Nixon-Eisenhower**
Foxall Lane
Berwyn, PA 19312
"Ex-President's Daughter"

**Norm Nixon**
607 Marguerita Avenue
Santa Monica, CA 90402
"Ex-Basketball Player"

**Yannick Noah**
20 rue Billancourt
F-92100 Boulogne FRANCE
"Tennis Player"

**Chelsea Noble**
P.O. Box 8665
Calabasas, CA 91372
"Actress"

**James Noble**
80 Baavater Lane
Black Rock, CT 06605
"Actor"

**Lyn Nofziger**
2000 Pennsylvania Ave. NW #365
Washington, DC 20037
"Political Advisor"

**Dr. Thomas Noguchi**
1110 Avoca Avenue
Pasadena, CA 91105
"Coroner"

**Natalija Nogulich**
11841 Kiowa Avenue #7
Los Angeles, CA 90049
"Actress"

**Philippe Noiret**
17 rue Durmont Dunville
F-75118 Paris FRANCE
"Actor"

**Christopher Nolan**
158 Vernon Avenue
Dublin, IRELAND
"Poet, Author"

**Kathleen Nolan**
250 West 57th Street #703
New York, NY 10107
"Actress"

**Tom Nolan**
1335 North Ontario Street
Burbank, CA 91505
"Writer"

**Gena Lee Nolin**
6230 Wilshire blvd. #171
Los Angeles, CA 90048
"Actress"

**Chuck Noll**
2121 George Hales Drive NW
Canton, OH 44708
"Ex-Football Coach"

**Nick Nolte**
6173 Bonsall Drive
Malibu, CA 90265
"Actor"

**Hideo Nomo**
Los Angeles Dodgers
1000 Elysian Park Avenue
Los Angeles, CA 90012
"Baseball Player"

**Kathleen Noone**
P.O. Box 57593
Sherman Oaks, CA 91403
"Actress"

**Peter Noone**
P.O. Box 77085
Orlando, Fl 32877
"Singer"

**Queen Noor**
Baab al-Salem Palace
Amman, Jordan
"Royalty"

**Clayton Norcross**
951 Galloway Street
Pacific Palisades, CA 90272
"Actor"

**Gen. Manuel Noriega**
#38699-079
Federal Metropolitan Correctional
Center
15801 Southwest 137th Avenue
Miami, FL 33177
"Prisoner of War"

**Greg Norman**
501 N. AIA Suite
Jupiter, FL 33477
"Golfer"

**Chuck Norris**
18653 Ventura Blvd. #751
Tarzana, CA 91356
"Actor"

**Terry Norris**
P.O. Box 877
Lakeside, CA 92040
"Boxer"

**Jay North**
290 NE First Avenue
Lake Butler, FL 32054
"Actor"

**Oliver North**
22570 Markley Circle #240
Dulles, VA 20166
"Former Military Lt. Col."

**Sheree North**
812 - 21st Street #C
Santa Monica, CA 90403
"Actress"

**Wayne Northrup**
21919 West Canon Drive
Topanga, CA 90290
"Actor"

**Edward Norton**
9465 Wilshire Blvd. #600
Beverly Hills, CA 90212
"Actor"

**Ken Norton**
416 1/2 Arcadia Avenue
Corona Del Mar, CA 92625
"Boxer"

**Deborah Norville**
P.O. Box 426
Mill Neck, NY 11765
"TV Show Host"

**Jack Noseworthy**
955 S. Carrillo Drive #300
Los Angeles, CA 90048
"Actor"

**Chris Noth**
9560 Wilshire Blvd. #516
Beverly Hills, CA 90212
"Actor"

**Don Nottingham**
2641 SE 40th Street
Ocala, FL 34480
"Football Player"

**Michael Nouri**
15304 Sunset Blvd. #208
Pacific Palisades, CA 90272
"Actor"

**William Novack**
3 Ashton
Newton, MA 02159
"Author"

**Robert Novak**
1750 Pennsylvania Avenue N.W.
Suite #1312
Washington, DC 20006
"News Journalist, Columnist"

**Don Novello**
P.O. Box 245
Fairfax, CA 94930
"Actor, Writer, Comedian"

**Eddie Nugent**
P.O. Box 1266
New York, NY 10150
"Actor"

**Ted Nugent**
4133 West Michigan Avenue
Jackson, MI 49202
"Singer, Guitarist"

**Ex-Sen. Sam Nunn**
75 14th Street Northeast #4810
Atalanta, GA 30309
"Politician"

**France Nuyen**
P.O. Box 18437
Beverly Hills, CA 90209
"Actress"

**Carrie Nye**
200 West 57th Street #900
New York, NY 10019
"Actress"

**Louis Nye**
1241 Corsica Drive
Pacific Palisdaes, CA 90272
"Actor, Comedian"

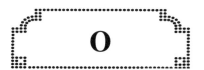

**Oak Ridge Boys**
88 New Shackle Island Road
Hendersonville, TN 37075
"C&W Group"

**Oasis**
54 Linhope Street
London NW1 6HL ENGLAND
"Gospel Group"

**John Oates**
9830 Wilshire Blvd.
Beverly Hills, CA 90212
"Singer, Songwriter"

**Hugh O'Brian**
10880 Wilshire Blvd. #410
Los Angeles, CA 90024
"Actor"

**Conan O'Brien**
30 Rockefeller Plaza
New York, NY 10012
"Talk Show Host"

**Cubby O'Brien**
2839 N. Surrey Drive
Carrollton, TX 75004
"Actor"

**Dan O'Brien**
One Hoosier Dome
Indianapolis, IN 46225
"Decathlete"

**Margaret O'Brien**
7440 Sepulveda Blvd.
North Tower #305
Van Nuya, CA 91405
"Actress"

**Billy Ocean**
32 Wilesden Lane
London NW6 7ST ENGLAND
"Singer"

**Jerry O'Connell**
9701 Wilshire Blvd., 10th Floor
Beverly Hills, CA 90212
"Actor"

**Mark O'Conner**
7957 Nita Avenue
Canoga Park, CA 91304
"Violinist"

**Sinead O'Conner**
43 Brook Green
London, W6 7EF, ENGLAND
"Singer"

**Des O'Connor**
23 Eyot Gardens
London W6 9TR ENGLAND
"Singer"

**Donald O'Connor**
P.O. Box 20204
Sedona, AZ 86341
"Actor, Director"

**Glynnis O'Connor**
2400 Whitman Avenue
Los Angeles, CA 90068
"Actress"

**Renee O'Connor**
400 S. Beverly Drive #216
Beverly Hills, CA 90212
"Actress"

**Sandra Day O'Connor**
1-1st Street, Northeast
Washington, DC 20543
"Supreme Court Justice"

**Tim O'Connor**
P.O. Box 458
Nevada City, CA 95959
"Actor"

**Anita O'Day**
21 Cobble Creek Drive
Tannersville, PA 18372
"Entertainer, Singer"

**Tony O'Dell**
417 Griffith Park Drive
Burbank, CA 91506
"Actor"

**Chris O'Donnell**
2029 Century Park East #500
Los Angeles, CA 90067
"Actor"

**Rosie O'Donnell**
40 West 57th Street
New York, NY 10019
"Actress"

**Al Oerter**
4745 Estero Blvd. #501
Ft. Meyers, FL 33931
"Executive, Discus Thrower"

**Ian Ogilvy**
46 Albermarle Street
London W1X 4PP ENGLAND
"Actor"

**Soon-Teck Oh**
128 North Kenwood Street #1
Burbank, CA 91505
"Actor"

**Jenny O'Hara**
1801 Avenue of the Stars #902
Los Angeles, CA 90067
"Actress"

**Michael O'Hara**
280 South Beverly Drive #400
Beverly Hills, CA 90212
"Writer"

**Dan O'Herlihy**
110 West 40th Street, #1500
New York, NY 10018
"Actor"

**The O'Jays**
1995 Broadway #501
New York, NY 10023
"R & B Group"

**Michael O'Keeffe**
1344 North Spaulding
Los Angeles, CA 90046
"Actor"

**Paul O'Keefe**
225 W. 83rd Street #9-5
New York, NY 10027
"Actor"

**Ken Olandt**
3500 West Olive #1400
Burbank, CA 91505
"Actor"

**Mike Oldfield**
252 - 260 Regent Street
London W1B 3BX ENGLAND
"Musician, Composer"

**Sally Oldfield**
100 Chalk Farm Road
London NW1 ENGLAND
"Singer"

**Gary Oldman**
9830 Wilshire Blvd.
Beverly Hills, CA 90212
"Actor"

**Michael O'Leary**
9200 Sunset Blvd. #1130
Los Angeles, CA 90069
"Actress"

**Ken Olin**
9701 Wilshire Blvd. 10th Floor
Beverly hills, CA 90212
"Actor"

**Lena Olin**
955 South Carrillo Drive #300
Los Angeles, CA 90048
"Actress"

**Edward James Olmos**
500 S. Buena Vista #MC1803
Burbank, CA 91521
"Actor"

**Gerald O'Loughlin**
P.O. Box 340832
Arleta, CA 91334
"Actor, Director"

**Ashley Olsen**
1801 Century Park East #1200
Los Angeles, CA 90067
"Actress"

**Mary Kate Olsen**
1801 Century Park East #1200
Los Angeles, CA 90048
"Actress"

**Nancy Olsen**
945 North Alpine Drive
Beverly Hills, CA 90210
"Actress"

**Mitchell Olson**
9899 Santa Monica Blvd., PBM
2002
Beverly Hills, CA 90212
"Survivor II Contestant"

**Saltan of Oman**
The Palace
Muslat OMAN
"Royalty"

**Jason O'Mara**
4 Kingly Street
London W1B 5PE ENGLAND
"Actor"

**Kate O'Mara**
1 Duchess Street
London W1N 3AB ENGLAND
"Actress"

**Athina Onassis**
88 Avenue Foch
F-75116 Paris FRANCE
"Richest Girl in the World"

**Griffin O'Neal**
21368 Pacific Coast Hwy
Malibu, CA 90265
"Screenwriter"

**Ryan O'Neal**
21368 Pacific Coast Highway
Malibu, CA 90265
"Actor"

**Shaquille O'Neal**
P.O. Box 951840
Lake Mary, FL 32795
"Basketball Player"

**Tatum O'Neal**
300 Central Park West #16-G
New York, NY 10024
"Actress"

**Jennifer O'Neil**
7500 W. Lake Mead Blvd. #492
Las Vegas, NV 89128
"Actress, Model"

**Ed O'Neill**
1122 South Roberston Blvd. #15
Los Angeles, CA 90035
"Actor"

**Tricia O'Neill**
15821 Ventura Blvd. #235
Encino, CA 91436
"Actress"

**Yoko Ono Lennon**
1 West 72nd Street
New York, NY 10023
"Singer, Songwriter"

**Michael Ontkean**
P.O. Box 1212
Malibu, CA 90265
"Actor"

**Marcel Ophuls**
10 rue Ernst-Deloison
92200 Neuilly, FRANCE
"Director, Producer"

**Alan Oppenhiemer**
1207 Beverly Green Drive
Beverly Hills, CA 90212
"Actor"

**Jerry Orbach**
1325 Ave. of the Americas, 15th Flr.
New York, NY 10019
"Actor"

**Cyril O'Reilly**
8436 W. Third Street #740
Los Angeles, CA 90048
"Actor"

**Tony Orlando**
9255 Sunset Blvd. #804
Los Angeles, CA 90069
"Singer"

**Yuri Orlov**
Cornell University
Newman Laboratory
Ithica, NJ 14853
"Scientist"

**Julia Ormond**
c/o Endeavor
9701 Wilshire Blvd., 10th Floor
Beverly Hills, CA 90212
"Actress"

**Bobby Orr**
15 Sleeper Street #105
Boston, MA 02210
"Ex-Hockey Player"

**Jimmy Orr**
3104 Glynn Avenue
Burnswick, GA 31520
"Football Player"

**Brian Orser**
1600 James Naismith Dr.
Gloucester Ontario
K1B 5N4 CANADA
"Skater"

**Jeffrey Osbourne**
P.O. Box 3172
Beverly Hills, CA 90212
"Singer, Songwriter"

**Ozzy Osbourne**
9830 Wilshire Blvd.
Beverly Hills, CA 90212
"Singer, Songwriter"

**Sharon Osbourne**
513 Doheny Road
Beverly Hills, CA 90210
"Wife of Ozzy Osbourne"

**Charles Osgood**
524 West 57th Steet
New York, NY 10019
"News Correspondent"

**Milo O' Shea**
40 West 72nd Street #17-A
New York, NY 10023
"Actor"

**Nagisa Osima**
4-11-5, Kugenuma-Matsugaoka
Fujisawa-Shi 251 JAPAN
"Director"

**K.T. Oslin**
704 - 18th Avenue South
Nashville, TN 37203
"Singer"

**Haley Joel Osment**
1420 Colina Drive
Glendale, CA 91208
"Actor"

**Cliff Osmond**
630 Bienvenida
Pacific Palisades, CA 90274
"Screenwriter"

**Donny Osmond**
P.O. Box 7122
Branson, MO 65616
"Singer"

**Ken Osmond**
9863 Wornom Avenue
Sunland, CA 91040
"Actor"

**Marie Osmond**
3325 N. University Avenue
Provo, UT 84604
"Singer, Actress"

**The Osmonds**
P.O. Box 7122
Branson, MO 65616
"Vocal Group"

**Jeff Osterhage**
210-D North Cordova
Burbank, CA 91505
"Actor"

**Gilbert O'Sullivan**
32 Willesden Lane, Kentishtown
London NW6 7ST ENGLAND
"Singer"

**Carre Otis**
550 North Larchmont Blvd.
Los Angeles, CA 90004
"Actress"

**Johnny Otis**
7105 Baker Lane
Sebastopol, CA 95472
"Singer, Guitarist"

**Annette O'Toole**
11936 Gorham Avenue #106
Los Angeles, CA 90049
"Actress"

**Peter O'Toole**
8 Baker Street
London W1M 1DA ENGLAND
"Actor"

**Merlene Ottey**
P.O. Box 120
Indianapolis, IN 46206
"Track & Field"

**Park Overall**
4843 Arcola Avenue
North Hollywood, CA 91601
"Actress"

**Paul Overstreet**
P.O. Box 320
Pregram, TN 37143
"Singer"

**Michael Ovitz**
9465 Wilshire Blvd. #510
Beverly Hills, CA 90212
"Talent Agent"

**Randy Owen**
Rt. #4
Ft. Payne, AL 35967
"Guitarist, Singer"

**Buck Owens**
3223 Sillect Avenue
Bakersfield, CA 93308
"Singer, Songwriter"

**Gary Owens**
18034 Ventura Blvd.
Encino, CA 91316
"Radio/TV Performer"

**Earl Owensby**
1 Motion Picture Blvd.
Shelby, NC 28152
"Director, Producer"

**Catherine Oxenberg**
9461 Chartville Blvd. #380
Beverly Hills, CA 90212
"Actress, Model"

**Frank Oz**
P.O. Box 20750
New York, NY 10023
"Puppeteer"

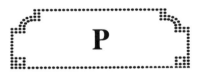

**Jack Paar**
9 Chateau Ridge Drive
Greenwich, CT 06830
"Ex-TV Show Host

**Pablo Cruise**
P.O. Box 770850
Orlando, FL 32877
"Rock & Roll Group"

**Judy Pace**
4139 Cloverdale
Los Angeles, CA 90008
"Actress"

**Al Pacino**
301 W. 57th Street #16
New York, NY 10019
"Actor"

**Ann Packer**
c/o Alfred A. Knopf, Inc.
201 East 50th Street
New York, NY 10022
"Author"

**Ex-Sen. Bob Packwood**
2201 Wisconsin Ave. NW #C-120
Washington, D.C. 20007
"Ex-Politician"

**Joanna Pacula**
1465 Lindacrest Drive
Beverly Hills, CA 90210
"Actress"

**Anita Page**
14840 Valerio Street
Van Nuys, CA 91405
"Actress"

**Bettie Page**
2641 South 53rd Street
Kansas City, KS 66106
"50's Pin-up Girl"

**Genevieve Page**
52 rue de Vaugirard
75004 Paris FRANCE
"Actress"

**Jimmy Page**
12 Oval Road
London NW1 7DH ENGLAND
"Guitarist"

**Patti Page**
404 Loma Larga drive
Solana Beach, CA 92075
"Singer"

**Debra Paget**
411 Karl Court
Houston, TX 77024
"Actress"

**Ashraf Pahlavi**
12 Avenue Montaigne
75016 Paris FRANCE
"Royalty"

**David Paich**
5323 Bellaire Avenue
No. Hollywood, CA 91607
"Composer, Conductor"

**Elaine Paige**
Arlon, Pinewood Road
Iver. Buckinghamshire
SL0 0NH ENGLAND
"Actress"

**Janis Paige**
1700 Rising Glen Road
Los Angeles, CA 90069
"Actress"

**Rev. Ian Paisley**
The Parsonage
17 Cyprus Avenue
Belfast BT5 5NT IRELAND
"Clergyman"

**Holly Palance**
2753 Roscomare
Los Angeles, CA 90077
"Actress"

**Jack Palance**
785 Tucker Road #G-206
Tehachapi, CA 93561
"Actor, Director"

**Ron Palillo**
1560 Broadway #1308
New York, NY 10036
"Actor"

**Michael Palin**
65-69 Shepard's Bush Green
London W12 8TX ENGLAND
"Actor, Writer"

**Arnold Palmer**
9000 Bay Hill Blvd.
Orlando, FL 32819
"Golfer"

**Betsy Palmer**
4040 Farmdale Avenue
Studio City, CA 91604
"Actress"

**Byron Palmer**
7044 Los Tilos Road
Los Angeles, CA 90068
"Actor"

**Gregg Palmer**
5726 Graves Avenue
Encino, CA 91316
"Actor"

**Gretchen Palmer**
15301 Ventura Blvd. #345
Sherman Oaks, CA 91403
"Actress"

**Jim Palmer**
530 Ocean Drive North
Juno Beach, FL 33408
"Ex-Baseball Player, Model"

**Peter Palmer**
216 Kingsway Drive
Temple Terrace, FL 33617
"Actor"

**Chazz Palminteri**
375 Greenwich St.
New York, NY 10013
"Actor"

**Gwyneth Paltrow**
8500 Wilshire Blvd. #700
Beverly Hils, CA 90212
"Actress"

**Leon E. Panetta**
100 Campus Center Bldg. 86E
CSU Monterey Bay
Seaside, CA 93955
"Former Goverment Offical"

**May Pang**
1619 Third Avenue #9D
New York, NY 10128
"John Lennon's ex-Mistress"

**Stuart Pankin**
9150 Wilshire Blvd. #350
Beverly Hills, CA 90212
"Actor"

**Joe Pantaliano**
600 Willow Avenue #3
Hoboken, NJ 07030
"Actor"

**Irene Papas**
Xenokratous 39
Athens-Kolanaki, GREECE
"Actress"

**Anna Paquin**
9465 Wilshire Blvd. #212
Beverly Hills, CA 90212
"Actress"

**Vanessa Paradis**
14 rue Lincoln
75008 Paris FRANCE
"Actress"

**Ara Paraseghian**
51767 Oakbrook Court
Granger, IN 46539
"Former College Coach"

**Jack Pardee**
P.O. Box 272
Grause, TX 77857
"Ex-Football Coach"

**Michael Pare**
15250 Ventura Blvd. #710
Sherman Oaks, CA 91403
"Actor"

**Gail Parent**
2001 Mandeville Canyon
Los Angeles, CA 90024
"Screenwriter"

**Judy Parfitt**
8383 Wilshire Blvd. #550
Beverly Hills, CA 90211
"Actress"

**Anne Parillaud**
20 rue Av. Rapp
F-75008 Paris FRANCE
"Actress"

**Johnny Paris**
195 Hannum Avenue
Rossford, OH 43460
"Singer"

**Ray Park**
P.O. Box 707
Renton, WA 98057
"Actor"

**Lara Parker**
P.O. Box 1254
Topanga, CA 90290
"Actress"

**Andrea Parker**
6250 Canoga Avenue
Woodland Hills, CA 91367
"Actress"

**Corey Parker**
10431 Scenario Lane
Los Angeles, CA 90077
"Actor"

**Dave Parker**
7131 Reading Road
Cincinnati, OH 45237
"Ex-Baseball Player"

**Eleanor Parker**
2195 La Paz Way
Palm Springs, CA 92262
"Actress"

**Fess Parker**
6200 Foxen Canyon Road
Los Olivos, CA 93441
"Actor"

**Jameson Parker**
1604 North Vista Avenue
Los Angeles, CA 90046
"Actor"

**Mary Louise Parker**
151 El Camino Drive
Beverly Hills, CA 90212
"Actress"

**Nathanial Parker**
10100 Santa Monica Blvd., #2500
Los Angeles, CA 90067
"Actor"

**Robert B. Parker**
94 Curtis Road
Bridgewater, CT 06752
"Author"

**Sarah Jessica Parker**
P.O. Box 69646
Los Angeles, CA 90069
"Actress"

**Suzy Parker**
770 Hot Springs Road
Santa Barbara, CA 93103
"Actress"

**Camilla Parker-Bowles**
St. James Palace
London SW1A 1BS ENGLAND
"Prince Charles' Friend"

**Heather Parkhurst**
8491 Sunset Blvd. #440
Los Angeles, CA 90069
"Actress"

**Michael Parkinson**
58 Queen Anne Street
London W1M 0DX ENGLAND
"Writer"

**Andrew Parks**
1830 Grace Avenue
Los Angeles, CA 90028
"Actor"

**Michael Parks**
1618 North Vine Street #614
Hollywood, CA 90028
"Actor"

**Rosa Parks**
65 Cadillac Square #2200
Detroit, MI 48206
"Mother of Civil Rights"

**Lee Roy Parnell**
P.O. Box 23451
Nashville, TN 37202
"Singer"

**Van Dyke Parks**
1801 Century Park E. #2400
Los Angeles, CA 90067
"Composer"

**Derek Parra**
P.O. Box 450639
Westlake, OH 44145
"Olympic Speedskater"

**Julie Parrish**
P.O. Box 247
Santa Monica, CA 90406
"Actress"

**Peter Parros**
P.O. Box 3055
West Orange, NJ 07052
"Actor"

**Estelle Parsons**
924 West End Avenue #T-5
New York, NY 10025
"Actress"

**Dolly Parton**
P.O. Box 150307
Nashville, TN 37215
"Singer, Actress"

**Stella Parton**
1906 Chet Atkins Place #502
Nashville, TN 37212
"Singer"

**Derek Partridge**
96 Broadway
Bexley Heath
Kent DA6 7DE ENGLAND
"Actor"

**Francoise Pascal**
89 Riverview Gardens
London SW12 ENGLAND
"Actress"

**Adrian Pasdar**
8942 Wilshire Blvd.
Beverly Hills, CA 90211
"Actor"

**Robert Pastorelli**
2751 Holly Ridge Drive
Los Angeles, CA 90068
"Actor"

**Sarah Paulson**
10390 Santa Monica Blvd. #300
West Los Angeles, CA 90025
"Actress"

**Michael Pate**
21 Bukdarra Road
Bellevue Hill 2023
AUSTRALIA
"Actor"

**Joe Paterno**
830 McKee Street
State College, PA 16803
"College Football Coach"

**Mandy Patinkin**
200 West 90th Street
New York, NY 10024
"Actress"

**Will Patton**
520 Washington Blvd. #903
Marina Del Rey, CA 90292
"Actor"

**Jason Patric**
112 S. Almont Drive
Los Angeles, CA 90048
"Actor"

**Butch Patrick**
302 Bluepoint Road
Holtsville, NY 11742
"Actor"

**Robert Patrick**
1122 S. Robertson Blvd. #15
Los Angeles, CA 90035
"Playwright"

**Floyd Patterson**
Springtown Road
P.O. Box 336
New Paltz, NY 12561
"Boxer"

**Lorna Patterson**
23852 Pacific Coast Hwy. #355
Malibu, CA 90265
"Actress"

**Neva Patterson**
2498 Maneville Canyon Road
Los Angeles, CA 90049
"Actress"

**Sandi Patty**
P.O. Box 2940
Anderson, IN 46018
"Singer"

**Adrian Paul**
P.O. Box 4593
North Hollywood, CA 91617
"Actor"

**Alexandra Paul**
1505 - 10th Street
Santa Monica, CA 90401
"Actress"

**Don Michael Paul**
606 N. Larchmont Blvd. #309
Los Angeles, CA 90004
"Actor"

**Les Paul**
78 Deerhaven Road
Mahwah, NJ 07430
"Guitarist"

**Jane Pauley**
30 Rockefeller Plaza
New York, NY 10012
"TV Show Host"

**Albert Paulsen**
733 N. Seward Street PH
Los Angeles, CA 90038
"Actor"

**Marisa Pavan**
4 Allee des Borouillards
F-75018 Paris, FRANCE
"Actress"

**Corey Paven**
2515 McKinney #930, Box 10
Dallas, TX 75201
"Golfer"

**Luciano Pavarotti**
Staatsoper, Oprnring 2
1010 Vienna AUSTRIA
"Tenor"

**Ria Pavia**
3500 West Olive Avenue, #1400
Burbank, CA 91505
"Actress"

**Bill Paxton**
9701 Wilshire Blvd. 10th Floor
Beverly Hills, CA 90212
"Actor"

**Johnny Paycheck**
P.O. Box 916
Hendersonville, TN 37077
"Singer"

**David Paymer**
1506 Pacific Street
Santa Monica, CA 90405
"Actor"

**Freda Payne**
1995 Broadway #501
New York, NY 10023
"Singer"

**Scherie Payne**
433 N. Camden Drive #400
Beverly Hills, CA 90210
"Singer"

**Amanda Pays**
11075 Santa Monica Blvd. #150
Los Angeles, CA 90025
"Actress, Model"

**Vinnie Pazienda**
64 Waterman Avenue
Cranston, RI 02910
"Boxer"

**Peaches & Herb**
1560 Broadway #1308
New York, NY 10036
"Music Duo"

**E. J. Peaker**
4935 Densmore Avenue
Encino, CA 91436
"Actress"

**Guy Pearce**
Box 478
Kings Cross
NSW 2011 AUSTRALIA
"Actor"

**Pearl Jam**
525 Broadway #500
New York, NY 10012
"Rock & Roll Group"

**Drew Pearson**
3721 Mt. Vernon Way
Plano, TX 75052
"Ex-Football Player"

**Durk Pearson**
P.O. Box 1067
Hollywood, FL 33022
"Scientist, Author"

**Nia Peeples**
P.O. Box 21833
Waco, TX 76702
"Actress"

**Larry Peerce**
9200 Sunset Blvd. #900
Los Angeles, CA 90069
"Actor"

**Amanda Peet**
955 South Carrilo Drive #300
Los Angeles, CA 90048
"Actress"

**Rodney Peete**
9171 Wilshire Blvd. #508
Beverly Hills, CA 90210
"Football Player"

**I. M. Pei**
88 Pine Street
New York, NY 10005
"Architect"

**Ashley Peldon**
P.O. Box 57593
Sherman Oaks, CA 91403
"Actress"

**Courtney Peldon**
P.O. Box 57593
Sherman Oaks, CA 91403
"Actress"

**Pele**
Rua Riachuelo 121-3
Andar-Fones 34-163335
Santos SP BRAZIL
"Soccer Player"

**Lisa Pelikan**
P.O. Box 57593
Sherman Oaks, CA 91403
"Actress"

**Ex-Sen. Claybourne Pell**
3425 Prospect Street, NW
Washington, D.C. 20007
"Ex-Politician"

**Rep. Nancy Pelosi**
2438 Rayburn House Office Bldg.
Washington, DC 20515
"Politician"

**Meeno Peluce**
2713 North Keystone
Burbank, CA 91504
"Actor"

**Elizabeth Pena**
P.O. Box 904
Topanga, CA 90290
"Actress"

**Federico Pena**
3517 Sterling Avenue
Alexandria, VA 22304
"ex-Government Official"

**Teddy Pendergrass**
1505 Flat Rock Road
Narberth, PA 19072
"Singer, Songwriter"

**Austin Pendleton**
155 East 76th Street
New York, NY 10021
"Comedian"

**Thao Penghlis**
7187 Macapa Drive
Los Angeles, CA 90068
"Actor"

**The Penguins**
19948 Mayall Street
Chatsworth, CA 91311
"Vocal Group"

**Susan Penhaligon**
109 Jermyn Street
London SW1 ENGLAND
"Actress"

**Ce Ce Peniston**
250 West 57th Street #821
New York, NY 10107
"Singer"

**Penn & Teller**
4132 South Rainbow Blvd., #377
Las Vegas, NV 89103
"Entertainment Duo"

**Chris Penn**
9560 Wilshire Blvd. #516
Beverly Hills, CA 90212
"Actor"

**Sean Penn**
2049 Century Park East #2500
Los Angeles, CA 90067
"Actor"

**Jonathan Penner**
8383 Wilshire Blvd. #550
Beverly Hills, CA 90211
"Actor"

**Ann Pennington**
701 N. Oakhurst Drive
Beverly Hills, CA 90210
"Actress, Model"

**Janice Pennington**
433 N. Camden Drive #600
Beverly Hills, CA 90210
"Model, Actress"

**Michael Pennington**
41 Marlborough Hill
London NW8 ENGLAND
"Actor"

**Joe Penny**
10453 Sarah
North Hollywood, CA 91602
"Actor"

**Sidney Penny**
6894 Parson Trail
Tujunga, CA 91042
"Actress"

**Roger Penske**
13400 Outer Drive West
Detroit, MI 48239
"Auto Racing Executive"

**Willie Pep**
Boxing Hall of Fame
1 Hall of Fame Drive
Canastota, NY 13032
"Boxer"

**Joe Pepitone**
32 Lois Lane
Farmingdale, NY 11735
"Ex-Baseball Player"

**Charles Percy**
1691-34th Street NW
Washington, DC 20007
"Ex-Senator"

**Shimon Peres**
10 Hayarkon Street
Box 3263
Tel Aviv 3263 ISRAEL
"Politician"

**Manny Perez**
648 Broadway #912
New York, NY 10012
"Actor"

**Rosie Perez**
112 South Almont Drive
Los Angeles, CA 90048
"Actress"

**Vincent Perez**
20 av. Rapp
F-75007 Paris FRANCE
"Actor"

**Elizabeth Perkins**
9150 Wilshire Blvd. #350
Beverly Hills, CA 90212
"Actress"

**Millie Perkins**
2511 Canyon Drive
Los Angeles, CA 90068
"Actress"

**Rhea Perlman**
P.O. Box 491246
Los Angeles, CA 90049
"Actress"

**Ron Perlman**
275 South Beverly Drive #215
Beverly Hills, CA 90212
"Actress"

**Ytzhak Pearlman**
c/o IMG
825 - 7th Avenue
New York, NY 10019
"Violinist"

**Mme. Isabel Peron**
Moreto 3
Los Jeronimos, E-28014
Madrid SPAIN
"Politician"

**H. Ross Perot**
1700 Lakeside Square
Dallas, TX 75251
"Data Executive"

**Gigi Perreau**
5841 Cantaloupe Avenue
Van Nuys, CA 91401
"Actress"

**Valerie Perrine**
Via Toscana 1
I-00187 Rome ITALY
"Actress, Model"

**Barbara Perry**
6926 La Presa Drive
Los Angeles, CA 90068
"Actress"

**Felton Perry**
540 South St. Andrews Place
Suite #5
Los Angeles, CA 90020
"Actor"

**Gaylord Perry**
P.O. Box 489
Spruce Pine, NC 28777
"Ex-Baseball Player"

**John Bennett Perry**
606 N. Larchmont Blvd. #309
Los Angeles, CA 90004
"Actor"

**Luke Perry**
137 N. Larchmont Blvd. #117
Los Angeles, CA 90004
"Actor"

**Matthew Perry**
1122 S. Robertson Blvd. #15
Los Angeles, CA 90035
"Actor"

**Steve Perry**
14575 SW Village Lane
Beaverton, OR 97007
"Singer, Composer"

**Willaim "Refridgerator" Perry**
1463 Edgefield Hwy.
Aiken, SC 29801
"Football Player"

**Nehemiah Persoff**
5847 Tampa Avenue
Tarzana, CA 91356
"Actor"

**The Persuaders**
225 West 57th Street, #500
New York, NY 10019
"R & B Group"

**Bill Pertwee**
25 Whitehall
London SW1A 2BS ENGLAND
"Actor"

**Joe Pesci**
1501 Broadway @43rd St. #2600
New York, NY 10036
"Actor"

**Donna Pescow**
6267 Paseo Canyon Drive
Malibu, CA 90265
"Actress"

**Pet Shop Boys**
Box 102, Stanmore
Middlesex HA7 2PY ENGLAND
"Rock & Roll Group"

**Peter, Paul & Mary**
121 Mt. Herman Way
Ocean Grove, NJ 07756
"Vocal Trio"

**Bernadette Peters**
323 West 80th Street
New York, NY 10024
"Actress"

**Brock Peters**
1420 Rising Glen Road
Los Angeles, CA 90069
"Actor, Writer, Director"

**House Peters Junior**
Motion Pictures Home
23388 Mulholland Drive
Woodland Hills, CA 91364
"Actor"

**Jon Peters**
630 Siena Way
Los Angeles, CA 90077
"Film Producer"

**Mike Peters**
1269 - 1st Street #8
Sarasota, FL 34236
"Cartoonist"

**Pat Petersen**
1634 Veteran Avenue
Los Angeles, CA 90025
"Actor"

**Paul Petersen**
14530 Denker Avenue
Gardena, CA 90247
"Actor"

**Wolfgang Petersen**
9830 Wilshire Blvd.
Beverly Hills, CA 90212
"Film Director"

**Gervase Peterson**
20 Hornblende Lane
Willingboro, NJ 08046
"CBS Survivor Show Contestant"

**Oscar Peterson**
2421 Hammond Road
Mississagua, Ontario
L5K 1T3 CANADA
"Musician"

**Dan Petry**
1808 Cartlen Drive
Placentia, CA 92670
"Ex-Baseball Player"

**Daniel Petrie**
13201 Haney Place
Los Angeles, CA 90049
"TV Director"

**Brittany Petros**
P.O. Box 27273
Los Angeles, CA 90027
"Appeared on Big Brother Show"

**Kyle Petty**
11 Branson Mill Road
Randleman, NC 27317
"Race Car Driver"

**Lori Petty**
4001 W. Alameda Ave. #301
Burbank, CA 91505
"Actress"

**Richard Petty**
311 Branson Mill Road, Box 86
Randleman, NC 27317
"Race Car Driver"

**Tom Petty**
1926 Contra Costa Blvd. #201
Pleasant Hill, CA 94523
"Rock & Roll Singer"

**Penny Peyser**
22039 Alizondo Drive
Woodland Hills, CA 91367
"Actress"

**Michelle Pfeiffer**
8500 Wilshire Blvd. #700
Beverly Hills, CA 90211
"Actress"

**Jo Ann Pflug**
2865 Lenox Road NE #509
Atlanta, GA 30324
"Actress"

**Dr. Phil**
555 Melrose Avenue
Mae West Bldg. 132
Los Angeles, CA 90038
"Advice Giver"

**Regis Philbin**
101 W. 67th Street #51A
New York, NY 10023
"TV Show Host"

**HRH Prince Philip**
Duke of Edinburgh
Buckingham Palace
London SW1 ENGLAND
"Royalty"

**Ryan Phillippe**
9150 Wilshire Blvd. #350
Beverly Hills, CA 90212
"Actor"

**Ethan Phillips**
4212 McFarlane Avenue
Burbank, CA 91505
"Actor"

**Gina Phillips**
6100 Wilshire Blvd. #1170
Los Angeles, CA 90048
"Actress"

**Jeffrey Phillips**
8436 West Thrid Street #740
Los Angeles, CA 90048
"Trombonist"

**Joseph C. Phillips**
8730 Sunset Blvd. #480
Los Angeles, CA 90069
"Actor"

**Julianne Phillips**
1505 - 10th Street
Santa Monica, CA 90401
"Actress, Model"

**Lou Diamond Phillips**
1122 S. Robertson Blvd. #15
Los Angeles, CA 90035
"Actor"

**Mackenzie Phillips**
805 Third Avenue #2900
New York, NY 10022
"Actress, Singer"

**Michelle Phillips**
4350 Berryman Avenue #4
Los Angeles, CA 90035
"Actress, Singer"

**Sam Phillips**
12424 Wilshire Blvd. #1000
Los Angeles, CA 90025
"Singer"

**Sian Phillips**
14 Petherton Road
London N5 ENGLAND
"Actress"

**Stone Phillips**
30 Rockefeller Plaza
New York, NY 10112
"News Journalist"

**Joaquin (Leaf) Phoenix**
1180 South Beverly Drive #608
Los Angeles, CA 90035

**Mike Piazza**
Box 864, Oakwood Lane
Valley Forge, PA 19481
"Baseball Player"

**Robert Picardo**
6500 Wilshire Blvd. #2200
Los Angeles, CA 90048
"Actor"

**Michel Piccoli**
11 rue de Lions St. Paul
4e Paris, FRANCE
"Actor"

**Paul Picerni**
P.O. Box 572257
Tarzana, CA 91356
"Actor"

**James Pickens Jr.**
8436 West Third Street #740
Los Angeles, CA 90048
"Actor"

**Donald Pickering**
Back Court
Manor House
Eastleach, Glos. ENGLAND
"Actor"

**Cindy Pickett**
662 North Palmas Avenue #305
Los Angeles, CA 90004
"Actress"

**Wilson Pickett**
P.O. Box 770850
Orlando, FL 32877
"R & B Singer"

**Vivian Pickles**
91 Regent Street
London W1R 8RU ENGLAND
"Actress"

**Ronald Pickup**
54 Crouch Hall Road
London N8 ENGLAND
"Actor"

**David Hyde Pierce**
4724 Cromwell Avenue
Los Angeles, CA 90027
"Actor"

**Mary Pierce**
525 Plymouth Road #317
Plymouth Meeting, PA 19462
"Tennis Player"

**Eric Pierpoint**
2199 Topanga Skyline Drive
Topanga, CA 90290
"Actor"

**Jimmy Piersall**
1105 Oakview Drive
Wheaton, IL 60187
"Ex-Baseball Player"

**Amy Pietz**
P.O. Box 81
Oak Creek, WI 53154
"Actress"

**Tim Pigott-Smith**
34-43 Russell Street
London WC2B 5HA ENGLAND
"Actor"

**Mitch Pileggi**
1122 S. Robertson Blvd. #15
Los Angeles, CA 90035
"Actor"

**Ray Pillow**
2802 Columbine Place
Nashville, TN 37204
"Singer"

**Bronson Pinchot**
9150 Wilshire Blvd. #350
Beverly Hills, CA 90212
"Actor"

**Philip Pine**
7034 Costello Avenue
Van Nuys, CA 91405
"Actor"

**Robert Pine**
4212 Ben Avenue
Studio City, CA 91604
"Actor, Director"

**Lou Piniella**
1005 Taray De Avila
Tampa, FL 33613
"Baseball Manager"

**Jada Pinkett-Smith**
9701 Wilshire Blvd., 10th Floor
Beverly Hills, CA 90212
"Actress"

**Pink Floyd**
370 City Road Islington
London W11 ENGLAND
"Rock & Roll Group"

**Vada Pinson**
710 31st Street
Oakland, CA 94609
"Baseball Player"

**Danny Pintauro**
5757 Wilshire Blvd. #473
Los Angeles, CA 90036
"Actor"

**Sir Harold Pinter**
2 St. Charles Place
London W10 6EG ENGLAND
"Screenwriter"

**Rowdy Roddy Piper**
18645 SW Farmington Rd. PMB
312
Aloha, OR 97007
"Wrestler"

**Scottie Pippen**
700 N.E. Multnomah Street #950
Portland, OR 97232
"Basketball Player"

**Joe Piscopo**
P.O. Box 258
Bernardsville, NJ 07924
"Actor"

**Marie-France Pisier**
3, Quai Malaquais
75006 Paris, FRANCE
"Actress"

**Dean Pitchford**
1701 Queens Road
Los Angeles, CA 90069
"Lyricist, Producer"

**Maria Pitillo**
8912 Burton Way
Beverly Hills, CA 90211
"Actress"

**Gene Pitney**
6201 - 39th Avenue
Kenosha, WI 53142
"Singer"

**Brad Pitt**
9150 Wilshire Blvd. #350
Beverly Hills, CA 90212
"Actor"

**Jeremy Pivan**
9701 Wilshire Blvd., 10th Floor
Beverly Hills, CA 90212
"Actor"

**Mary Kay Place**
9911 W. Pico Blvd. #PH-A
Los Angeles, CA 90035
"Actress, Writer"

**Robert Plant**
12 Oval Road
London NW1 7DH ENGLAND
"Singer, Songwriter"

**Platinum Blonde**
P.O. Box 1223, Station F.
Toronto, Ontario
M4Y 2T8 CANADA
"Rock & Roll Group"

**Howard Platt**
9200 Sunset Blvd. #1130
Los Angeles, CA 90069
"Actor"

**Oliver Platt**
9460 Wilshire Blvd. #700
Beverly Hills, CA 90212
"Actor"

**The Platters**
2756 N. Green Valley Parkway #449
Las Vegas, NV 89014
"Vocal Group"

**Gary Player**
Box 785629
Sandton 2146 SOUTH AFRICA
"Golfer"

**John Pleshette**
2643 Creston Drive
Los Angeles, CA 90068
"Actor, Writer"

**Suzanne Pleshette**
10375 Wilshire Blvd. #5B
Los Angeles, CA 90024
"Actress"

**George Plimpton**
541 East 72nd Street
New York, NY 10021
"Author"

**Martha Plimpton**
9465 Wilshire Blvd. #600
Beverly Hills, CA 90211
"Model, Actress"

**Joan Plowright**
76 Oxford Street
London W1R 1RB ENGLAND
"Actress"

**Eve Plumb**
9200 Sunset Blvd. #1130
Los Angeles, CA 90069
"Actress"

**Christopher Plummer**
49 Wampum Hill Road
Weston, CT 06883
"Actor"

**Scotty Plummer**
909 Parkview Avenue
Lodi, CA 95240
"Singer"

**Jim Plunkett**
51 Kilroy Way
Atherton, CA 94025
"Ex-Football Player"

**Rosanna Podesta**
Via Bartolemeo Ammanatti 8
00187 Rome, ITALY
"Actress"

**Sylvia Poggioli**
c/o National Public Radio
2025 "M" Street NW
Washington, DC 20036
"News Correspondent"

**Buster Poindexter**
9200 Sunset Blvd. #900
Los Angeles, CA 90069
"Singer"

**Anita Pointer**
12060 Crest Court
Beverly Hills, CA 90210
"Singer"

**Priscilla Pointer**
151 El Camino Drive
Beverly Hills, CA 90211
"Actress"

**Ruth Pointer**
1900 Avenue of the Stars #1640
Los Angeles, CA 90067
"Singer"

**Pointer Sisters**
1900 Avenue of the Stars, #1640
Los Angeles, CA 90067
"Vocal Trio"

**Sydney Poitier**
9255 Doheny Road
Los Angeles, CA 90069
"Actor, Writer, Producer"

**Roman Polanski**
201 rue de Faubourg-St.-Honore
75008 Paris, FRANCE
"Actor, Writer, Director"

**The Police**
194 Kensington Park Road
London W11 2ES ENGLAND
"Rock & Roll Group"

**Sydney Pollack**
9830 Wilshire Blvd.
Beverly Hills, CA 90212
"Writer, Producer"

**Cheryl Pollak**
275 S. Beverly Drive #215
Beverly Hills, CA 90212
"Actress"

**Tracy Pollan**
62 Chelsea Piers #303
New York, NY 10011
"Actress"

**Jonathan Pollard**
Federal Reformatory
Marion, IL 62959
"Israeli Spy, Traitor"

**Michael J. Pollard**
520 S. Burnside Avenue #12-A
Los Angeles, CA 90036
"Actor"

**LuAnne Ponce**
3500 West Olive Avenue, #1400
Burbank, CA 91505
"Actress"

**Carlo Ponti**
6 rue Charles Bonnet
CH-1206 Geneve SWITZERLAND
"Film Producer"

**Iggy Pop**
307 - 7th Avenue #807
New York, NY 10001
"Singer"

**Paulina Porizkova**
18 E. 53rd Street #1400
New York, NY 10022
"Model"

**Jean Porter**
3945 Westfall Drive
Encino, CA 91436
"Actress"

**Marina Oswald Porter**
1850 WFM Road 550
Rockwell, TX 75087
"Widow of Lee Harvey Oswald"

**Natalie Portman**
9465 Wilshire Blvd.
Beverly Hills, CA 90212
"Actress"

**Parker Posey**
1216 North 6th Avenue
Laurel, MS 39440
"Actress"

**Vladimir Posner**
1125-16th Street N.W.
Washington, DC 20036
"Russian Spokesman"

**Markie Post**
10153 1/2 Riverside Drive
Suite #333
Toluca Lake, CA 91602
"Actress"

**Tom Poston**
1 North Venice Blvd. #106
Venice, CA 90291
"Actor"

**Carol Potter**
151 El Camino Drive
Beverly Hills, CA 90210
"Actress"

**Annie Potts**
P.O. Box 29400
Los Angeles, CA 90029
"Actress"

**Cliff Potts**
8383 Wilshire Blvd. #954
Beverly Hills, CA 90211
"Actor"

**CCH Pounder**
121 North San Vicente Blvd.
Beverly Hills, CA 90211
"Actor"

**Paula Poundstone**
1223 Broadway #162
Santa Monica, CA 90404
"Comedienne, TV Show Host"

**Gen. Colin L. Powell**
1317 Ballantra Farm Drive
McLean, VA 22101
"Ex-Military Leader"

**Jane Powell**
150 West End Avenue #26C
New York, NY 10023
"Actress"

**Randolph Powell**
2644 highland Avenue
Santa Monica, CA 90405
"Actor"

**Robert Powell**
10 Pond Place
London SW3 6QJ ENGLAND
"Actor"

**Susan Powell**
6333 Bryn Mawr Drive
Los Angeles, CA 90068
"Actress"

**Romina Power**
I-72020 Cellino San Marco
(Brindise) ITALY
"Actress"

**Udana Power**
1962 Beachwood Drive #202
Los Angeles, CA 90068
"Actress"

**Mala Powers**
10543 Valley Spring Lane
North Hollywood, CA 91602
"Actress"

**Stefanie Powers**
P.O. Box 67981
Los Angeles, CA 90067
"Actress"

**Michael Praed**
c/o Marathon Entertainment
89 Fifth Avenue, 10th Floor
New York, NY 10003
"Actor"

**Laurie Prange**
1519 Sargent Place
Los Angeles, CA 90026
"Actress"

**Joan Prather**
31647 Sea Level Drive
Malibu, CA 90265
"Actress"

**Paula Prentiss**
P.O. Box 57593
Sherman oaks, CA 91403
"Actress"

**Micheline Presle**
6 rue Antoine Dubois
F 75006 Paris, FRANCE
"Actress"

**Lisa-Marie Presley**
1167 Summit Drive
Beverly Hills, CA 90210
"Elvis' Daughter"

**Priscilla Presley**
1167 Summit Drive
Beverly Hills, CA 90210
"Actress, Model"

**ex-Sen. Larry Pressler**
2812 Davis Avenue
Alexandria, VA 22302
"Politician"

**Lawrence Pressman**
15033 Encanto Drive
Sherman Oaks, CA 91403
"Actor"

**Billy Preston**
5410 West 61st Street
Los Angeles, CA 90056
"Singer"

**Kelly Preston**
15821 Ventura Blvd. #460
Encino, CA 91436
"Actress"

**The Pretenders**
24 Ives Street
London SW3 2ND ENGLAND
"Vocal Group"

**Andre Previn**
180 West 80th Street #206
New York, NY 10024
"Composer, Conductor"

**Francoise Previne**
37 rue de Ponthieu
F-75008 Paris FRANCE
"Actor"

**Leontyne Price**
9 Van Dam Street
New York, NY 10003
"Soprano"

**Lloyd Price**
95 Horseshoe Hill Road
Pound Ridge, NY 10576
"Actor"

**Marc Price**
8444 Magnolia Drive
Los Angeles, CA 90046
"Actor"

**Mark Price**
2923 Streetsboro Road
Richfield, OH 44286
"Basketball Player"

**Nick Price**
900 S. US Hwy. 1 #105
Jupiter, FL 33477
"Golfer"

**Ray Price**
1031 East Battlefield Street #224
Springfield, MO 65807
"Singer"

**Charlie Pride**
P.O. Box 670507
Dallas, TX 75367
"Singer"

**Maxi Priest**
853 Broadway #711
New York, NY 10003
"Reggae Singer"

**Pat Priest**
13775-A Mono Way #220
Sonora, CA 95370
"Actor"

**Barry Primus**
2735 Creston Drive
Los Angeles, CA 90068
"Actor, Director"

**Prince**
7801 Audubon Road
Chanhassen, MN 55317
"Singer, Songwriter, Actor"

**Clayton Prince**
3500 West Olive Avenue, #1400
Burbank, CA 91505
"Actor"

**Jonathan Prince**
526 North Camden Drive
Beverly Hills, CA 90210
"Actor"

**Victoria Principal**
120 S. Spalding Drive #205
Beverly Hills, CA 90212
"Actress"

**Andrew Prine**
3364 Longridge Avenue
Sherman Oaks, CA 91403
"Actor"

**Joan Pringle**
3500 West Olive #1400
Burbank, CA 91505
"Actress"

**Freddie Prinz Jr.**
8942 Wilshire Blvd.
Beverly Hills, CA 90211
"Actor"

**Jurgen Prochnow**
8942 Wilshire Blvd.
Beverly Hills, CA 90211
"Actor"

**The Proclaimers**
P.O. Box 309
Edinburgh EH9 1JE SCOTLAND
"Rock & Roll Group"

**Ronnie Prophet**
1227 Saxon Drive
Nashville, TN 37215
"Singer, Songwriter"

**Paul Provenza**
10921 Wilshire Blvd. #1009
Los Angeles, CA 90024
"Actor"

**Dorothy Provine**
8832 Ferncliff N.E.
Bainbridge Island, WA 98110
"Actress"

**Dave Prowse**
P.O. Box 1181
Croydon CR9 7BQ ENGLAND
"Actor"

**Chef Paul Prudhomme**
2424 Chartres
New Orleans, LA 70117
"Famous Chef"

**Jeanne Pruett**
1906 Chet Atkins Place #502
Nashville, TN 37212
"Singer"

**Jonathan Pryce**
46 Albermarle Street
London W1X 4PP ENGLAND
"Actor"

**Richard Pryor**
16847 Bosque Drive
Encino, CA 91436
"Actor, Comedian"

**Public Enemy**
151 El Camino Drive
Beverly Hills, CA 90212
"Rap Group"

**Wolfgang Puck**
805 North Sierra Drive
Beverly Hills, CA 91210
"Chef, Restaurateur"

**Gary Puckett**
10710 Seminoele Blvd. 33
Seminoel, FL 33778
"Singer, Songwriter"

**Tommy Puett**
16621 Cerulean Court
Chino Hills, CA 91709
"Actor"

**Keshia Knight Pulliam**
P.O. Box 866
Teaneck, NJ 07666
"Actress"

**Bill Pullman**
9560 Wilshire Blvd. #500
Beverly Hills, CA 90212
"Actor"

**Liselotte Pulver**
Villa Bip, Perroy
Kanton Vandois SWITZERLAND
"Actress"

**Dr. Bernard Punsley**
1415 Granvia Altemeia
Rancho Palos Verdes, CA 90274
"Actor"

**Lee Purcell**
3300 Foothill Blvd
P.O. Box 1258
La Crescenta, CA 91224
"Actress"

**Sarah Purcell**
6525 Esplanada Street
Playa del Rey, CA 90293
"Actress"

**Linda Purl**
13775-A Mono Way #220
Sonora, CA 95370
"Actress"

**John Putch**
3972 Sunswept Drive
Studio City, CA 91604
"Actor"

**President Vladimir Putin**
Congress of People's Deputies
Federal Republic Bldg.
Moscow, RUSSIA
"President of Russia"

**Thomas Pynchon**
34 Beacon Street
Boston, MA 02108
"Author"

**Natasha Pyne**
43A Princess Road
Regent's Park
London NW1 8JS ENGLAND
"Actress"

**Monty Python**
34 Thistlewaite Road
London E5 0QQ ENGLAND
"Comedy Group"

**Dennis Quaid**
P.O. Box 742625
Houston, TX 77274
"Actor"

**Randy Quaid**
10100 Santa monica Blvd. #2500
Los Angeles, CA 90067
"Actor"

**Megan Quann**
One Olympic Plazza
Colorado Springs, CO 80909
"Olympic Gold Medalist Swimmer"

**Robert Quarry**
11032 Moorpark St. #A-3
No. Hollywood, CA 91602
"Actor"

**Suzi Quatro**
P.O. Box 770850
Orlando, FL 32877
"Singer"

**Anna Quayle**
4 Guilford Road, Brighton
Sussex ENGLAND
"Actress"

**Dan Quayle**
2425 East Camelback Road #1080
Phoenix, AZ 85016
"Ex-Vice President U.S.A."

**Marilyn Tucker-Quayle**
2425 East Camelback Road #1080
Pheonix, AZ 85016
"Wife of Dan Quayle"

**Queen**
9565 Wilshire Blvd. #505
Beverly Hills, CA 90212
"Rock & Roll Group"

**Quiet Riot**
2002 Hogback Road #20
Ann Arbor, MI 48105
"Rock & Roll Group"

**Joan Quigley**
1055 California Street #14
San Francisco, CA 94108
"Astrologer"

**Linnea Quigley**
2608-1 N. Ocean Blvd. #126
Pompano Beach, CA 33062
"Actress, Model"

**Denis Quilley**
22 Willow Road
London NW3 ENGLAND
"Actor, Singer"

**Kathleen Quinlan**
P.O. Box 861
Rockaway, OR 97136
"Actress"

**Aldan Quinn**
151 El Camino Drive
Beverly Hills, CA 90069
"Actor"

**Anthony Quinn**
420 Poppasquash Road
Bristol, RI 02809
"Actor, Director"

**Carmel Quinn**
456 Park Avenue
Leonia, NJ 01605
"Singer, Comedienne, Storyteller"

**Anthony Tyler Quinn**
8949 Sunset Blvd. #201
Los Angeles, CA 90069
"Actor"

**Francesco Quinn**
3910 Woodcliff Road
Sherman Oaks, CA 91403
"Actor"

**Sally Quinn**
3014 "N" Street NW
Washington, DC 20007
"Journalist"

**Brandon Quinton**
9899 Santa Monica Blvd., PBM 202
Beverly Hills, CA 90212
"Survivor Show Contestan"

**Robin Quivers**
c/o WXRX
40 West 57 Street #1400
New York, NY 10019
"Talk Show Personality"

# R

**Alan Rachins**
1274 Capri
Pacific Palisades, CA 90272
"Actor, Writer, Director"

**Cassidy Rae**
1801 Ave. of the Stars #902
Los Angeles, CA 90067
"Actress"

**Charlotte Rae**
8721 Sunset Blvd. #210
Los Angeles, CA 90069
"Actress"

**Deborah Raffin**
301 North Canon Drive #214
Beverly Hills, CA 90210
"Actress"

**Kaye Lani Rae Rafko**
4932 Frary Lane
Monroe, MI 48161
"Former Miss America"

**Hashemi Rafsanjani**
Ali Shariati Avenue
Tehran IRAN
"President of Iran"

**Gerald Rafshoon**
3028 "Q" Street N.W.
Washington, DC 20006
"Former Presidential Aide"

**John S. Ragin**
5706 Briarcliff Road
Los Angeles, CA 90068
"Actor"

**Lisa Raggio**
9460 Wilshire Blvd. #300
Beverly Hills, CA 90212
"Actress"

**Bobby Rahal**
5 New Albany Farms Road
New Albany, OH 43054
"Race Car Driver"

**Steve Railsback**
11684 Ventura Blvd. #581
Studio City, CA 91604
"Actor"

**Ted Raimi**
252 North Larchmont Blvd. #200
Los Angeles, CA 90004
"Actor"

**Gillian Raine**
13 Billing Road
London SW10 ENGLAND
"Actress"

**Luise Rainer**
54 Eaton Mews North
London SW1 XAS ENGLAND
"Actress"

**Ford Rainey**
3821 Carbon Canyon
Malibu, CA 90265
"Actor"

**Bonnie Raitt**
3575 Cahuenga Blvd. W. #450
Los Angeles, CA 90068
"Singer"

**John Raitt**
1164 Napoli Drive
Pacific Palisades, CA 90272
"Actor"

**Sheryl Lee Ralph**
938 South Longwood
Los Angeles, CA 90019
"Actress"

**Vera Hruba Ralston**
4121 Crecienta Drive
Santa Barbara, CA 93110
"Actress"

**Raul Ramirez**
Avenida Ruiz
65 Sur Ensenda
Baja California, MEXICO
"Tennis Player"

**Harold Ramis**
160 Euclid Avenue
Glencoe, IL 60022
"Actor, Writer, Director"

**Pres. Fidel Ramos**
Malacanang Palace
Manila PHILIPPINES
"Politician"

**Charlotte Rampling**
1 Ave. Emile Augier
F-78290 Croissy-Sur Seine
FRANCE
"Actress"

**John & Patsy Ramsey**
100 Peachtree Street #2140
Atlanta, GA 30303
"Suspected in Daughter's Death"

**Tony Randall**
1 West 81st Street #6-D
New York, NY 10024
"Actor, Director"

**Josh Randall**
8730 Sunset Blvd. #490
Los Angeles, CA 90069
"Actor"

**Teddy Randazzo**
5254 Oak Island Road
Orlando, FL 32809
"Singer"

**Theresa Randle**
1018 Meadowbrook Avenue
Los Angeles, CA 90019
"Actress"

**Boots Randolph**
4798 Lickton Pike
White Creek, TN 37189
"Saxophonist"

**Jane Randolph**
875 Comstock Avenue
Los Angeles, CA 90024
"Actress"

**John Randolph**
1850 North Whitley Place
Los Angeles, CA 90028
"Actor"

**Joyce Randolph**
295 Central Park West #18-A
New York, NY 10024
"Actress"

**Willie Randolph**
648 Juniper Place
Franklin Lakes, NJ 07417
"Ex-Baseball Player"

**Sue Raney**
P.O. Box 2040
New York, NY 10101
"Singer"

**Rep. Charles B. Rangel (NY)**
House Rayburn Bldg. #2354
Washington, DC 20515
"Politician"

**Kenny Rankin**
9255 Sunset Blvd. #804
Los Angeles, CA 90069
"Singer, Songwriter"

**Prunella Ransome**
59 Frith Street
London W1 ENGLAND
"Actress"

**Sally Jessy Raphael**
249 Quaker Hill Road
Pawling, NY 12564
"TV Show Host"

**David Rasche**
121 North San Vicente Blvd.
Beverly Hills, CA 90211
"Actor"

**Ahmad Rashad**
450 Harmon Meadow Blvd.
Secaucus, NJ 07094
"Ex-Football Player, Sportcaster"

**Phylicia Rashad**
25 Magnolia Avenue
Mt. Vernon, NY 10553
"Actress"

**Dan Rather**
524 West 57th Street
New York, NY 10019
"Newscaster"

**RATT**
1818 Illion Street
San Diego, CA 92110
Rock & Roll Group"

**John Ratzenberger**
9255 Sunset Blvd. #1010
Los Angeles, CA 90069
"Actor"

**Eddy Raven**
1071 Bradley Road
Gallatin, TN 37066
"Singer, Songwriter"

**Betsy Rawls**
100 International Golf Drive
Daytona Beach, FL 32124
"Golfer"

**Lou Rawls**
109 Fremont Place
Los Angeles, CA 90005
"Singer"

**Marguerite Ray**
1329 North Vista #106
Los Angeles, CA 90046
"Actress"

**Collin Raye**
P.O. Box 530
Reno, NV 89504
"Singer"

**Paula Raymond**
1122 1/2 N. Larrabee
Los Angeles, CA 90069
"Actress"

**Chris Rea**
122 Holland Park Avenue
London W11 4UA ENGLAND
"Singer, Guitarist"

**Peggy Rea**
10331 Riverside Drive #204
Toluca Lake, CA 91602
"Actress"

**Stephen Rea**
861 Sutherland Avenue
London W9 ENGLAND
"Actor"

**James Read**
9229 Sunset Blvd. #315
Los Angeles, CA 90069
"Actor"

**Ralph Read**
P.O. Box 1990
Chesapeake, VA 23327
"Christian Spokesman"

**Michael Reagan**
15260 Ventura Blvd. #500
Sherman Oaks, CA 91403
"Ex-President's Son"

**Nancy Reagan**
668 St. Cloud Road
Los Angeles, CA 90077
"Ex-First Lady, Actress"

**Ronald Reagan**
668 St. Cloud Road
Los Angeles, CA 90077
"Actor, Ex-President"

**Ron Reagan, Jr.**
2612 28th Avenue W.
Seattle, WA 98199
"TV Show Host, Dancer"

**Jeff Reardon**
4 Martwood Lane
Palm Beach Gardens, FL 33410
"Ex-Baseball Player"

**Rex Reason**
20105 Rhapsody Road
Walnut, CA 91789
"Actor"

**Rhodes Reason**
P.O. Box 503
Gladstone, OR 97027
"Actor"

**James Rebhorn**
145 West 45th Street #1203
New York, NY 10036
"Actor"

**Peter Reckell**
P.O. Box 2704-462
Huntington Beach, CA 92647
"Actor"

**Red Hot Chili Peppers**
729 7th Avenue #1600
New York, NY 10019
"Music Group"

**Leon Redbone**
179 Aquestong Road
New Hope, PA 18938
"Singer, Guitarist"

**Juli Redding**
P.O. Box 1806
Beverly Hills, CA 90212
"Actress"

**Helen Reddy**
2029 Century Park E. #600
Los Angeles, CA 90067
"Singer"

**Quinn Redeker**
8075 Third Street #303
Los Angeles, CA 90048
"Actor, Writer"

**Robert Redford**
1101-E Montana Avenue
Santa Monica, CA 90403
"Actor, Director"

**Lynn Redgrave**
121 North San Vicente Blvd.
Beverly Hills, CA 90211
"Actress"

**Vanessa Redgrave**
2D Wimpole Street
London W1N 7AA ENGLAND
"Actress"

**Sumner Redstone**
Viacom Inc.,
1515 Broadway
New York, NY 10036
"Media Executive"

**Gabrielle Reece**
5111 Ocean Front Walk #4
Marina del Rey, CA 90291
"Model"

**Alaina Reed-Hall**
10636 Rathburn
Northridge, CA 91326
"Actress"

**Jerry Reed**
153 Rue De Grande
Brentwood, TN 37027
"Singer, Actor"

**Lou Reed**
2550 Laurel Pass Avenue
Los Angeles, CA 90046
"Music Group"

**Margaret Reed**
524 West 57th Street #5330
New York, NY 10019
"Actress"

**Pamela Reed**
1505 - 10th street
Santa Monica, CA 90401
"Actress"

**Rex Reed**
1 West 72nd Street #86
New York, NY 10023
"Film Critic"

**Shanna Reed**
1327 Brinkley Avenue
Los Angeles, CA 90049
"Actress"

**Della Reese**
55 West 900 South
Salt Lake City, UT 84101
"Singer, Actress"

**Roger Rees**
1505 - 10th Street
Santa Monica, CA 90401
"Actor"

**Trevor Rees-Jones**
Oswestry
Shropshire, ENGLAND
"Princess Di's Ex-Bodyguard"

**Christopher Reeve**
RR #2
Bedford, NY 10506
"Actor"

**Dana Reeve**
RR #2
Bedford, NY 10506
"Wife of Christopher Reeve"

**Del Reeves**
1300 Division Street #102
Nashville, TN 37203
"Singer"

**Diane Reeves**
P.O. Box 66
Englishtown, NJ 07726
"Singer"

**Julie Reeves**
P.O. Box 300
Russell, KY 41169
"Singer"

**Keanu Reeves**
8500 Wilshire Blvd. #700
Beverly Hills, CA 90211
"Actor"

**Martha Reeves**
P.O. Box 1821
Ojai, CA 93024
"Singer"

**Joe Regalbuto**
724-24th Street
Santa Monica, CA 90402
"Actor"

**Donald T. Regan**
240 McLaws Circle #142
Williamsburg, VA 23185
"Former Secretary of Treasury"

**Duncan Regehr**
2501 Main Street
Santa Monica, CA 90405
"Actor"

**Paul Regina**
2911 Canna Street
Thousand Oaks, CA 91360
"Actor"

**Regine**
502 Park Avenue
New York, NY 10022
"Singer"

**William Rehnquist**
2329 N. Glebe Road
Arlington, VA 22207
"Supreme Court Chief Justice"

**Tanja Reichert**
1404-510 West Hastings Street
Vancouver BC V6B 1L8 CANADA
"Actress"

**Daphne Maxwell Reid**
1 New Millennium Drive
Petersburg, VA 23805
"Actress"

**Elliott Reid**
1850 N. Whitley Avenue
Los Angeles, CA 90028
"Actor, Writer"

**Frances Reid**
235 Oceano Drive
Los Angeles, CA 90049
"Actress"

**Tara Reid**
124 West 60th Street #39-D
New York, NY 10023
"Actress"

**Tim Reid**
1 New Millennium Drive
Petersburg, VA 23805
"Actor"

**Charles Nelson Reilly**
2341 Gloaming Way
Beverly Hills, CA 90210
"Actor"

**John Reilly**
602 North Las Palmas Avenue
Los Angeles, CA 90004
"Actor"

**Carl Reiner**
714 North Rodeo Drive
Beverly Hills, CA 90210
"Actor, Director"

**Judge Reinhold**
15332 Antioch Street, PMB 723
Pacific Palisades, CA 90272
"Actor"

**Ann Reinking**
40 West 57th Street
New York, NY 10019
"Actress"

**Paul Reiser**
11845 West Olympic Blvd. #1125
Los Angeles, CA 90064
"Actor"

**Rock Reiser**
9014 Melrose Avenue
West Hollywood, CA 90069
"Actor"

**Ivan Reitman**
900 Cold Springs Road
Montecito, CA 93108
"Director, Producer"

**R.E.M.**
170 College Avenue
Athens, GA 30601
"Rock & Roll Group"

**Leah Remini**
3500 West Olive Avenue #1400
Burbank, CA 91505
"Actress"

**Line Renaud**
5 rue de Bois de Boulogne
F-75116 Paris FRANCE
"Actress"

**Liz Renay**
3708 San Angelo Avenue
Las Vegas, NV 89102
"Burlesque"

**Brad Renfro**
8383 Wilshire Blvd. #550
Beverly Hills, CA 90212
"Actor"

**Mel Renfro**
4120 International Parkway
Carrollton, TX 75007
"Ex-Football Player"

**Jack Reno**
P.O. Box 1001
Florance, KY 41052
"Singer"

**Janet Reno**
P.O. Box 162117
Miami, FL 33116
"ex-Attorney General"

**Jean Reno**
11 rue de la Croix Boissee
F-91540 Mennecy FRANCE
"Actor"

**Claudio Renya**
1801 South Prairie Avenue
Chicago, IL 60616
"Soccer Player"

**REO Speedwagon**
1100 Glendon Avenue #2000
Los Angeles, CA 90024
"Rock & Roll Band"

**Alain Resnis**
70 rue des Plantes
75014 Paris, FRANCE
"Film Director"

**Robert Ressler**
P.O. Box 187
Spotsylvania, VA 22553
Law Enforcement Consultant"

**James B. Reston**
4714 Hunt Avenue
Chevy Chase, MD 20815
"Journalist"

**Mary Lou Retton**
114 White Avenue
Fairmont, WV 26554
"Gymnast, Actress"

**Gloria Reuben**
151 El Camino Drive
Beverly Hills, CA 90212
"Actress"

**Paul Reubens**
P.O. Box 29373
Los Angeles, CA 90029
"Actor"

**Paul Revere & The Raiders**
P.O. Box 1821
Ojai, CA 93024
"Rock & Roll Group"

**Clive Revill**
15029 Encanto Drive
Sherman Oaks, CA 91403
"Actor"

**Judy Reyes**
10100 Santa Monica Blvd. #2500
Los Angeles, CA 90067
"Actress"

**Burt Reynolds**
P.O. Box 3288
Tequesta, FL 33469
"Actor, Director"

**Debbie Reynolds**
6514 Lankershim Blvd.
North Hollywood, CA 91606
"Actress"

**Gene Reynolds**
2034 Castillian Drive
Los Angeles, CA 90068
"Actor, Director"

**James Reynolds**
1925 Hanscom Drive
South Pasadena, CA 91030
"Actor"

**Kevin Reynolds**
151 El Camino Drive
Beverly Hills, CA 90212
"Film Director"

**Ryan Reynolds**
9701 Wilshire Blvd., 10th Floor
Beverly Hills, CA 90212
"Actor"

**Ving Rhames**
1158 - 26th Street #549
Santa Monica, CA 90403
"Actor"

**Alicia Rhett**
59 Tradd Street
Charleston, SC 29401
"Actress"

**Donnelly Rhodes**
3500 West Olive Avenue #1400
Burbank, CA 91505
"Actor"

**Dusty Rhodes**
240 Datura Street
Henderson, NV 89104
"Wrestler"

**Madlyn Rhue**
23388 Mulholland Drive
Woodland Hills, CA 91364
"Actress"

**Busta Rhymes**
8383 Wilshire Blvd. #550
Beverly Hills, CA 90211
"Rap Singer"

**John Rhys-Davies**
3428 Oak Glen Drive
Los Angeles, CA 90068
"Actor"

**Alfonso Ribeiro**
3353 Blair Drive
Los Angeles, CA 90068
"Actor"

**Giovanni Ribisi**
1122 S. Robertson Blvd. #15
Los Angeles, CA 90035
"Actor"

**Marissa Ribisi**
9560 Wilshire Blvd. #500
Los Angeles, CA 90010
"Actress"

**Christina Ricci**
8942 Wilshire Blvd.
Beverly Hills, CA 90211
"Actress"

**Anne Rice**
1239 First Street
New Orleans, LA 70130
"Writer"

**Bobby G. Rice**
505 Canton Pass
Madison, TN 37115
"Singer"

**Dr. Condoleezza Rice**
1600 Pennsylvania Avenue NW
Washington, DC 20500
"Government Offical"

**Donna Rice-Hughes**
P.O. Box 888
Fairfax, VA 22030
"Personalist"

**Jerry Rice**
3725 Jefferson Court
Redwood City, CA 94062
"Football Player"

**Jim Rice**
RR #8
Anderson, SC 29621
"Ex-Baseball Player"

**Sir Tim Rice**
96 Castlemere Plaza
North Andover, MA 01845
"Lyricist"

**Adam Rich**
21848 Vantage Avenue
Chatsworth, CA 91311
"Actor"

**Christopher Rich**
11500 West Olympic Blvd. #510
Los Angeles, CA 90064
"Actor"

**Elaine Rich**
500 South Sepulveda Blvd.
Los Angeles, CA 90049
"Producer"

**John Rich**
2501 Colorado Ave. #350
Santa Monica, CA 90404
"Writer, Producer"

**Matty Rich**
9560 Wilshire Blvd. #500
Beverly Hills, CA 90210
"Director"

**Cliff Richard**
Queen Anne House
Weybridge, Surrey ENGLAND
"Singer, Actor"

**Ann Richard**
P.O. Box 684746
Austin, TX 78768
"Ex-Governor"

**Ariana Richards**
6500 Wilshire Blvd. #2200
Los Angeles, CA 90048
"Actress"

**Denise Richards**
9465 Wilshire Blvd. #600
Beverly Hills, CA 90212
"Actress"

**Emelie Richards**
P.O. Box 7052
Arlington, VA 22207
"Actress"

**Evan Richards**
1800 Avenue of the Starts, #400
Los Angeles, CA 90067
"Actor"

**Kieth Richards**
"Redlands" West Whittering
Near Chichester Sussex
ENGLAND
"Actor"

**Michael Richards**
9171 Wilshire Blvd. #406
Beverly Hills, CA 90210
"Actor"

**Governor Bill Richardson**
State Capitol, Room 400
Santa Fe, NM 87501
"Governor of NM"

**Bobby Richardson**
P.O. Box 2000
Lynchburg, VA 24506
"Ex-Basketball Player"

**Elliot Richardson**
1100 Crest Lane
McLean, VA 22101
"Diplomat"

**Ian Richardson**
131 Lavender Sweep
London SW11 ENGLAND
"Actor"

**LaTanya Richardson**
9057-C Nemo Street
West Hollywood, CA 90069
"Actress"

**Miranda Richardson**
7 St. George's Square
London SW1V 2HX ENGLAND
"Actress"

**Natasha Richardson**
200 Fulham Road
London SW10 9PN ENGLAND
"Actress"

**Patricia Richardson**
253a - 26th Street
Santa Monica, CA 90402
"Actress"

**Lionel Richie**
9012 West Olympic Blvd. #200
Beverly Hills, CA 90211
"Singer, Songwriter"

**Peter Mark Richman**
5114 Del Moreno Drive
Woodland Hills, CA 91364
"Actor"

**Branscombe Richmond**
1706 Palo Verde Drive
Alamogordo, NM 88310
"Actor, Stuntman"

**Andy Richter**
315 S. Beverly Drive #216
Beverly Hills, CA 90212
"Ex-Late Night Show Co-Host"

**Jason James Richter**
112 South Almont Drive
Los Angeles, CA 90048
"Actor"

**Les Richter**
1405 Via Vallarta
Riverside, CA 92506
"Football Player"

**Lindsey Richter**
9899 Santa Monica Blvd., PMB
2002
Beverly Hills, CA 90212
"Survivor TV Show Contestant"

**Don Rickles**
10249 Century Woods Drive
Los Angeles, CA 90067
"Comeidan, Actor"

**Alan Rickman**
76 Oxford Street
London W1N 0AX ENGLAND
"Actor"

**Dr. Sally Ride**
9500 Gillman Drive
MS 0221
La Jolla, CA 92093
"Astronaut"

**Ex Gov. Tom Ridge**
1600 Pennsylvania Avenue NW
Washington, DC 20500
"Government Offical"

**Leni Riefenstahl**
Tengstrasse 20
D-80798 Munich
GERMANY
"Film Director"

**Joshua Rifkind**
4526 Wilshire Blvd. #200
Los Angeles, CA 90010
"Conductor"

**Cathy Rigby**
110 East Wilshire #200
Fullerton, CA 92632
"Gymnast"

**Dame Diana Rigg**
4 Great Portland Street
London W1W 8PA ENGLAND
"Actress"

**Righteous Brothers**
9841 Hot Springs Drive
Huntington Beach, CA 92646
"Vocal Group"

**Dave Righetti**
552 Magdalena Avenue
Los Altos, CA 94024
"Ex-Basketball Player"

**Robin Riker-Halsey**
1089 North Oxford Avenue
Los Angeles, CA 90029
"Actress"

**Jeannie C. Riley**
906 Granville Road
Franklin, TN 37064
"Singer"

**Pat Riley**
180 Arvida Parkway
Miami, FL 33156
"Basketball Coach"

**Jack Riley**
400 South Beverly Drive #101
Beverly Hills, CA 90212
"Actor, Writer"

**Michael Riley**
9200 Sunset Blvd. #900
Los Angeles, CA 90069
"Actor"

**LeAnn Rimes**
1801 Whitehall Lane
Garland, TX 75043
"Singer"

**Molly Ringwald**
19 West 44 Street #1000
New York, NY 10036
"Actress"

**Lisa Rinna**
1465 Lindacrest Drive
Beverly Hills, CA 90210
"Actress"

**ex Mayor Richard Riordan**
141 North Bristol Avenue
Los Angeles, CA 90049
"Mayor of Los Angeles"

**Kelly Ripa**
646 Juniper Place
Franklin Lakes, NJ 07417
"Actress"

**Cal Ripken, Jr.**
10801 Tony Drive #A
Lutherville, MD 21093
"Baseball Player"

**Rodney Allen Rippey**
3939 Veselich Avenue #351
Los Angeles, CA 90039
"Actor"

**Robby Rist**
10635 Santa Monica #130
Los Angeles, CA 90025
"Actor"

**The Ritchie Family**
4100 West Flagler #B-2
Miami, FL 33134
"Vocal Group"

**Guy Ritchie**
1 Horse & Dolphin Yard
London W1V 7LG ENGLAND
"Writer, Director"

**Jill Richie**
1180 South Beverly Drive #608
Los Angeles, CA 90035
"Actress"

**Lionel Ritchie**
9012 West Olympic Blvd. #200
Beverly Hills, CA 90211
"R & B Singer"

**Lee Ritenour**
11808 Dorothy Street #108
Los Angeles, CA 90049
"Guitarist"

**John Ritter**
1205 Benedict Canyon
Beverly Hills, CA 90210
"Actor"

**Mrs. Tex Ritter**
14151 Valley Vista
Sherman Oaks, CA 91423
"Tex Ritter's Widow"

**Chita Rivera**
c/o Shapiro + Lobel
111 West 40th Street
New York, NY 10018
"Actress, Singer, Dancer"

**Geraldo Rivera**
620 Ave. of the Americas #600
New York, NY 10011
"TV Show Host, Author"

**Jorge Rivero**
Salvador Novo 71
Cuyoacan 21 D.F. MEXICO
"Actor"

**Joan Rivers**
P.O. Box 1150, FDR Station
New York, NY 10150
"Comedienne, TV Show Host"

**Johnny Rivers**
12358 Venture Blvd. #342
Studio City, CA 91604
"Singer, Songwriter"

**Vincent Riverside**
5757 Wilshire Blvd. #2200
Los Angeles, CA 90036
"Actor"

**Jacques Rivette**
20 Blvd. de la Bastille
75012 Paris, FRANCE
"Film Director"

**Phil Rizzuto**
P.O. Box 193
Massapequa, NY 11758
"Ex-Baseball Player"

**Sam Robards**
2530 Riverbend Drive
Crested Butte, CO 81224
"Actor"

**David Robb**
151 El Camino Drive
Beverly Hills, CA 90212
"Actor"

**Lynda Bird Johnson-Robb**
612 Chain Bridge Raod
Mc Lean, VA 22101
"Ex-President's Daughter"

**Seymour Robbie**
9980 Liebe Drive
Beverly Hills, CA 90210
"TV Director"

**Brian Robbins**
10960 Ventura Blvd. #200
Studio City, CA 91604
"Actor"

**Tim Robbins**
c/o Havoc Inc.
16 W. 19th Street, 12th Floor
New York, NY 10011
"Actor"

**Jane Robelot**
524 West 57th Street
New York, NY 10019
"TV Show Host"

**Beverly Roberts**
30912 Ariana Lane
Laguna Niguel, CA 92677
"Actress"

**Cokie Roberts**
5315 Bradley Blvd.
Bethesda, MD 20814
"News Correspondent"

**Doris Roberts**
6225 Quebec Drive
Los Angeles, CA 90068
"Actress, Director"

**Eric Roberts**
12025 1/2 Ventura Blvd.
Studio City, CA 91604
"Actor"

**Jake "The Snake" Roberts**
P.O. Box 3859
Stamford, CT 06905
"Wrestler"

**Julia Roberts**
156 Fifth Avenue #711
New York, NY 10010
"Actress"

**Louie Roberts**
2401 - 12th Avenue South
Nashville, TN 37203
"Singer, Guitarist"

**Oral Roberts**
P.O. Box 2187
Tulsa, OK 74171
"Evangelist"

**Pernell Roberts**
20395 Seaboard Road
Malibu, CA 90265
"Actor"

**Robin Roberts**
504 Terrace Hill Road
Temple Terrace, FL 33617
"Ex-Baseball Player"

**Steven Roberts**
5315 Bradley Blvd.
Bethesda, MD 20814
"Columnist"

**Tanya Roberts**
1122 South Roberston Blvd. #15
Los Angeles, CA 90035
"Actress"

**Tony Roberts**
970 Park Avenue #8-N
New York, NY 10028
"Actor"

**Cliff Robertson**
325 Dunmere Drive
La Jolla, CA 92037
"Actor, Writer, Director"

**Dale Robertson**
P.O. Box 850707
Yukon, OK 73085
"Actor"

**Kathleen Robertson**
9460 Wilshire Blvd. #700
Beverly Hills, CA 90212
"Actress"

**Oscar Robertson**
621 Tusculum Avenue
Cincinatti, OH 45226
"Ex-Basketball Player"

**Pat Robertson**
1000 Centerville Turnpike
Virginia Beach, VA 23463
"Evangelist"

**Andrew Robinson**
2671 Byron Place
Los Angeles, CA 90046
"Actor"

**Anne Robinson**
19 Victoria Grove
London W8 5RW ENGLAND
"Weakest Link TV Show Host"

**Brooks Robinson**
9210 Baltimore National Pike
Elillcot, MD 21042
"Ex-Baseball Player"

**Bumber Robinson**
2572 Gallcia
La Verne, CA 91750
"Actor"

**Charles Robinson**
10000 Santa Monica Blvd. #305
Los Angeles, CA 90067
"Actor"

**Chris Robinson**
12706 E. Pacific Circle #202
Aurora, CO 80014
"Actor, Director"

**David Robinson**
P.O. Box 530
San Antonio, TX 78292
"Basketball Player"

**Frank Robinson**
15557 Aqua Verde Drive
Los Angeles, CA 90024
"Ex-Baseball Player & Manager"

**Glen Robinson**
1001 North Fourth Street
Milwaukee, WI 53203
"Basketball Player"

**Holly Robinson-Peet**
112 South Almont Drive
Los Angeles, CA 90048
"Actress"

**Mrs. Jackie (Rachel) Robinson**
3 West 35th Street
New York, NY 10001
"Widow of Jackie Robinson"

**Janice Robinson**
1122 "B" Street #308
Hayward, CA 94541
"Singer, Songwriter"

**Jay Robinson**
13757 Milbank Avenue
Sherman Oaks, CA 91403
"Actor"

**Randall Robinson**
1744 "R" Street NW
Washington, DC 20009
"Social Activist"

**Smokey Robinson**
12702 Landale Street
Studio City, CA 91604
"Singer, Songwriter"

**Andy Robustelli**
460 Summer Street
Stamford, CT 06901
"Ex-Football Player"

**Alex Rocco**
1755 Ocean Oaks Road
Carpinteria, CA 93013
"Actor"

**Eugene Roche**
9911 West Pico Blvd., #PH-A
Los Angeles, CA 90035
"Actor"

**Debbie Rochon**
P.O. Box 1299
New York, NY 10009
"Actress"

**Lela Rochon**
250 W. 57th Street #1610
New York, NY 10107
"Actress"

**Chris Rock**
1740 Broadway #1500
New York, NY 10019
"Comedian"

**David Rockefeller, Jr.**
30 Rockefeller Plaza #506
New York, NY 10112
"Businessman"

**Sen. John D. Rockefeller IV (WV)**
Senate Hart Bldg. #109
Washington, DC 20510
"Politician"

**Mrs. Nelson Rockefeller**
30 Rockefeller Plaza #5600
New York, NY 10112
"Wife of Nelson Rockefeller"

**Sharon Rockefeller**
1515 Barberry
Charleston, WV 25314
"Wife of John D. Rockefeller"

**John Rocker**
c/o Cleveland Indians
2401 Ontario street
Cleveland, OH 44115
"Baseball Player"

**The Rockers**
P.O. Box 3859
Stamford, CT 06905
"R & B Group"

**Robert Rockwell**
18428 Coastline Drive
Malibu, CA 90265
"Actor"

**Sam Rockwell**
9 Desbrosses Street #200
New York, NY 10013
"Actor"

**Jay Rodan**
76 Oxford Street
London W1N OAX ENGLAND
"Actor"

**Marcia Rodd**
11738 Moorpark Street #C
Studio City, CA 91604
"Actress"

**Anton Rodgers**
The White House
Lower Basildon
Berkshire ENGLAND
"Actor"

**Jimmie Rodgers**
P.O. Box 685
Forsyth, MO 65653
"Singer, Songwriter"

**ex-Rep. Peter Rodino, Jr.**
Seton Hall
400 South Orange Avenue
South Orange, NJ 07079
"Former US Congressman"

**Dennis Rodman**
P.O. Box 5870
Orange, CA 92863
"Basketball Player"

**Chi Chi Rodriguez**
3916 Clock Pointe Trail #101
Stow, OH 44224
"Golfer"

**Freddy Rodriguez**
1505 - 10th Street
Santa Monica, CA 90401
"Actor"

**Jennifer Rodriguez**
P.O. Box 450639
Westlake, OH 44145
Olympic Speed Skating  Medalist"

**Johnny Rodriguez**
P.O. Box 427
San Marcos, TX 78667
"Singer, Songwriter"

**Tommy Roe**
P.O. Box 26037
Minneapolis, MN 55426
"Singer, Songwriter"

**Daniel Roebuck**
1314 Scott Road
Burbank, CA 91501
"Actor"

**Nicholas Roeg**
14 Courtnell Street
London W2 5BX ENGLAND
"Film Director"

**Bill Rogers**
353 The Marketplace
Fanuil Hall
Boston, MA 02109
"Runner"

**Mr. Rogers (Fred)**
4802 - 5th Avenue
Pittsburgh, PA 15213
"TV Show Host"

**Joy Rogers**
4141 West Kling Street #3
Burbank, CA 91505
"Actress"

**Kasey Rogers**
23401 Park Sorrento #24
Calabasas, CA 91302
"Actress"

**Kenny Rogers**
2910 Poston Avenue
Nashville, TN 37203
"Singer, Songwriter"

**Melody Rogers**
2051 Nichols Canyon Road
Los Angeles, CA 90046
"Actress, TV Show Host"

**Mimi Rogers**
11693 San Vicente Blvd. #241
Los Angeles, CA 90049
"Actress"

**Paul Rogers**
9 Hillside Gardens
London N6 5SU ENGLAND
"Actor"

**Suzanne Rogers**
11266 Canton Drive
Studio City, CA 91604
"Actress"

**Tristan Rogers**
6500 Wilshire Blvd. #2200
Los Angeles, CA 90048
"Actor"

**Wayne Rogers**
11828 La Grange Avenue
Los Angeles, CA 90025
"Actor, Writer, Director"

**Fred Roggin**
3000 West Alameda Avenue
Burbank, CA 91523
"TV Show Host"

**Eric Rohmer**
26 Ave. Pierre-Ler-De-Serbie
F-75116 Paris, FRANCE
"Film Director"

**Clayton Rohner**
6924 Treasure Trail
Los Angeles, CA 90068
"Actor"

**Al Roker**
2200 Fletcher Drive
FT. Lee, NJ 07024
"TV Weatherman"

**Rolling Stones**
252 Regent Street #100
London W1B 3BX ENGLAND
"Rock & Roll Group"

**Ed Rollins**
510 King Street, #302
Alexandria, VA 22314
"Political Consultant"

**Sonny Rollins**
193 Brighton Avenue
Boston, MA 02134
"Saxophonist"

**Matt Roloff**
23985 Grossen Road
Hillsboro, OR 97124
"Author with Dwarfism"

**Freddie Roman**
889 S. Brentwood Blvd. #201
St. Louis, MO 63105
"Comedian"

**Roman Holiday**
P.O. Box 475
London W1 ENGLAND
"Rock & Roll Group"

**Ray Romano**
4000 Warner Blvd., Bldg. 131
Burbank, CA 91522
"Actor"

**The Romantics**
1924 Spring Street
Paso Robles, CA 93446
"Music Group"

**Richard Romanus**
14011 Ventura Blvd. #213
Sherman Oaks, CA 91403
"Actor"

**George Romero**
P.O. Box 5617
Beverly Hills, CA 90210
"Filmmaker, Screenwriter"

**Ned Romero**
12724 Ventura Blvd. #506
Sherman Oaks, CA 91403
"Actor"

**Rebecca Romijn-Stamos**
94171 Wilshire Blvd. #300
Beverly Hills, CA 90210
"Actress"

**Linda Ronstadt**
c/o Trident Media
152 - 58th Street, 16th Floor
New York, NY 10019
"Singer"

**Michael Rooker**
275 S. Beverly Drive #215
Beverly Hills, CA 90212
"Actor"

**Andy Rooney**
254 Rowayton Avenue
Rowayton, CT 06853
"Writer, Actor, Director"

**Mickey Rooney**
P.O. Box 3186
Thousand Oaks, CA 91359
"Actor"

**Axl Rose**
5055 Latigo Canyon Road
Malibu, CA 90265
"Singer"

**Charlie Rose**
524 West 57th Street
New York, NY 10019
"Talk Show Host"

**Jamie Rose**
3500 W. Olive Avenue #1400
Burbank, CA 91505
"Actress"

**Rose Marie**
6916 Chisholm Avenue
Van Nuys, CA 91406
"Singer"

**Pete Rose**
8144 Glades Road
Boca Raton, FL 33434
"Ex-Baseball Player"

**Sherrie Rose**
1758 Laurel Canyon Blvd.
Los Angeles, CA 90046
"Actress"

**Roseanne**
5 Crest Road
Rolling Hills, CA 90274
"Actress"

**Alan Rosenberg**
P.O. Box 5617
Beverly Hills, CA 90210
"Actor"

**Stuart Rosenberg**
1984 Coldwater Canyon
Beverly Hills, CA 90210
"Writer, Producer"

**Rick Rosenthal**
2501 Colorado Avenue #350
Santa Monica, CA 90404
"Film Director"

**Barney Rosenzweig**
P.O. Box 48005
Los Angeles, CA 90048
"TV Writer, Producer"

**Ken Rosewall**
111 Pentacost Avenue
Turramurra NSW 2074
AUSTRALIA
"Tennis Player"

**Francesco Rosi**
Via Gregoriana 36
I-00187 Rome, ITALY
"Film Director"

**Charlotte Ross**
9200 Sunset Blvd. #1130
Los Angeles, CA 90069
"Actress"

**Diana Ross**
P.O. Box 11059
Glenville Station
Greenwich, CT 06831
"Singer, Actress"

**Jonathan Ross**
34/42 Cleveland Street
London W1P 5SB ENGLAND
"Actor"

**Katherine Ross**
33050 Pacific Coast Hwy.
Malibu, CA 90265
"Actress"

**Marion Ross**
1180 S. Beverly Drive #301
Los Angeles, CA 90035
"Actress"

**Stan Ross**
1410 North Gardner
Los Angeles, CA 90046
"Actor"

**Tracee Ellis Ross**
c/o Girlfriends/UPN
11800 Wilshire Blvd.
Los Angeles, CA 90025
"Actress"

**Dan Rostenkowski**
1372 West Evergreen Street
Chicago, IL 60622
"Ex-Congressman"

**Walt Rostow**
1 Wildwind Point
Austin, TX 78746
"Economist"

**Kyle Rote, Jr.**
6075 Poplar Avenue #920
Memphis, TN 38119
"Ex-Football Player"

**Andrea Roth**
4526 Wilshire Blvd.
Los Angeles, CA 90010
"Actress"

**David Lee Roth**
455 Bradford Street
Pasadena, CA 91105
"Singer, Songwriter"

**Matt Roth**
P.O. Box 5617
Beverly Hills, CA 90210
"Actor"

**John Rothman**
9229 Sunset Blvd. #710
Los Angeles, CA 90069
"Actor"

**Cynthia Rothrock**
2633 Lincoln Blvd. #103
Santa Monica, CA 90405
"Actress"

**Richard Roundtree**
8436 West Third Street #740
Los Angeles, CA 90048
"Actor"

**Mickey Rourke**
8942 Wilshire Blvd.
Beverly Hills, CA 90211
"Actor"

**The Roustabouts**
P.O. Box 25371
Charlotte, NC 28212
"Bluegrass Group"

**Kelly Rowan**
151 El Camino Drive
Beverly Hills, CA 90212
"Actor"

**Alan Rowe**
8 Sherwood Close
London SW13 ENGLAND
"Actor"

**Debbie Rowe-Jackson**
435 N. Roxbury Drive
Beverly Hills, CA 90210
"Michael Jackson's wife"

**Misty Rowe**
P.O. Box 294
Cos Cob, CT 05807
"Actress"

**Nicholas Rowe**
52 Shaftesbury Avenue
London WIV 7DE ENGLAND
"Poet, Dramatist"

**Victoria Rowell**
195 S. Beverly Drive #400
Beverly Hills, CA 90212
"Actress"

**Betty Rowland**
125 N. Barrington Avenue #103
Los Angeles, CA 90049
"Burlesque"

**Dave Rowland**
P.O. Box 121089
Nashville, TN 37212
"Singer"

**Gena Rowlands**
7917 Woodrow Wilson Drive
Los Angeles, CA 90046
"Actress"

**Patsy Rowlands**
265 Liverpool Rd.
London N1 1LX ENGLAND
"Actress"

**J. K. Rowlings**
c/o Scholastic Press
555 Broadway
New York, NY 10012
"Harry Potter Author"

**Steve Roxton**
6 Thornton Road, Leytonstone
London E11 ENGLAND
"Actor"

**Billy Joe Royal**
304 Somerset Way
Newport, NC 28570
"Singer, Songwriter"

**Darrell Royal**
2100 North College Avenue
Bethany, OK 73008
"Ex-Football Coach"

**Kenneth Royce**
3 Abbott's Close, Andover
Hants. SP11 7NP ENGLAND
"Author"

**Pamela Roylance**
292 S. LaCienega Blvd. #217
Beverly Hills, CA 90211
"Actress"

**Pete Rozelle**
P.O. Box 9686
Rancho Santa Fe, CA 92067
"Former Football Commissioner"

**Mike Rozier**
I-85 & Suwanee Road
Suwanee, GA 30174
"Football Player"

**John Rubinstien**
19531 Collier Street
Tarzana, CA 91356
"Actor"

**Zelda Rubinstein**
8730 Sunset Blvd. #270
Los Angeles, CA 90069
"Actress"

**Paul Rudd**
9465 Wilshire Blvd. #517
Beverly Hills, CA 90212
"Actor"

**Ricky Rudd**
P.O. Box 4060
Mooresville, NC 28117
"Race Car Driver"

**Al Ruddy**
1601 Clearview Drive
Beverly Hills, CA 90210
"Film Writer, Producer"

**Rita Rudner**
2934 Beverly Glen Circle #389
Los Angeles, CA 90077
"Comedienne"

**Alan Rudolph**
15760 Ventura Blvd. #16
Encino, CA 91436
"Film Writer, Producer"

**Mercedes Ruehl**
9830 Wilshire Blvd.
Beverly Hills, CA 90212
"Actress"

**Jimmy Ruffin**
102 Ryder's Lane
East Brunswick, NJ 08816
"Singer"

**Rufus**
7250 Beverly Blvd #200
Los Angeles, CA 90036
"R&B Group"

**Mark Ruiz**
201 South Capitol Avenue #430
Indianapolis, IN 46206
"Diver"

**Janice Rule**
105 West 72nd Street #12B
New York, NY 10023
"Actress"

**Donald Rumsfeld**
Department of Defense
The Pentagon
Washington, DC 20301
"Ex-Government Official"

**Run D.M.C.**
225 West 57th Street #500
New York, NY 10109
"Rap Group"

**Todd Rundgren**
P.O. Box 1821
Ojai, CA 93024
"R & B Group"

**Marla Runyan**
P.O. Box 120
Indianapolis, IN 46206
"Legally Blind Runner"

**Jennifer Runyon**
5130 N. Lakemont Lane
Boise, ID 83703
"Actress"

**Barbara Rush**
1709 Tropical Avenue
Beverly Hills, CA 90210
"Actress"

**Geoffrey Rush**
129 Bourke Street
Wooloomooloo NSW 2011
Australia
"Actor"

**Jennifer Rush**
145 Central Park West
New York, NY 10023
"Singer"

**Salman Rushdie**
c/o Rogers, Ttd.
49 Blenheim Crescent
London W11 ENGLAND
"Author"

**Patrice Rushen**
P.O. Box 6278
Altadena, CA 91003
"Singer"

**Dean Rusk**
620 Hills Street
Athens, GA 30601
"ex-Secy. of State"

**Robert Rusler**
112 South Almont Drive
Los Angeles, CA 90048
"Actor"

**Bill Russell**
9415 SE 52nd Street
Mercer Island, WA 98040
"Basketball Player"

**Bing Russell**
229 E. Gainsborough Road
Thousand Oaks, CA 91360
"Actor"

**Brenda Russell**
9200 Sunset Blvd. #900
Los Angeles, CA 90069
"Singer"

**Cazzie Russell**
Savannah College
P.O. Box 3146
Savannah, GA 31402
"Basketball Player"

**Jane Russell**
2430 Ridgemark Drive
Santa Maria, CA 93455
"Actress"

**Johnny Russell**
P.O. Box Drawer 37
Hendersonville, TN 37077
"Singer, Songwriter"

**Ken Russell**
16 Salisbury Place
London W1H 1FH ENGLAND
"Film Director"

**Keri Russell**
1122 S. Robertson Blvd., #15
Los Angeles, CA 90035
"Actress"

**Kimberly Russell**
11617 Laurelwood Drive
Studio City, CA 91604
"Actress"

**Kurt Russell**
1422 Capi Avenue
Pacific Palisades, CA 90272
"Actor"

**Leon Russell**
2000 S. Dixie Hwy.
West Palm Beach, FL 33401
"Singer, Songwriter"

**Mark Russell**
3201 33rd Place NW
Washington, DC 20008
"Satirist, Comedian"

**Nipsey Russell**
889 S. Brentwood Blvd. #201
St. Louis, MO 63105
"Comedian"

**Theresa Russell**
9434 Lloyd Crest Drive
Beverly Hills, CA 90210
"Actress"

**Tim Russert**
3124 Woodley Road, NW
Washington, D.C. 20008
"TV Show Host"

**Rene Russo**
253A - 26th Street #199
Santa Monica, CA 90402
"Actress"

**Emily Rutherford**
9150 Wilshire Blvd. #350
Beverly Hills, CA 90212
"Actress"

**Johnny Rutherford**
4919 Black Oak Lane
Fort Worth, TX 76114
"Race Car Driver"

**Kelly Rutherford**
P.O. Box 492266
Los Angeles, CA 90049
"Actress"

**Susan Ruttan**
11103 Kling Street
Toluca Lake, CA 91602
"Actress"

**Fran Ryan**
4204 Woodland
Burbank, CA 91505
"Actress"

**JERI LYNN RYAN**
P.O. Box 260098
Encino, CA 91426
"Actress"

**Marisa Ryan**
1450 South Robertson Blvd.
Los Angeles, CA 90035
"Actress"

**Meg Ryan**
151 El Camino Drive
Beverly Hills, CA 90212
"Actress"

**Mitchell Ryan**
30355 Mulholland Drive
Cornell, CA 91301
"Actor"

**Nolan Ryan**
P.O. Box 1534
Alvin, TX 77512
"Ex-Baseball Player"

**Peggy Ryan**
1821 East Oakley Blvd.
Las Vegas, NV 89104
"Actress"

**Bobby Rydell**
P.O. Box 148
Dresher, PA 19025
"Singer"

**Christopher Rydell**
911 North Sweetzer #C
Los Angeles, CA 90069
"Actor"

**Mark Rydell**
1 Topsail
Marina del Rey, CA 90292
"Actor, Director"

**Winona Ryder**
8500 Wilshire Blvd. #700
Beverly Hills, CA 90211
"Actress"

**Ann Ryerson**
935 Gayley Avenue
Los Angeles, CA 90024
"Actress"

**Leony Rysanek**
D-88682
Attenbeuren GERMANY
"Soprano"

**Jim Ryun**
Rt. 3, Box 62-B
Lawrence, KS 66044
"Track Athlete"

**Daryl Sabara**
c/o Endeavor
9701 Wilshire Blvd., 10th Floor
Beverly Hills, CA 90212
"Actor"

**Gabriela Sabatini**
35/35 Grosvenor Street
London W1K 4QX ENGLAND
"Tennis Player"

**Michael Sabatino**
13538 Valleyheart Drive
Sherman Oaks, CA 91423
"Actor"

**Antonio Sabato Jr.**
P.O. Box 9462
Marina del Rey, CA 90295
"Actor"

**Brett Saberhagen**
5535 Amber Circle
Calabasas, CA 91302
"Baseball Player"

**Robert Sacchi**
203 N. Gramercy Place
Los Angeles, CA 90004
"Actor"

**Andrew Sachs**
25 Whitehall
London SW1A 2BS ENGLAND
"Actor"

**Madame Jehan El-Sadat**
2310 Decatur Place N.W.
Washington, DC 20008
"Widower of Anwar"

**Sade**
10 Great Malborough Street
London W1V 2LP ENGLAND
"Singer, Songwriter"

**William Sadler**
8383 Wilshire Blvd. #550
Beverly Hills, CA 90211
"Actor"

**Morley Safer**
51 West 52nd Street
New York, NY 10019
"News Journalist"

**Katey Sagal**
7095 Hollywood Blvd. #792
Los Angeles, CA 90028
"Actress"

**Liz Sagal**
4526 Wilshire Blvd.
Los Angeles, CA 90010
"Actress

**Francoise Sagan**
Equemauville F-14600
Honfleur FRANCE
"Author"

**Jeff Sagansky**
145 Ocean Avenue
Santa Monica, CA 90402
"TV Executive"

**Carole Bayer Sager**
10761 Bellagio Road
Los Angeles, CA 90077
"Singer, Songwriter"

**Bob Saget**
1122 South Roberston Blvd. #15
Los Angeles, CA 90035
"Comedian"

**Mort Sahl**
1441 Third Avenue #12C
New York, NY 10028
"Comedian, Writer"

**Eva Marie Saint**
10590 Wilshire Blvd. #408
Los Angeles, CA 90024
"Actress"

**Susan Saint James**
174 West Street #54
Litchfield, CT 06759
"Actress"

**Jill St. John**
1500 Old Oak Road
Los Angeles, CA 90077
"Actress"

**Lyn St. James**
2570 W. International Speedway #F
Daytona, FL 32114
"Race Car Driver"

**Sara St. James**
P.O. Box 3384
Cleveland, OH 37320
"Pornstar"

**Matthew St. Patrick**
c/o Greenblatt-Janollari
1438 North Gower
Hollywood, CA 90028
"Actor"

**Yves St. Laurent**
5 av Marceau
F-75116 Paris FRANCE
"Fashion Designer"

**Pat Sajak**
10202 W. Washington Blvd. #5300
Culver City, CA 90232
"TV Show Host"

**Jamie Sale**
11160 River Valley Road
P.O. Box 3180
Edmonton AB T5J 2G7 CANADA
"Figure Skater"

**Meredith Salenger**
9255 Sunset Blvd. #1010
W. Hollywood, CA 90069
"Actress"

**Soupy Sales**
245 East 35th Street
New York, NY 10016
"Actor, Comedian"

**Pierre Salinger**
La Bastiderose, 99 Cherin Des
Croupieres Lethor FRANCE
"News Correspondent"

**Illya Salkind**
1000 Universal Plaza
Orlando, FL 32819
"Film Producer"

**Jennifer Salt**
9045 Elevado Street
West Hollywood, CA 90069
"Actress"

**Salt-N-Pepa**
250 W. 57th Street #821
New York, NY 10107
"Rap Group"

**Sam The Sham**
6123 Old Brunswick Road
Arlington, TN 38002
"Singer, Songwriter"

**Richie Sambora**
4970 Summit View Drive
Thousand Oaks, CA 91362
"Guitarist"

**Emma Samms**
2934 1/2 N. Beverly Glen Circle
Suite #417
Los Angeles, CA 90077
"Actress"

**Pete Sampras**
525 Plymouth Road #317
Plymouth Meeting, PA 19462
"Tennis Player"

**Jeffrey D. Sams**
9200 Sunset Blvd., #1130
Los Angeles, CA 90069
"Actor"

**Ron Samuels**
P.O. Box 1690
Rancho Mirage, CA 92270
"Talent Agent"

**David Sanborn**
27171 Grayfox Street
Malibu, CA 90365
"Musician"

**Roselyn Sanchez**
400 North Gardner Street
Los Angeles, CA 90035
"Actress"

**Aitana Sanchez-Gijon**
8730 Sunset Blvd. #490
Los Angeles, CA 90069
"Actress"

**Casey Sander**
145 S. Fairfax Avenue #310
Los Angeles, CA 90036
"Actor"

**Beverly Sanders**
12218 Morrison Street
Valley Village, CA 91607
"Actress"

**Doug Sanders**
8828 Sandringham
Houston, TX 77024
"Golfer"

**Mariene Sanders**
175 Riverdale Drive
New York, NY 10024
"Television Writer, Director"

**Richard Sanders**
P.O. Box 1644
Woodinville, WA 98072
"Actor, Writer"

**Summer Sanders**
450 Harmon Meadow Blvd.
Secaucus, NJ 07094
"Swimmer"

**William Sanderson**
P.O. Box 691471
West Hollywood, CA 90069
"Actor"

**Adam Sandler**
9150 Wilshire Blvd., 350
Beverly Hills, CA 90212
"Actor"

**Jay Sandrich**
610 North Maple Drive
Beverly Hills, CA 90210
"Actor, Director"

**Julian Sands**
1287 Ozeta Terrace
Los Angeles, CA 90069
"Actor"

**Tommy Sands**
P.O. Box 770850
Orlando, FL 32877
"Actor, Singer"

**Baby Sandy**
(Sandra Lee Henville Magee)
6846 Haywood
Tujunga, CA 91042
"Actress"

**Gary Sandy**
P.O. Box 4146
North Hollywood, CA 91607
"Actor"

**Isabel Sanford**
2501 Colorado Avenue #350
Santa Monica, CA 90404
"Actress"

**Carlos Santana**
P.O. Box 10348
San Rafael, CA 94912
"Singer"

**Merlin Santana**
300 South Raymond Avenue #11
Pasadena, CA 91105
"Actor"

**Benito Santiago**
2267 NW 199th Street
Miami, FL 33056
"Baseball Player"

**Tessie Santiago**
1450 South Robertson Blvd.
Los Angeles, CA 90035
"Actress"

**Santo & Johnny**
217 Edgewood Avenue
Clearwater, FL 34615
"Vocal Duo"

**Ron Santo**
1721 Meadow Lane
Bannockburn, IL 60015
"Ex-Baseball Player"

**Reni Santoni**
247 South Beverly Drive #102
Beverly Hills, CA 90212
"Actor"

**Al Sapienza**
P.O. Box 691240
West Hollywood, CA 90069
"Actor"

**HRH Sarah, Dutchess of York**
Sunningham Park
Berkshire Windsor ENGLAND
"Royalty"

**Chris Sarandon**
3500 West Olive Avenue #920
Burbank, CA 91505
"Actor"

**Susan Sarandon**
40 West 57th Street
New York, NY 10019
"Actress"

**Sen. Paul Sarbanes (MD)**
Senate Hart Bldg. #309
Washington, DC 20510
"Politician"

**Vincent Sardi, Jr.**
234 West 44th Street
New York, NY 10036
"Restaurateur"

**Joseph Sargent**
8827 Beverly Blvd.
Los Angeles, CA 90048
"Film Director, Producer"

**Michael Sarrazin**
9920 Beverly Grove
Beverly Hills, CA 90210
"Actor"

**Vidal Sassoon**
1163 Calle Vista
Beverly Hills, CA 90210
"Hair Stylist"

**Paul Satterfield**
400 S. Beverly Drive #101
Beverly Hills, CA 90212
"Actor"

**Ben Savage**
1450 South Robertson Blvd. #15
Los Angeles, CA 90035
"Actor"

**Fred Savage**
1122 S. Robertson Blvd. #15
Los Angeles, CA 90035
"Actor"

**John Savage**
11300 W. Olympic Blvd. #610
Los Angeles, CA 90064
"Actor"

**Randy Savage**
7650 Bayshore Drive #10038
St. Petersburg, FL 33706
"Wrestler"

**Tracie Savage**
6212 Banner Avenue
Los Angeles, CA 90038
"Actress"

**Doug Savant**
252 N. Larchmont Blvd. #200
Los Angeles, CA 90004
"Actor"

**David Saville**
28 Colomb Street
London SW10 9EW ENGLAND
"Actor"

**Julia Sawalha**
34-43 Russell Street
London WC2B 5HA ENGLAND
"Actress"

**Sawyer Brown**
5200 Old Harding Road
Franklin, TN 37064
"Rock & Roll Group"

**Diane Sawyer**
147 Columbus Avenue
New York, NY 10023
"Broadcast Journalist"

**Steve Sax**
201 Wesley Court
Roseville, CA 95661
"ex-Baseball Player"

**John Saxon**
P.O. Box 492480
Los Angeles, CA 90049
"Actor, Writer"

**Peggy Say**
438 Lake Shore Drive
Cadiz, KY 42211
"Sister Of American Hostage"

**Gale Sayers**
1150 Feehanville Drive
Mt. Prospect, IL 60056
"Ex-Football Player"

**Anne Sayre**
1268 East 14th Street
Brooklyn, NY 11230
"Actress"

**Raphael Sbarge**
4526 Wilshire Blvd.
Los Angeles, CA 90046
"Actor"

**Boz Scaggs**
9460 Wilshire Blvd. #310
Beverly Hills, CA 90212
"Singer, Songwriter"

**Prunella Scales**
18-21 Jermyn Street
London SW1 ENGLAND
"Actress"

**Antonin Scalia**
6713 Wemberly Way
McLean, VA 22101
"Supreme Court Justice"

**Jack Scalia**
23049 Calvert Street
Woodland Hills, CA 91367
"Actor"

**Michele Scarabelli**
9157 Sunset Blvd. #215
Los Angeles, CA 90069
"Actress"

**Diana Scarwid**
P.O. Box 3614
Savannah, GA 31404
"Actress"

**Francesco Scavullo**
216 East 63rd Street
New York, NY 10021
"Photographer"

**Richard Schaal**
612 Gulf Blvd. #9
Indian Rocks Beach, FL 33785
"Actor"

**Johnathon Schaech**
4739 Lankershim Blvd.
North Hollywood, CA 91602
"Actor"

**George Schaeffer**
1040 Woodland Drive
Beverly Hills, CA 90210
"TV Director, Producer"

**William Schallert**
14920 Ramos Place
Pacific Palisades, CA 90272
"Actor"

**Anne Schedeen**
4526 Wilshire Blvd.
Los Angeles, CA 90010
"Actress"

**Roy Scheider**
P.O. Box 364
Sagaponack, NY 11962
"Actor"

**Judge Judy Scheindlin**
5842 Sunset Blvd., #303
Hollywood, CA 90028
"TV Judge"

**Catherine Schell**
Postfache 8000504, D-51005
Koln, GERMANY
"Actress"

**Maria Schell**
A-9451 Preitenegg
AUSTRIA
"Actress"

**Maximilian Schell**
2869 Royston Place
Beverly Hills, CA 90210
"Actor"

**August Schellenberg**
1320 Waterside Drive
Dallas, TX 75218
"Actor"

**Bo Schembechler**
1904 Boulder Drive
Ann Arbor, MI 48104
"Ex-College Football Coach"

**Chris Schenkel**
7101 North Kalorama Road
Leesburg, IN 46538
"Sportscaster"

**Bob Schieffer**
2438 Belmont Road NW
Washington, DC 20008
"Broadcast Journalist"

**Claudia Schiffer**
342 Madison Avenue #1900
New York, NY 10173
"Model"

**Lalo Schifrin**
710 North Hillcrest Road
Beverly Hills, CA 90210
"Composer, Conductor"

**Walter M. Schirra, Jr.**
16834 Via de Santa Fe
Rancho Santa Fe, CA 92067
"Astronaut"

**Steve Schirripa**
8436 West 3rd Street #740
Los Angeles, CA 90048
"Actor"

**Phyllis Schlafly**
68 Fairmont
Alton, IL 62002
"Author, Politician"

**George Schlatter**
400 Robert Lane
Beverly Hills, CA 90210
"Writer, Producer"

**John Schlesinger**
P.O. Box 1362
Desert Hot Springs, CA 92240
"Film Director"

**Dr. Laura Schlessinger**
25065 Ashley Ridge Road
Hidden Hills, CA 91302
"Radio Show Host"

**Edwin Schlossberg**
641 Avenue of the Americas
New York, NY 10011
"Artist"

**Max Schmeling**
Sonnenweg 1
D-21279 Hollenstedt
GERMANY
"Ex-Boxer"

**Helmut Schmidt**
Die Ziet, Speersport 1
Hamburg 20095 GERMANY
"Ex-Chancellor"

**John Schneider**
8436 West 3rd Street #740
Los Angeles, CA 90048
"Actor, Writer, Singer"

**Rob Schneider**
12250 Addison Street
Valley Village, CA 91607
"Actor"

**Stephen Schnetzer**
448 West 44th Street
New York, NY 10036
"Actor"

**Gina Schock**
P.O. Box 4398
North Hollywood, CA 91617
"Drummer, Singer"

**Carolyn Hunt Schoellkopf**
100 Crescent #1700
Dallas, TX 75201
"Businesswoman"

**Daniel Schorr**
3113 Woodley Road
Washington, DC 20008
"Broadcast Journalist"

**Marge Schott**
Great American Ball Park
Cincinnati, OH 45202
"Baseball Team Owner"

**David Schramm**
3521 Berry Drive
Studio City, CA 91604
"Actor"

**Tex Schramm**
9355 Sunnybrook
Dallas, TX 75220
"Football Team Executive"

**Gerhard Schroder**
c/o Federal Chancellery
Willy-Brandtstr. 1
10557 Berlin GERMANY
"Chancellor"

**Barbet Schroeder**
9830 Wilshire Blvd.
Beverly Hills, CA 90212
"Film Director"

**Patricia Schroeder**
c/o Assoc. of Amer. Publishers
71 - 5th Avenue
New York, NY 10003
"Ex-Politician"

**Mark Schubb**
9744 Wilshire Blvd. #308
Beverly Hills, CA 90212
"Actor"

**John Schuck**
1501 Broadway #703
New York, NY 10036
"Actor"

**Budd Schulberg**
P.O. Box 707, Brookside
Westhampton Beach, NY 11978
"TV Writer"

**Dr. Robert Schuller**
P.O. Box 100
Garden Grove, CA 92842
"Motivational & Author"

**Dwight Schultz**
3172 Dona Susana Drive
Stuido City, CA 91604
"Actor"

**Matt Schulze**
P.O. Box 5617
Beverly Hills, CA 90210
"Actor"

**Paul Schulze**
9150 Wilshire Blvd. #350
Beverly Hills, CA 90212
"Actor"

**Joel Schumacher**
11766 Wilshire Blvd. #1610
Los Angeles, CA 90025
"Writer, Producer"

**Sen. Charles Schumer (NY)**
313 Hart Senate Building
Washington, DC 20510
"Politicain"

**Diane Schuur**
33042 Ocean Ridge
Dana Point, CA 92629
"Singer"

**Neil Schwartz**
23427 Schoolcraft Avenue
Canoga Park, CA 91304
"Actor"

**Sherwood Schwartz**
1865 Carla Ridge Dr.
Beverly Hills, CA 90210
"TV Writer, Producer"

**Arnold Schwarzenegger**
3110 Main Street #300
Santa Monica, CA 90405
"Actor"

**Elisabeth Schwarzkopf**
Rebhusstr. 29
CH-8126 Zunnikon
Zurich, SWITZERLAND
"Opera Singer"

**Gen. Norman Schwarzkopf**
400 North Ashley Drive #3050
Tampa, FL 33609
"Military Leader"

**David Schwimmer**
1122 South Roberston Blvd. #15
Los Angeles, CA 90035
"Actor"

**Rusty Schwimmer**
1450 South Robertson Blvd.
Los Angeles, CA 90035
"Actress"

**Hanna Schygulla**
Leopoldstr. 19
D-80802 Munich GERMANY
"Actress"

**Patti Scialfa**
1224 Benedict Canyon
Beverly Hills, CA 90210
"Singer"

**Leonard Sciascia**
Viale Scaduto 10/B
I-90144 Palermo, ITALY
"Author"

**Annabella Sciorra**
8383 Wilshire Blvd. #550
Beverly Hills, CA 90211
"Actress"

**Mike Scioscia**
444 Fargo Street
Thousand Oaks, CA 91360
"Baseball Player"

**Dean Scofield**
12304 Santa Monica Blvd. #104
Los Angeles, CA 90025
"Actor"

**Paul Scofield**
The Gables
Balcombe, Sussex ENGLAND
"Actor"

**Tracy Scoggins**
10100 Santa Monica Blvd. #410
Los Angeles, CA 90067
"Actress, Model"

**Peter Scolari**
500 S. Sepulveda Blvd. #500
Los Angeles, CA 90049
"Actor"

**The Scooters**
15190 Encanto Drive
Sherman Oaks, CA 91403
"Rock & Roll Group"

**Martine Scorsese**
445 Park Avenue #700
New York, NY 10022
"Film Writer, Producer"

**Izabella Scorupco**
Volrumlehenkatu 20
00150 Helsinki FINLAND
"Actress"

**Campbell Scott**
200 West 57th Street #900
New York, NY 10019
"Actor"

**Coltin Scott**
195 South Beverly Drive #400
Beverly Hills, CA 90212
"Actor"

**Col. David Scott**
30 Hackamore Lane #1
Bell Canyon, CA 91307
"NASA Astronaut"

**Dr. Gene Scott**
1615 Glendale Avenue
Glendale, CA 91205
"TV Show Host, Teacher"

**Jacqueline Scott**
12216 Moorpark Street
Studio City, CA 91604
"Actress"

**Jean Bruce Scott**
11250 Addison Street
Valley Village, CA 91607
"Actress"

**Judson Scott**
P.O. Box 2744
Toluca Lake, CA 91610
"Actor"

**Kathryn Leigh Scott**
5757 Wilshire Blvd. #473
Los Angeles, CA 90036
"Actress"

**Klea Scott**
1180 S. Beverly Drive #608
Los Angeles, CA 90035
"Actress"

**Lizabeth Scott**
8277 Hollywood Blvd.
Los Angeles, CA 90069
"Actress"

**Martha Scott**
14054 Chandler Blvd.
Van Nuys, CA 91401
"Actress"

**Melody Thomas Scott**
25151 Jim Bridger Road
Hidden Hills, CA 91302
"Actress"

**Pippa Scott**
10850 Wilshire Blvd. #250
Los Angeles, CA 90024
"Actress"

**Ridley Scott**
7920 Sunset Blvd.
Los Angeles, CA 90046
"Film Director"

**Seann William Scott**
9100 Wilshire Blvd., #615-E
Beverly Hills, CA 90210
"Actor"

**Tom Everett Scott**
9560 Wilshire Blvd. #516
Beverly Hills, CA 90212
"Actor"

**Williard Scott**
30 Rockerfeller Plaza #304
New York, NY 10012
"TV Weatherman"

**Renato Scotto**
61 West 62nd Street #6F
New York, NY 10023
"Soprano"

**General Brent Scowcroft**
350 Park Avenue #2600
New York, NY 10022
"Ex-Military, Politician"

**William W. Scranton**
201 Pennsylvania Avenue #231
Scranton, PA 18503
ex-Gov. of Pennsylvanis"

**Earl Scruggs**
P.O. Box 40313
Nashville, TN 37204
"Banjoist, Songwriter"

**Vin Scully**
P.O. Box 559
Salisbury, NC 28144
"Sportscaster"

**Ryan Seacrest**
2700 Colorado Avenue #400
Santa Monica, CA 90404
"Actor"

**Steven Seagal**
151 El Camino Drive
Beverly Hills, CA 90212
"Actor"

**Bob Seagren**
25301 Prado De Los Arboles
Calabasas, CA 91302
"Actor"

**Jenny Seagrove**
76 Oxford Street
London W1D 1BS ENGLAND
"Actress"

**Seal**
27A Floral Street #300
Covent Garden
London WC2E 9DQ ENGLAND
"Singer"

**Dan Seals**
38 Music Square East #300
Nashville, TN 37203
"Singer, Songwriter"

**Junior Seau**
1640 Camino del Rio North
San Diego, CA 92108
"Football Player"

**Tom Seaver**
1761 Diamond Mountain Road
Calistoga, CA 94515
"Ex-Baseball Player"

**John Sebastian**
2431 Briarcrest Road
Beverly Hills, CA 90210
"Singer, Songwriter"

**Alice Sebold**
c/o Little Brown & Co.
34 Beacon Street
Boston, MA 02108
"Author"

**Jon Secada**
420 Jefferson Avenue
Miami Beach, FL 33139
"Singer"

**Kyle Secor**
9150 Wilshire Blvd. #350
Beverly Hills, CA 90212
"Actor"

**Gen. Richard Secord**
1 Pennsylvania Plaza #2400
New York, NY 10119
"Miltary Leader"

**Jon Seda**
420 Jefferson Avenue
Miami Beach, FL 33139
"Actor"

**Neil Sedaka**
201 East 66th Street #3N
New York, NY 10021
"Singer, Songwriter"

**Frank Sedgman**
28 Bolton Avenue
Hampton, Victoria 3188
AUSTRALIA
"Tennis Player"

**Kyra Sedgwick**
P.O. Box 668
Sharon, CT 06069
"Actress"

**Pete Seeger**
P.O. Box 431
Duchess Junction
Beacon, NY 12508
"Singer, Songwriter"

**Erich Segal**
Wolfson College
Oxford OX2 66D ENGLAND
"Author"

**George Segal**
515 N. Robertson Blvd.
Los Angeles, CA 90048
"Actor"

**Jonathan Segal**
P.O. Box 3059
Tel Aviv 61030 ISRAEL
"Actor"

**Michael Segal**
27 Cyprus Avenue, Finchley
London N3 1SS ENGLAND
"Actor"

**Pamela Segall**
8675 W. Washington Blvd. #293
Culver City, CA 90232
"Actress"

**Bob Seger**
567 Purdy
Birmingham, MI 48009
"Singer"

**Pancho Segura**
194 Bellevue Avenue
Newport, RI 02840
"Tennis Player"

**Jason Sehorn**
c/o NY Giants
Giants Stadium
East Rutherford, NJ 07073
"Football Player"

**Emmanuella Seigner**
3 Quai Malaquais
F-75006 Paris FRANCE
"Actress"

**Jerry Seinfeld**
147 S. El Camino Drive #205
Beverly Hills, CA 90212
"Comedian, Actor"

**Seka**
1122 White Rock
Dixon, IL 60121
"Actress, Model"

**David Selby**
15152 Encanto Drive
Sherman Oaks, CA 91403
"Actor"

**Monica Seles**
1266 East Main Street #4
Stamford, CT 06902
"Tennis Player"

**Bud Selig**
c/o County Coliseum
Milwaukee, WI 53214
"Baseball Team Owner"

**Connie Selleca**
15030 Ventura Blvd. #916
Sherman Oaks, CA 91403
"Actress"

**Tom Selleck**
10560 Wilshire Blvd. #1606
Los Angeles, CA 90068
"Actor"

**Milton Selzer**
1751 Emerald Isle Way
Oxnard, CA 93035
"Actor"

**Suzanne Sena**
6310 San Vicente Blvd. #200
Los Angeles, CA 90048
"Celebrity Homes Host"

**Maurice Sendak**
200 Chestnut Hill Road
Ridgefield, CT 06877
"Illustrator, Artist"

**The Serendipity Singers**
P.O. Box 142
Wauconda, IL 60084
"Vocal Group"

**Yahoo Serious**
12/33 East Crescent Street
McMahons Point NSW 2060
AUSTRLIA
"Actor, Director"

**Pepe Serna**
127 Ruby Avenue
Newport Beach, CA 92661
"Actor"

**Michel Serrauot**
201 rue Du Fauboug-Street-Honore
F-75008 Paris FRANCE
"Actor"

**Sesame Street**
1329 Braddock Place
Alexandria, VA 22314
"Children TV Show"

**Johnny Seven**
11213 McLennan Avenue
Granada Hills, CA 91344
"Actor, Director"

**Doc Severinsen**
4275 White Pine Lane
Santa Ynez, CA 93460
"Trumpeter"

**The Sex Pistols**
252 - 260 Regent Street
London SW13 OAT ENGLAND
"Music Group"

**Jane Seymour**
23852 Pacific Coast Hwy., PMB 337
Malibu, CA 90265
"Actress, Model"

**Stephanie Seymour**
5415 Oberlin Drive
San Diego, CA 92121
"Model"

**Ted Shackelford**
12305 Valleyheart Drive
Studio City, CA 91604
"Actor"

**Paul Shaffer**
1697 Broadway
New York, NY 10019
"Keyboardist"

**Peter Shaffer**
200 Fulham Road
London SW10 ENGLAND
"Screenwriter"

**Steve Shagan**
10390 Wilshire Blvd. #705
Los Angeles, CA 90024
"Writer, Producer"

**Shakira**
420 Jefferson Avenue
Miami Beach, FL 33132
"Singer"

**Kula Shakur**
39-A Gramercy Park N. #1-C
New York, NY 10010
"Music Band"

**Donna Shalala**
University of Miami
230 Ashe Bldg.
Coral Gables, FL 33124
"ex-Sec. Health & Human Service"

**Shalamar**
707-18th Avenue So.
Nashville, TN 37203
"R&B Group"

**Gene Shalit**
225 East 79th Street
New York, NY 10021
"Film Critic"

**Yitzhak Shamir**
Belt Amot Mishpat 8 Shaul
Hamelech Blvd.
Tel Aviv 64733 ISRAEL
"Politician"

**Garry Shandling**
c/o Endeavor
9701 Wilshire Blvd., 10th Floor
Beverly Hills, CA 90212
"Comedian, Actor, Director"

**Shanice**
1800 Argyle Avenue #408
Hollywood, CA 90028
"Singer"

**Ravi Shankar**
17 Warden Court
Gowalia Tank Road
Bombay 36 INDIA
"Satarist"

**Michael Shanks**
1122 South Robertson Blvd. #15
Los Angeles, CA 90035
"Actor"

**Esther Shapiro**
617 North Alta Drive
Beverly Hills, CA 90210
"TV Writer, Producer"

**Richard Shapiro**
617 North Alta Drive
Beverly Hills, CA 90210
"TV Writer, Producer"

**Robert Shapiro**
2121 Avenue of the Stars #1900
Los Angeles, CA 90067
"Attorney"

**Omar Sharif**
BP 41
F-78380 Bougival FRANCE
"Actor"

**Barbara Sharma**
P.O. Box 29125
Los Angeles, CA 90029
"Actress"

**Ariel Sharon**
38 Rehou King George
Tel Aviv, 61231 Israel
"Prime Minister"

**Don Sharp**
80 Castelnau
London SW13 9EX ENGLAND
"TV Writer, Executive"

**Rev. Al Sharpton**
1941 Madison Avenue #2
New York, NY 10035
"Social Activist"

**William Shatner**
11288 Ventura Blvd. #725
Studio City, CA 91604
"Actor"

**David Shatraw**
544 North Poinsettia Pl.
Los Angeles, CA 90036
"Actor"

**Grant Shaud**
151 El Camino Drive
Beverly Hills, CA 90036
"Actor"

**Charles Shaughnessy**
P.O. Box 7314
Santa Monica, CA 90406
"Actor"

**Mel Shavelson**
11947 Sunshine Terrace
North Hollywood, CA 91604
"Writer, Producer"

**Earnie Shavers**
30 Doreen Avenue
Moretown, Wirral
Merseyside CH46 6DN ENGLAND
"Boxer"

**Helen Shaver**
1505 - 10th Street
Santa Monica, CA 90401
"Actress"

**Artie Shaw**
2127 West Palos Court
Newbury Park, CA 91320
"Orchestra Leader"

**Martin Shaw**
204 Belswins Lane
Hemel, Hempstead
Hertfordshire, ENGLAND
"Actor"

**Stan Shaw**
4526 Wilshire Blvd.
Los Angeles, CA 90010
"Actor"

**Tommy Shaw**
1225 N. Meadow Pkwy. #100
Roswell, GA 30076
"Singer, Songwriter"

**Wallace Shawn**
3 East 48th Street
New York, NY 10017
"Playwright

**David Shawyer**
16 Rylett Road
London W12 ENGLAND
"Actor"

**George Beverly Shea**
1300 Harmon Place
Minneapolis, MN 55403
"Singer"

**Harry Shearer**
1900 West Pico Blvd.
Santa Monica, CA 90405
"TV Writer, Director"

**George Shearing**
1220 General MacArthur Drive
Brentwood, TN 37027
"Actor"

**SheDaisy**
3310 West End Avenue #500
Nashville, TN 37203
"Country Sister-Trio Group"

**Ally Sheedy**
11766 Wilshire Blvd. #1610
Los Angeles, CA 90025
"Actress"

**Doug Sheehan**
4019-137 Goldfinch Street
San Diego, CA 92103
"Actor"

**Patty Sheehan**
8395 Panorama Drive
Reno, NV 89511
"Golfer"

**Gail Sheehy**
300 East 57th Street #18-D
New York, NY 10022
"Author, Journalist"

**Charlie Sheen**
10580 Wilshire Blvd.
Los Angeles, CA 90024
"Actor"

**Martin Sheen**
6916 Dune Drive
Malibu, CA 90265
"Actor, TV Director"

**Craig Sheffer**
5699 Kanan Road #275
Agoura, CA 91301
"Actor"

**Gary Sheffield**
2267 Northwest 199th Street
Miami, FL 33056
"Baseball Player"

**Johnny Sheffield**
834 First Avenue
Chula Vista, CA 92011
"Actor"

**Sen. Richard C. Shelby (AL)**
Senate Hart Bldg. #110
Washington, DC 20515
"Politician"

**Sidney Sheldon**
9100 Wilshire Blvd. #1000 West
Beverly Hills, CA 90212
"Writer"

**Sheila E**
1005 North Alfred Street #2
West Hollywood, CA 90069
"Singer"

**Art Shell**
2318 Walker Drive
Lawrenceville, GA 30043
"Ex-Football Player"

**Barbara Shelley**
91 Regent Street
London W1R 7TB ENGLAND
"Actress"

**Deborah Shelton**
2265 Westwood Blvd. #251
Los Angeles, CA 90064
"Actress"

**Shenandoah**
P.O. Box 1574
Goodlettsville, TN 37070
"Music Group"

**Jean Shepard**
1300 Division Street #102
Nashville, TN 37203
"Singer"

**Sam Shepard**
8942 Wilshire Blvd.
Beverly Hills, CA 90211
"Actor, Director"

**Cybill Shepherd**
1122 S. Robertson Blvd. #15
Los Angeles, CA 90035
"Actress, Model"

**T.G. Sheppard**
P.O. Box 510
Dundee, IL 60118
"Singer"

**Jamey Sheridan**
8942 Wilshire Blvd.
Beverly Hills, CA 90211
"Actor"

**Liz Sheridan**
125 South Sycamore Avenue
Los Angeles, CA 90036
"Actress"

**Bobby Sherman**
108 North Orlando Avenue #4
Los Angeles, CA 90048
"Singer, Actor"

**Vincent Sherman**
6355 Sycamore Meadows
Malibu, CA 90265
"Film Director"

**Pres. Edward Shevardnadze**
c/o State Council
Tbilisi GEORGIA
"Politician"

**Brooke Shields**
335 North Maple Drive #351
Beverly Hills, CA 90210
"Actress, Model"

**Robert Shields**
P.O. Box 2284
Sedona, AZ 86339
"Jewelry Maker & Mime"

**James Shigeta**
10635 Santa Monica Blvd. #130
Los Angeles, CA 90025
"Actor"

**Armin Shimerman**
1505 - 10th Street
Santa Monica, CA 90401
"Actor"

**Sab Shimono**
12711 Ventura Blvd. #440
Studio City, CA 91604
"Actor"

**Talia Shire**
16633 Ventura Blvd. #1450
Encino, CA 91436
"Actress"

**The Shirelles**
P.O. Box 100
Clifton, NJ 07011
"Singing Group"

**William Shockley**
6345 Balboa Blvd. #375
Encino, CA 91316
"Actor"

**Bill Shoemaker**
2545 Fairfield Place
San Marino, CA 91108
"Horse Racer"

**Pamela Susan Shoop**
13547 Ventura Blvd. #105
Sherman Oaks, CA 91423
"Actress"

**Pauly Shore**
8491 Sunset Blvd. #700
W. Hollywood, CA 90069
"Actor"

**Roberta Shore**
P.O. Box 71639
Salt Lake City, UT 84171
"Actress"

**Lonnie Shorr**
707 18th Avenue South
Nashville, TN 37203
"Comedian"

**Bobby Short**
444 East 57th Street #9E
New York, NY 10022
"Actor, Singer"

**Martin Short**
9150 Wilshire Blvd. 3350
Beverly Hills, CA 90212
"Actor"

**Frank Shorter**
558 Utica Court
Boulder, CO 80304
"Track Athlete"

**Steve Shortridge**
1707 Clearview Drive
Beverly Hills, CA 90210
"Actor"

**Grant Show**
937 South Tremaine
Los Angeles, CA 90019
"Actor"

**Jean Shrimpton**
Abbey Hotel
Penzance
Cornwall ENGLAND
"Actress"

**Kin Shriner**
3915 Benedict Canyon
Sherman Oaks, CA 91423
"Actor"

**Wil Shriner**
5313 Quakertown Avenue
Woodland Hills, CA 91364
"Actor, Writer, Comedian"

**Eunice Kennedy Shriver**
9109 Harrington Drive
Potomac, MD 20854
"Ex-President's Sister"

**Maria Shriver**
3110 Main Street #300
Santa Monica, CA 90405
"Broadcast Journalist"

**Pam Shriver**
401 Washington Avenue #902
Baltimore, MD 21204
"Tennis Player"

**R. Sargent Shriver**
1325 "G" Street NW
Washington, DC 20005
"Politician"

**Andrew Shue**
16255 Ventura Blvd. #920
Encino, CA 91436
"Actor"

**Elisabeth Shue**
1146 Sierra Alta Way
Los Angeles, CA 90069
"Actress"

**Don Shula**
16 Indian Creek Island
Miami Lakes, FL 33154
"Football Coach"

**George P. Shultz**
776 Dolores Street
Stanford, CA 94305
"Ex-Government Official"

**M. Night Shyamalan**
9560 Wilshire Blvd. #500
Beverly Hills, CA 90212
"Film Director, Actor, Writer"

**Jane Siberry**
1505 W. 2nd Avenue #200
Vancouver, BC V6H 3Y4
CANADA
"Singer, Guitarist"

**Hugh Sidey**
1050 Connecticut Avenue
Washington, DC 20036
"Columnist"

**Siegfried & Roy**
1639 North Valley Drive
Las Vegas, NV 89109
"Circus Act"

**Casey Siemaszko**
P.O. Box 5617
Beverly Hills, CA 90210
"Actor"

**Gregory Sierra**
8050 Selma Avenue
Los Angeles, CA 90046
"Actor"

**Jamie Lynn Sigler**
One Huntington Quad #3N07
Melville, NY 11747
"Actress"

**Sanford Sigoloff**
320 Cliffwood Avenue
Los Angeles, CA 90049
"Business Executive"

**Cynthia Sikes**
250 Delfern Drive
Los Angeles, CA 90077
"Actress"

**James B. Sikking**
4526 Wilshire Blvd.
Beverly Hills, CA 90210
"Actor"

**Karen Sillas**
P.O. Box 725
Wading River, NY 11792
"Actress"

**Beverly Sills**
RFD, Lambert's Cove Road
Vineyard Haven, MA 02568
"Soprano"

**Henry Silva**
8747 Clifton Way #305
Beverly Hills, CA 90210
"Actor"

**Ron Silver**
8942 Wilshire Blvd. #219
Beverly Hills, CA 90211
"Actor"

**Fred Silverman**
1642 Mandeville Canyon
Los Angeles, CA 90049
TV Executive, Producer"

**Jonathan Silverman**
2255 Mountain Oak Drive
Los Angeles, CA 90068
"Actor"

**Alicia Silverstone**
1122 S. Robertson Blvd. #15
Los Angeles, CA 90035
"Actress"

**Curt Simmons**
200 Park Road
Prospectville, PA 19002
"Baseball Player"

**Dick Simmons**
3215 Silver Cliff Drive
Prescott, AZ 86303
"Actor"

**Gene Simmons**
8730 Sunset Blvd. #200
Los Angeles, CA 90069
"Singer, Actor, Composer"

**Henry Simmons**
P.O. Box 5617
Beverly Hills, CA 90210
"Actor"

**Jaason Simmons**
43 Navy Street #300
Venice, CA 90291
"Actor"

**Jean Simmons**
636 Adelaide Way
Santa Monica, CA 90402
"Actress"

**Richard Simmons**
3215 Silver Cliff Circle
Prescott, AZ 86303
"Exercise Instructor"

**Larry Simms**
P.O. Box 55
Gray River, WA 98621
"Actor"

**Phil Simms**
252 West 71st Street
New York, NY 10023
"Ex-Football Player"

**Carly Simon**
P.O. Box 679
Branford, CT 06405
"Singer"

**Neil Simon**
10745 Chalon Road
Los Angeles, CA 90077
"Dramatist"

**Paul Simon**
Southern Ilinois University
Carbondale, IL 62901
"Ex-Senator"

**Paul Simon**
c/o Dan Klores
386 Park Avenue S., 10th Floor
New York, NY 10019
"Singer, Songwriter

**Simone Simon**
5 rue de Tilsitt
75008 Paris, FRANCE
"Actress"

**Simple Minds**
252-260 Regent Street
London W1B 3BX ENGLAND
"Rock & Roll Group"

**Simply Red**
Lock Keeper Cottage
Century Street
Manchester M3 4QL ENGLAND
"Rock & Roll Group"

**ex-Sen Alan Simpson**
1201 Sunshine Avenue
Cody, WY 82414
"Politician"

**Arnelle Simpson**
11661 San Vicente Blvd. #632
Los Angeles, CA 90049
"O.J.'s Daughter"

**Ashlee Simpson**
5700 Wilshire Blvd., 5th Floor
Los Angeles, CA 90036
"Actress, Singer, Dancer"

**Jason Simpson**
11661 San Vicente Blvd. #632
Los Angeles, CA 90049
"O.J.'s Son"

**Jessica Simpson**
c/o Hoffman
20 West 55th Street, 11th Floor
New York, NY 10019
"Singer"

**O.J. Simpson**
9450 SW 112th Street
Miami, FL 33176
"Ex-Football Player"

**Billy Sims**
230 S. MacArthur Blvd. #1111
Coppell, TX 75019
"Ex-Football Player"

**Frank Sinatra, Jr.**
3219 W. Brigantine Ave. #200
Brigantine Beach, NJ 08203
"Singer"

**Nancy Sinatra, Jr.**
P.O. Box 10236
Beverly Hills, CA 90210
"Singer, Actress"

**Ray Sinatra**
1234 S. 8th Place
Las Vegas, NV 89104
"Composer, Conductor"

**Tina Sinatra**
c/o Goldwyn Studios
1041 North Formosa Avenue
Los Angeles, CA 90046
"Singer"

**Sinceros**
25 Buliver Street
Shephard's Bush
London W12 8AR ENGLAND
"Rock & Roll Group"

**Donald Sinden**
60 Temple Fortune Lane
London NW11 ENGLAND
"Actor"

**Lori Singer**
1465 Linda Crest Drive
Beverly Hills, CA 90210
"Actress"

**Marc Singer**
15821 Ventura Blvd. #235
Encino, CA 91436
"Actor"

**John Singleton**
P.O. Box 92547
Pasadena, CA 91107
"Director"

**Margie Singleton**
P.O. Box 567
Hendersonville, TN 37077
"Singer, Guitarist"

**Penny Singleton**
15245 La Maida Street #101
Sherman Oaks, CA 91403
"Actress"

**Gary Sinise**
9150 Wilshire Blvd. #350
Beverly Hills, CA 90212
"Actor"

**Sirhan Sirhan #B21014**
Corcoran State Prison
P.O. Box 8800
Corcoran, CA 93212
"Robert Kennendy's Killer"

**Tony Sirico**
9150 Wilshire Blvd. #350
Beverly Hills, CA 90212
"Actor"

**Marina Sirtis**
4526 Wilshire Blvd.
Los Angeles, CA 90010
"Actress"

**Sisqo**
9100 Wilshire Blvd. #400W
Beverly Hills, CA 90212
"R&B Singer"

**Jeremy Sisto**
1505 - 10th Street
Santa Monica, CA 90401
"Actor"

**Sister Sledge**
173 Main Street
Ossining, NY 10562
"Vocal Group"

**Tom Sizemore**
9100 Wilshire Blvd., West Tower #600
Beverly Hills, CA 90212
"Actor"

**Ricky Skaggs**
329 Rockland Road
Hendersonville, TN 37075
"Singer, Guitarist"

**Michael Skakel**
Garner Corr. Institution
Garner Street
New Town, MA 02258
"Accused killer of Martha Moxley"

**Tom Skerritt**
1122 S. Robertson Blvd. #15
Los Angeles, CA 90035
"Actor"

**Skid Row**
2002 Hogback Road #20
Ann Arbor, MI 48105
"Rock & Roll Group"

**Moose Skowron**
1118 Beachcomber Drive
Schaumburg, IL 60193
"Ex-Baseball Player"

**Michael Skupin**
2734 Wabum Road
White Lake, MI 48386
"Survivor Show Contestant"

**Ione Skye**
8794 Lookout Mountain Avenue
Los Angeles, CA 90046
"Actress"

**Mark Slade**
38 Joppa Road
Worcester, MA 01602
"Actor"

**Christian Slater**
1122 S. Robertson Blvd. #15
Los Angeles, CA 90035
"Actor"

**Helen Slater**
1327 Brinkley Avenue
Los Angeles, CA 90049
"Actress"

**Robert F. Slatzer**
3033 Hollycrest Drive #2
Los Angeles, CA 90068
"Writer, Producer"

**Brandon Slay**
6155 Lehman Avenue
Colorado Springs, CO 80918
Wrestler"

**Percy Sledge**
9850 Sandalfoot Blvd. #458
Boca Raton, FL 33428
"Singer"

**Erika Siezak**
40 West 57th Street
New York, NY 10019
"Actress"

**Grace Slick**
c/o B. Thompson
2051 Third Street
San Francisco, CA 94107
"Singer"

**Curtis Sliwa**
c/o Guardian Angeles
763 - 8th Avenue
New York, NY 10036
"Guardian Angels Founder"

**Lindsay Sloane**
9200 Sunset Blvd. #1130
Los Angeles, CA 90069
"Actress"

**Joey Slotnick**
P.O. Box 5617
Beverly Hills, CA 90210
"Actor"

**James Sloyan**
920 Kagawa Street
Pacific Palisades, CA 90272
"Actor"

**Mary Small**
165 W. 66th Street
New York, NY 10023
"Actress"

**Jean Smart**
151 El Camino Drive
Beverly Hills, CA 90212
"Actress"

**Pamela Smart #93G0356**
Bedford Hills Correctional Facility
Bedford Hills, NY 10507
"ex-School Teacher"

**Smashing Pumpkins**
9830 Wilshire Blvd.
Beverly Hills, CA 90212
"Rock & Roll Group"

**Eleanor Smeal**
900 N. Stafford St. #1217
Arlington, VA 22003
"Social Activist"

**Yakov Smirnoff**
3750 West 76 Country Blvd.
Branson, MO 65616
"Comedian"

**Allison Smith**
1505 - 10th Street
Santa Monica, CA 90401
"Actress"

**Anna Deavere-Smith**
9830 Wilshire Blvd.
Beverly Hills, CA 90212
"Actress"

**Anna Nicole Smith**
330 Washington Blvd. #609
Marina del Rey, CA 90292
"Actress, Playmate"

**Bubba Smith**
5178 Sunlight Place
Los Angeles, CA 90016
"Actor, ex-Football Player"

**Charlie Martin Smith**
980 Cedarcliff Court
Westlake Village, CA 91362
"Actor"

**Connie Smith**
38 Music Square east #300
Nashville, TN 37203
"Singer"

**Cotter Smith**
15332 Antioch Street #800
Pacific Palisades, CA 90272
"Actor"

**Derek Smith**
201 Bramblewood Lane
East Amherst, NY 14051
"Actor"

**Emmitt Smith**
1 Cowboy Parkway
Irving, TX 75063
"Football Player"

**Gregory Smith**
4570 Van Nuys Blvd. #171
Sherman Oaks, CA 91403
"Actor"

**Hillary B. Smith**
8730 Sunset Blvd. #480
Los Angeles, CA 90069
"Actress"

**Ian Smith**
Gwenoro Farm
Shurugwi ZIMBABWE
"Ex-Government Official"

**Ilan Mitchell Smith**
104-60 Queens Blvd. #10-C
Fox Hills, NY 11375
"Actor"

**Jaclyn Smith**
10398 Sunset Blvd. #1200
Los Angeles, CA 90077
"Actress, Model"

**Karin Smith**
2300 Palisades Street
Los Osos, CA 93402
"Actress"

**Kathy Smith**
P.O. Box 491433
Los Angeles, CA 90049
"Actress"

**Keely Smith**
3434 Onelda Way
Las Vegas, NV 89109
"Actress"

**Kurtwood Smith**
1146 North Center Avenue #521
Glendale, CA 91202
"Actor"

**Lane Smith**
10100 Santa Monica Blvd. #2500
Los Angeles, CA 90067
"Actor"

**Lewis Smith**
3172 Dona Susana Drive
Studio City, CA 91604
"Actor"

**Liz Smith**
160 East 38th Street
New York, NY 10016
"Film Critic, Columnist"

**Lois Smith**
c/o I/A
235 Park Avenue South #700
New York, NY 10003
"Actress"

**Madeline Smith**
62 Chiswick Road
London W4 ISY ENGLAND
"Actress"

**Dame Maggie Smith**
76 Oxford Street
London W1N 0AX ENGLAND
"Actress"

**Margo Smith**
P.O. Box 1169
Franklin, TN 37065
"Singer"

**Martha Smith**
13775-A Mono Way #220
Sonora, CA 95370
"Actress, Model"

**Michael W. Smith**
25 Music Square West
Nashvile, TN 37203
"Guitarist"

**O.C. Smith**
1650 Broadway #508
New York, NY 10019
"Singer"

**Ozzie Smith**
P.O. Box 7117
Chesterfield, MO 63006
"Ex-Baseball Player"

**Rex Smith**
13701 Riverside Drive #201
Sherman Oaks, CA 91423
"Actor"

**Roger Smith**
2707 Benedict Canyon
Beverly Hills, CA 90210
"Actor, Writer"

**Sammi Smith**
Route #4, Box 362
Bristow, OK 74010
"Singer"

**Shawnee Smith**
1875 Century Park East #2250
Los Angeles, CA 90067
"Actress"

**Shelley Smith**
182 South Mansfield Avenue
Los Angeles, CA 90036
"Actress"

**Stan Smith**
194 Bellevue Avenue
Newport, RI 02840
"Tennis Player"

**Susan Smith**
#4901-1104-94
Women's Correctional Facility
4450 Broad River Road
Columbia, SC 29210
"Convicted of Killing Children"

**Taran Noah Smith**
12665 King Street
North Hollywood, CA 91604
"Actor"

**Vince Smith**
P.O. Box 1221
Pottsville, PA 17901
"Singer, Songwriter"

**Will Smith**
8500 Wilshire Blvd. #700
Beverly Hills, CA 90211
"Actor"

**William Smith**
3250 W. Olympic Blvd. #67
Santa Monica, CA 90404
"Actor"

**Dr. William Kennedy Smith**
Physicians Against Land Mines
351 East Huron #225
Chicago, IL 60611
"Physician"

**William Smithers**
2202 Anacapa Street
Santa Barbara, CA 93105
"Actor"

**Bill Smitrovich**
5075 Amestoy Avenue
Encino, CA 91316
"Actor"

**Jimmy Smits**
P.O. Box 49922
Barrington Station
Los Angeles, CA 90049
"Actor"

**Dick Smothers**
6442 Coldwater Canyon Ave. 107-B
N. Hollywood, CA 91606
"Comedian, Actor"

**Tom Smothers**
6442 Coldwater Canyon Ave. 107-B
N. Hollywood, CA 91606
"Comedian, Actor"

**Marcus Smythe**
Waters & Nicolosi
1501 Broadway
New York, NY 10036
"Actor"

**Snapcase**
P.O. Box 711966
Salt Lake City, UT 84171
"Punk Band"

**J.C. Snead**
1751 Pinnacle Drive #1500
McLean, VA 22102
"Golfer"

**Stephen Snedden**
1875 Century Park East #2250
Los Angeles, CA 90067
"Actor"

**Tom Sneva**
3301 East Valley Vista Lane
Paradise Valley, AZ 85253
"Race Car Driver"

**Dee Snider**
69 Broad Street #C
Red Bank, NJ 07701
"Singer of 90's)

**Mike Snider**
P.O. Box 140710
Nashville, TN 37214
"Bluegrass Musician"

**Wesley Snipes**
9560 Wilshire Blvd. #500
Beverly Hills, CA 90211
"Actor"

**Carrie Snodgress**
16650 Schoenborn
Sepulveda, CA 91343
"Actress"

**Snoop Doggy Dog**
3986 Swartmore Court
Claremont, CA 91711
"Rap Singer"

**Phoebe Snow**
2458 Zorada Drive
Los Angeles, CA 90046
"Singer"

**Sen. Olympia Snowe (ME)**
Senate Russell Building #495
Washington, DC 20510
"Politicain"

**Lord Snowdon**
22 Lauceston Place
London, W1 ENGLAND
"Photographer"

**Liza Snyder**
121 North San Vicente Blvd.
Beverly Hills, CA 90211
"Actress"

**Tom Snyder**
9536 Wilshire Blvd. #500
Beverly Hills, CA 90212
"Talk Show Host"

**Barry Sobel**
9000 Sunset Blvd. #1200
Los Angeles, CA 90069
"Comedian"

**Leelee Sobieski**
8265 Sunset Blvd. #201
Los Angeles, CA 90046
"Actress"

**Steve Sohmer**
2625 Larmar Road
Los Angeles, CA 90068
"TV Director"

**Marla Sokoloff**
9465 Wilshire Blvd. #600
Beverly Hills, CA 90212
"Child Actress"

**Stephen Solarz**
241 Dover Street
Brooklyn, NY 11235
"Ex-Congressman"

**Bruce Solomon**
14011 Ventura Blvd. #202
Sherman Oaks, CA 91423
"Actor"

**Brett Somers**
4 Willow Wall
Westport, CT 06880
"Actress"

**Suzanne Somers**
8899 Beverly Blvd. #713
Los Angeles, CA 90048
"Actress, Singer"

**Elke Sommer**
Atzelaberger Street 46
D-9I08O Marloffstein GERMANY
"Actress"

**Bonnie Somerville**
8383 Wilshire Blvd. #550
Beverly Hills, CA 90211
"Actress, Singer"

**Stephen Sondheim**
246 East 49th Street
New York, NY 10017
"Composer, Lyricist"

**Barry Sonnenfield**
9830 Wilshire Blvd.
Beverly Hills, CA 90212
"Film Director, Producer"

**Susan Sontag**
470 West 24th Street
New York, NY 10011
"Essayist, Writer, Novelist

**Princess Soraya**
Ave. Montaigne
75008 Paris FRANCE
Dancer, Actress, Print Model"

**Kevin Sorbo**
8651 East Lake Drive
Burnaby BC V5A 4T7 CANADA
"Actor"

**Louise Sorel**
10808 Lindbrook Drive
Los Angeles, CA 90024
"Actress"

**Ted Sorenson**
1285 Avenue of the Americas
New York, NY 10019
"Former Government Official"

**Aaron Sorkin**
9701 Wilshire Blvd., 10th Flr.
Beverly Hills, CA 90212
"TV Plot Writer"

**Arleen Sorkin**
623 Beverly Glenn Blvd.
Los Angeles, CA 90024
"Writer, Producer"

**Mira Sorvino**
120 West 45th Street #3601
New York, NY 10036
"Actress"

**Paul Sorvino**
110 East 87th Street
New York, NY 10128
"Actor"

**Sammy Sosa**
1060 West Addison Street
Chicago, IL 60613
"Baseball Player"

**David Soul**
863 North Beverly Glen
Los Angeles, CA 90077
"Actor, Singer, Director"

**David Souter**
34 Cilley Hill Road
Weare, NH 03281
"Supreme Court Justice"

**Joe South**
3051 Claremont Road NE
Atlanta, GA 30329
"Singer, Songwriter"

**Southern Belles**
11150 West Olympic Blvd.
Suite #1100
Los Angeles, CA 90064
"Wrestling Tag Team"

**Catherine Spaak**
Viale Parioli 59
00197 Rome, ITALY
"Actress"

**Sissy Spacek**
Rt. 22, #640
Cobham, VA 22929
"Actress"

**Kevin Spacey**
151 El Camino Drive
Beverly Hills, CA 90212
"Actor"

**David Spade**
707 North Beverly Drive
Beverly Hills, CA 90210
"Actor"

**James Spader**
9530 Heather Road
Beverly Hills, CA 90210
"Actor"

**Warren Spahn**
658 Meadowood Drive
Broken Arrow, OK 74011
"Ex-Baseball Player"

**Douglas Spain**
9200 Sunset Blvd. #1130
Los Angeles, CA 90069
"Actor"

**Joe Spano**
1505 - 10th Street
Santa Monica, CA 90401
"Actor"

**Vincent Spano**
P.O. Box 4602
Valley Village, CA 91617
"Actor"

**Hal Sparks**
9560 Wilshire Blvd. #500
Beverly Hills, CA 90211
"Actor, Singer"

**Camilla Spary**
10140 Cielo Drive
Beverly Hills, CA 90210
"Actress"

**Boris Spassky**
Skatertny Pereulok 5
Moscow RUSSIA
"Chess Player"

**Billy Joe Spears**
10 Sandforth Road
Liverpool L12 1JY ENGLAND
"Singer"

**Britney Spears**
P.O. Box 590009
Orlando, FL 32859
"Singer"

**Sen. Arlen Specter (PA)**
Senate Hart Bldg. #530
Washington, DC 20510
"Politician"

**Phil Spector**
686 S. Arroyo Parkway #175
Pasadena, CA 91105
"Record Producer"

**Ronnie Spector**
1560 Broadway #1308
New York, NY 10036
"Singer"

**Scott Speedman**
9701 Wilshire Blvd. #1000
Beverly Hills, CA 9022
"Actor"

**Sebastian Spence**
1005 Cambie Street
Vancouver BC V6B 5L7 CANADA
"Actor"

**Aaron Spelling**
5700 Wilshire Blvd. #575
Los Angeles, CA 90036
"TV Producer"

**Tori Spelling**
1836 Courtney Terrace
Los Angeles, CA 90046
"Actress"

**Gerry Spence**
15 South Jackson
Jackson, WY 83001
"Attorney"

**Sebastian Spence**
1005 Cambie Street
Vancouver BC V6B 5L7 CANADA
"Actor"

**Bud Spencer**
Via Cortina d'Ampezzo 156
00191 Rome, ITALY
"Actor"

**Earl Charles Spencer**
Althorpe House, Gr. Brington
Northamptonshire NN7 4HG
ENGLAND
"Princess Di's Brother"

**John Spencer**
10316 Viretta Lance
Los Angeles, CA 90077
"Actor"

**Linda Spencer**
Harvard University
1 Longfellow Hall
13 Applan Way
Cambridge, MA 02138
"Survivor Show Contestant"

**Victor Spencer-Churchill**
6 Cumberland Mansions
George Street
London W1 ENGLAND
"Viscount"

**Wendy Jo Sperber**
4110 Wetzel Drive
Sherman Oaks, CA 91423
"Actress"

**Penelope Spheeris**
7920 Sunset Blvd.
Los Angeles, CA 90046
"Director, Producer"

**Spice Girls**
35 Parkgate Rd., Unit 32
Ransomes Dock
London SWII 4NP ENGLAND
"Female Music Group"

**David Spielberg**
10537 Cushdon Avenue
Los Angeles, CA 90064
"Actor"

**Steven Spielberg**
P.O. Box 8520
Universal City, CA 91608
"Director, Producer"

**Mickey Spillane**
P.O. Box 265
Murrells Inlet, SC 29576
"Writer"

**Sandy Spillman**
1353 Alvarado Terrace
Los Angeles, CA 90017
"Actor"

**Spinal Tap**
4268 Hazeltine Avenue
Sherman Oaks, CA 91423
"Rock & Roll Group"

**Brent Spiner**
8383 Wilshire Blvd. 3550
Beverly Hills, CA 90211
"Actor"

**Leon Spinks**
209 Jones Street
Hollister, MO 65672
"Ex-Boxer"

**Michael Spinks**
250 West 57th Street
New York, NY 10107
"Boxer"

**Spinners**
3750 Hudson Manor Terrace #3A-E
Riverdale, NY 10463
"Vocal Group"

**Mark Spitz**
383 Dalehurst
Los Angeles, CA 90077
"Swimmer"

**Split Ends**
136 New Kings Road
London SW6 ENGLAND
"Rock & Roll Group"

**Roger Spottiswoods**
151 El Camino Drive
Beverly Hills, CA 90212
"Film Director"

**Michael Spound**
3500 W. Olive Avenue #920
Burbank, CA 91505
"Actor"

**G.D. Spardin**
P.O. Box 1294
San Luis Obispo, CA 93406
"Actor"

**Latrell Sprewell**
1001 San Gabriel Blvd.
San Gabriel, CA 91775
"Basketball Player"

**Jerry Springer**
454 North Columbus Drive #200
Chicago, IL 60611
"Talk Show Host"

**Rick Springfield**
515 Ocean Avenue
Santa Monica, CA 90402
"Singer, Guitarist"

**Bruce Springsteen**
1224 Benedict Canyon
Beverly Hills, CA 90210
"Singer, Guitarist"

**Steve Spurrier**
17050 Silver Charm Place
Leesburg, VA 20176
"College Football Coach"

**Spyro Gyro**
926 Horseshoe Road
Suffern, NY 10901
"Jazz Group"

**Billy Squier**
P.O. Box 231251
New York, NY 10023
"Singer, Guitarist"

**Rebecca Staab**
8840 Wilshire Blvd. #200
Los Angeles, CA 90048
"Actress"

**Nick Stabile**
6363 Wilshire Blvd. #419
Los Angeles, CA 90048
"Actor"

**Ken Stabler**
260 North Joachim Street
Mobile, AL 36603
"Ex-Football Player"

**Robert Stack**
321 St. Pierre Road
Los Angeles, CA 90077
"Actor"

**Timothy Stack**
10635 Santa Monica Blvd. #130
Los Angeles, CA 90025
"Actor"

**Craig Stadler**
1851 Alexander Bell Drive #410
Reston, VA 20191
"Golfer"

**Jim Stafford**
P.O. Box 6366
Branson, MO 65616
"Singer"

**Jo Stafford**
2339 Century Hill
Los Angeles, CA 90067
"Singer"

**Nancy Stafford**
P.O. Box 11807
Marina del Rey, CA 90295
"Actress"

**Lesley Stahl**
524 West 57th Street
New York, NY 10019
"Journalist"

**Lisa Stahl**
13775-A Mono Way #220
Sonora, CA 95370
"Actress"

**Joan Staley**
24516-B Windsor Drive
Valencia, CA 91355
"Actress"

**Frank Stallone**
10668 Eastborne #206
Los Angeles, CA 90025
"Actor"

**Sasha Stallone**
9 Bevery Park
Beverly Hills, CA 90210
"Ex-Wife of Sylvester Stallone"

**Sylvester Stallone**
30 Beverly Park
Beverly Hills, CA 90210
"Actor"

**Lynn Stalmaster**
12400 Wilshire Blvd. #920
Los Angeles, CA 90025
"Casting Director"

**John Stamos**
9255 Sunset Blvd. #1010
Los Angeles, CA 90069
"Actor"

**Terrence Stamp**
4 Windmill Street
London W1P 1HF ENGLAND
"Actor"

**John Standing**
28 Broomhouse Road
London SW6 ENGLAND
"Actor"

**Dennis Stanfill**
908 Oak Grove Avenue
San Marino, CA 91108
"Business Executive"

**Arnold Stang**
257 Park Avenue South #900
New York, NY 10010
"Actor"

**Bernadette Stanis**
9300 Wilshire Blvd. #410
Beverly Hills, CA 90212
"Actress"

**Florence Stanley**
6300 Wilshire Blvd. #910
Los Angeles, CA 90048
"Actress"

**Ralph Stanley**
3368 Guernsey Avenue
Memphis, TN 38122
"Blue Grass Band"

**BerNadette Stannis**
9460 Wilshire Blvd. #300
Beverly Hills, CA 90212
"Actress"

**Lisa Stansfield**
Box 59, Ashwall
Herfordshire SG 5NG ENGLAND
"Singer"

**Harry Dean Stanton**
14527 Mulholland Drive
Los Angeles, CA 90077
"Actor"

**Jean Stapleton**
5757 Wilshire Blvd. #PH-5
Los Angeles, CA 90036
"Actress"

**Maureen Stapleton**
1-14 Morgan Manor
Lenox, MA 01240
"Actress"

**Jo Jo Starbuck**
202 South Michigan Street #810
South Bend, IN 46523
"Ice Skater"

**Koo Stark**
52 Shaftesbury Avenue
London W1 ENGLAND
"Actress"

**Ray Stark**
232 South Mapleton Drive
Los Angeles, CA 90077
"TV Producer"

**Bart Starr**
2647 Rocky Ridge Lane
Birmingham, AL 35216
"Ex-Football Player"

**Kay Starr**
708 Palisades Drive
Pacific Palisades, CA 90272
"Singer"

**Kenneth Starr**
c/o Pepperdine Law School
24255 Pacific Coast Hwy.
Malibu, CA 90265
"Attorney"

**Ryan Starr**
c/o Freemantle Media
2700 Colorado Avenue, 4th Floor
Santa Monica, CA 90404
"Singer"

**Starship (Jefferson Airplane)**
9850 Sandalfoot Blvd. #458
Boca Raton, FL 33428
"Rock & Roll Group"

**Jason Statham**
151 El Camino Drive
Beverly Hills, CA 90212
"Actor"

**Statler Brothers**
P.O. Box 492
Hernando, MS 38632
"Vocal Group"

**Roger Staubach**
6912 Edelweiss Circle
Dallas, TX 75240
"Ex-Football Player"

**Amy Steel**
1505 - 10th Street
Santa Monica, CA 90401
"Actress"

**Allan Steele**
1640 South Sepulveda Blvd. #218
Los Angeles, CA 90025
"Actor"

**Barbara Steele**
2460 Benedict Canyon
Beverly Hills, CA 90210
"Actress"

**Danielle Steele**
P.O. Box 1637
Murray Hill Station
New York, NY 10156
"Novelist"

**Tommy Steele**
3 Burlington Lane
London W4 2TH ENGLAND
"Actor, Singer"

**Mary Steenburgen**
8500 Wilshire Blvd. #700
Beverly Hills, CA 90211
"Actress"

**Gwen Stefani**
P.O. Box 8899
Anaheim, CA 92812
"Singer"

**Ben Stein**
602 N. Crescent Drive
Beverly Hills, CA 90210
"Writer"

**David Steinberg**
16117 Royal Oak Road
Encino, CA 91436
"Comedian, Actor, Writer"

**George Steinbrenner**
P.O. Box 25077
Tampa, FL 33622
"Baseball Executive"

**Gloria Steinem**
118 East 73rd Street
New York, NY 10021
"Author, Feminist"

**Jake Steinfeld**
622 Toyopa Drive
Pacific Palisades, CA 90272
"Actor, Bodybuilder"

**Herb Stempel**
105 - 1B 66th Avenue
Flushing, NY 11375
"Quiz Show Host"

**Ingemar Stenmark**
1 Annociade 17, Av. de l'Annociade
Monte Carlo, MONACO
"Skier"

**Princess Stephanie**
Maison Clos St. Martin
F-St. Remy de Provence
FRANCE
"Royalty"

**George Stephanopoulos**
c/o ABC News
1717 De Sales Street NW
Washington, D.C. 20036
"ex-White House Official"

**James Stephens**
8271 Melrose Avenue #110
Los Angeles, CA 90046
"Actor, Director"

**Laraine Stephens**
10800 Chalon Road
Los Angeles, CA 90077
"Actress"

**Jan Stephenson**
P.O. Box 705
Windemere, FL 34786
"Golfer"

**Steppenwolf**
P.O. Box 1821
Ojai, CA 93024
"Rock & Roll Group"

**Jan Sterling**
c/o Motion Picture Home
23388 Mulholland
Woodland Hills, CA 91364
"Actress"

**Daniel Stern**
P.O. Box 6788
Malibu, CA 90264
"Actor"

**Howard Stern**
101 West 67th Street
New York, NY 10021
"Shock Radio Host"

**Frances Sternahgen**
152 Sutton Manor Road
New Rochelle, NY 10805
"Actress"

**Andrew Stevens**
9460 Wilshire Blvd. #300
Beverly Hills, CA 90212
"Actor"

**Brinke Stevens**
P.O. Box 8900
Universal City, CA 91618
"Actress, Model"

**Cat Stevens**
(aka Yusef Islam)
81677 Munich GERMANY
"Singer, Songwriter"

**Connie Stevens**
426 South Roberston Blvd.
Los Angeles, CA 90048
"Actress, Singer"

**Fisher Stevens**
151 El Camino Drive
Beverly Hills, CA 90212
"Actor"

**George Stevens, Jr.**
John F. Kennedy Center
Washington, DC 20566
"Director, Producer"

**Kaye Stevens**
10580 Des Moines Avenue
Northridge, CA 91326
"Actress"

**Mick Stevens**
P.O. Box 344
West Tisbury, MA 02575
"Cartoonist"

**Rise Stevens**
930 Fifth Avenue
New York, NY 10021
"Mezzo-Soprano"

**Shadow Stevens**
2934 North Beverly Glen Circle
#399
Los Angeles, CA 90077
"Radio-TV personality"

**Stella Stevens**
1608 N. Cahuenga Blvd. #649
Los Angeles, CA 90028
"Actress"

**Sen. Ted Stevens (AK)**
Senate Hart Bldg. #522
Washington, DC 20510
"Politician"

**Warren Stevens**
14155 Magnolia Blvd. #27
Sherman Oaks, CA 91403
"Actor"

**Adlai Stevenson III**
20 North Clark Street #750
Chicago, IL 60602
"Ex-Governor"

**Parker Stevenson**
4526 Wilshire Blvd.
Los Angeles, CA 90010
"Actor"

**Teofilo Stevenson**
Hotel Havana Libre
Havana, CUBA
"Boxer"

**Alana Stewart**
9200 Sunset Blvd. #900
Los Angeles, CA 90069
"Actress"

**Catherine Mary Stewart**
9560 Wilshire Blvd, #500
Beverly Hills, CA 90212
"Actress"

**French Stewart**
9560 Wilshire Blvd. #500
Beverly Hills, CA 90212
"Actor"

**Jackie Stewart**
24 Rte. de Divonne
1260 Nyon, SWITZERLAND
"Ex-Race Car Driver"

**Martha Stewart**
19 Newtown Turnpike
Westport, CT 06880
"Society Caterer, Author"

**Patrick Stewart**
233 Wilshire Blvd. #600
Santa Monica, CA 90401
"Actor"

**Peggy Stewart**
11139 Hortense Street
North Hollywood, CA 91602
"Actress"

**Rod Stewart**
1122 South Robertson Blvd. #15
Los Angeles, CA 90035
"Singer, Songwriter"

**Donna Stewart-Hardway**
P.O. Box 777
Pinch, WV 25156
"Munchkin in Wizard of Oz"

**Michael Stich**
Bayerstr. 383, A-5071
Saizburg/Wals-Siezenheim AUS-
TRIA
"Tennis Player"

**David Ogden Stiers**
8675 W. Washington Blvd. #203
Culver City, CA 90232
"Actor"

**Robert Stigwood**
122 East 42nd Street
New York, NY 10017
"Film Producer"

**Ben Stiller**
1122 S. Robertson Blvd. #15
Los Angeles, CA 90035
"Actor"

**Jerry Stiller**
118 Riverside Drive #5A
New York, NY 10024
"Comedian, Actor, Writer"

**Stephen Still**
191 North Phelps Avenue
Winter Park, FL 32789
"Singer"

**Stacey Stillman**
1 Market Plaza, 31st Floor
San Francisco, CA 94105
"Survivor Show Contestant"

**Sting**
2 The Grove
Highgate Village
London N6 6JUENGLAND
"Singer, Actor, Composer"

**Barbara Stock**
14945 Ventura Blvd. #228
Sherman Oaks, CA 91403
"Actress"

**Adm. James B. Stockdale**
Hoover Institution
Stanford, CA 94305
"Ross Perot's V.P. Select"

**Karl-Heinz Stockhausen**
Stockhausen-Verlag
D-51515 Kuerten, GERMANY
"Composer"

**Dick Stockton**
Fox - TV
205 West 67th Street
New York, NY 10021
"TV Sports Announcer"

**Dean Stockwell**
1875 Centuty Park East #2250
Los Angeles, CA 90067
"Actor"

**John Stockwell**
344 S. Rossmore Avenue
Los Angeles, CA 90029
"Actor"

**Brandon Stoddard**
241 North Glenroy Avenue
Los Angeles, CA 90049
"Film-TV Executive

**Elvis Stojko**
1600 Jane Naismith Drive
Gloucester, Ontario
K1B 5N4 CANADA
"Ice Skater"

**Mink Stole**
3155 Ettrick Street
Los Angeles, CA 90027
"Actress"

**David Stollery**
3203 Bern Court
Laguna Beach, CA 92651
"Actor"

**Eric Stoltz**
4116 W. Magnolia Blvd. #101
Burbank, CA 91505
"Actor"

**Peter Stomare**
1129 North Poinsettia Drive
West Hollywood, CA 90046
"Actor"

**Doug Stone**
P.O. Box 388
Springfield, TN 37172
"Singer"

**Oliver Stone**
520 Broadway #600
Santa Monica, CA 90401
"Film Writer, Director"

**Sharon Stone**
15030 Ventura Blvd. #710
Sherman Oaks, CA 91403
"Actress, Model"

**Tom Stoppard**
34-43 Russell Street
London WC2B 5HA ENGLAND
"Dramatist"

**Larry Storch**
330 West End Avenue #17-F
New York, NY 10023
"Actor"

**Gale Storm**
23831 Bluehill Bay
Dana Point, CA 92629
"Actress, Singer"

**Jim Storm**
13576 Cheltenham Drive
Serman Oaks, CA 91423
"Actor"

**Tempest Storm**
P.O. Box 15154
Newport Beach, CA 92659
"Burlesque Actress"

**Peter Stomare**
1129 Poinsettia Drive
West Hollywood, CA 90046
"Actor"

**John Stossel**
211 Central Park West #15K
New York, NY 10024
"Broadcast Journalist"

**Madeleine Stowe**
9560 Wilshire Blvd. #516
Beverly Hills, CA 90212
"Actress"

**Michael Stoyanov**
3172 Dona Susana Drive
Studio City, CA 91604
"Actor"

**Julie Strain**
8491 Sunset Blvd. #1850
Los Angeles, CA 90069
"Actress"

**George Strait**
1000 -18th Avenue South
Nashville, TN 37212
"Singer, Songwriter"

**Hank Stram**
194 Belle Terre Blvd.
Covington, LA 70483
"Ex-Football Coach"

**Robin Strand**
4118 Elmer
North Hollywood, CA 91607
"Actor"

**Deborah Strang**
247 S. Beverly Drive #102
Beverly Hills, CA 90212
"Actress"

**Curtis Strange**
137 Thomas Dale
WIlliamsburg, VA 23185
"Golfer"

**Robin Strasser**
P.O. Box 1872
Ojai, CA 93024
"Actress"

**Gil Stratton**
4227-B Colfax Avenue #B
Studio City, CA 91604
"Sportscaster"

**Peter Straub**
53 West 85th Street
New York, NY 10026
"Novelist"

**Robert Strauss**
1333 New Hampshire Ave. NW
Suite #400
Washington, DC 20005
"Politician"

**Strawberry Blondes**
Box 33
Pontypool
Gwent NP4 7YU ENGLAND
"British Band"

**Stray Cats**
113 Wardour Street
London W1 ENGLAND
Rock & Roll Band"

**Meryl Streep**
8500 Wilshire Blvd. #700
Beverly Hills, CA 90212
"Actress"

**Barbara Streisand**
118 S. Beverly Drive #201
Beverly Hills, CA 90212
"Singer, Actress, Director"

**Amzie Strickland**
1329 North Ogden Drive
Los Angeles, CA 90046
"Actress"

**Gail Strickland**
14732 Oracle Place
Pacific Palisades, CA 90272
"Actress"

**Sherry Stringfield**
9560 Wilshire Blvd. #516
Beverly Hills, CA 90212
"Actress"

**Elaine Stritch**
125 Gloucester Road
London SW7 YTE ENGLAND
"Actress"

**Herbert L. Strock**
1630 Hilts Avenue #205
Los Angeles, CA 90024
"Writer, Producer"

**Shiloh Strong**
6212 Banner Avenue
Los Angeles, CA 90038
"Actor"

**Don Stroud**
P.O. Box 1496
Manhattan Beach, CA 90266
"Actor"

**Kerri Strug**
1122 S. Robertson Blvd. #15
Los Angeles, CA 90035
"Gymnast"

**Sally Struthers**
8721 Sunset Blvd.
Los Angeles, CA 90046
"Actress"

**Barbara Stuart**
6399 Wilshire Blvd. #414
Los Angeles, CA 90048
"Actress"

**Gloria Stuart**
884 South Bundy Drive
Los Angeles, CA 90049
"Actress"

**Marty Stuart**
2100 West End Avenue #1000
Nashville, TN 37203
"C&W Singer"

**Maxine Stuart**
1801 Avenue of the Stars #902
Los Angeles, CA 90067
"Actress"

**Roy Stuart**
4948 Radford Avenue
North Hollywood, CA 91602
"Actor"

**Wes Studi**
P.O. Box 740282
Dallas, TX 75374
"Actor"

**Geoff Stults**
11365 Ventura Blvd. #100
Studio City, CA 91604
"Actor"

**Shannon Sturgess**
4526 Wilshire Blvd.
Los Angeles, CA 90010
"Actress"

**William Styron**
12 Rucum Road
Roxbury, CT 06783
"Author"

**David Suchet**
169 Queensgate #8A
London SW7 5EH ENGLAND
"Actor"

**Alan Sues**
9014 Dorrington Avenue
Los Angeles, CA 90048
"Actor"

**Helena Sukova**
1 Avenue Grande Bretagne
Monte Carlo, Monaco
"Tennis Player"

**Danny Sullivan**
414 E. Cooper Street #201
Aspen, CO 81611
"Race Car Driver"

**Kathryn D. Sullivan**
333 West Broad STreet
Columbus, OH 44215
"Astronaut"

**Susan Sullivan**
8642 Allenwood Road
Los Angeles, CA 90046
"Actress"

**Tom Sullivan**
30 Glenmoor Drive
Englewood, CO 80110
"Singer, Songwriter"

**Sultan of Brunei**
Bandar Seri
Begawan BRUNEI
"Royalty"

**Arthur Ochs Sulzberber**
229 West 43rd Street
New York, NY 10036
"Newspaper Publisher"

**Yma Sumac**
333 Valencia Street #450
San Francisco, CA 94103
"Singer"

**Cree Summer**
17328 Ventura Blvd. #242
Encino, CA 91316
"Actress"

**Donna Summer**
1325 Avenue of the Americas
New York, NY 10019
"Singer"

**Eleanor Summerfield**
10 Kildare Terrace
London W2 ENGLAND
"Actress"

**Yale Summers**
9490 Cherokee Lane
Beverly Hills, CA 90210
"Actor"

**John Sununu**
24 Samoset Drive
Salem, NH 03079
"Former Governor"

**Nicolas Surovy**
121 North San Vicente Blvd.
Beverly Hills, CA 90211
"Actor"

**Survivor**
P.O. Box 1821
Ojai, CA 93024
"Rock & Roll Group"

**Todd Susman**
11462 Poema Place #34-102
Chatsworth, CA 91311
"Actor"

**Rick Sutcliff**
25911 - 99th Street
Lee's Summit, MO 64053
"ex-Baseball Player"

**Donald Sutherland**
9830 Wilshire Blvd.
Beverly Hills, CA 90212
"Actor"

**Kiefer Sutherland**
132 So. Rodeo Drive, #300
Beverly Hills, CA 90212
"Actor"

**James Sutorius**
14014 Milbank Street #1
Sherman Oaks, CA 91423
"Actor"

**Don Sutton**
1145 Mountain Ivy Drive
Roswell, GA 30075
"Ex-Baseball Player"

**Hal Sutton**
212 Texas Street #117
Shreveport, LA 71101
"Golfer"

**Janet Suzman**
52/53 Poland Street
London W1F 7LX ENGLAND
"Actress"

**Bo Svenson**
247 S. Beverly Drive #102
Beverly Hills, CA 90212
"Actor"

**Jimmy Swaggart**
8912 World Ministry Avenue
Baton Rouge, LA 70810
"Evangelist"

**Caskey Swaim**
1605 North Cahuenga Blvd. #202
Los Angeles, CA 90028
"Actor"

**Dominique Swain**
151 El Camino Drive
Beverly Hills, CA 90212
"Actress"

**Michael Swan**
13576 Cheltenham Drive
Sherman Oaks, CA 91423
"Actor"

**Hilary Swank**
9100 Wilshire Blvd., West Tower
#600
Burbank, CA 90212
"Actress"

**Lynn Swann**
506 Hegner Way #2
Sewickley, PA 15143
"Ex-Football Player"

**Kristy Swanson**
2934 1/2 N. Beverly Glen Circle
#416
Los Angeles, CA 90077
"Actress"

**Don Swayze**
247 S. Beverly Drive #102
Beverly Hills, CA 90212
"Actor"

**Patrick Swayze**
132 S. Rodeo Drive, #300
Beverly HIlls, CA 90212
"Actor"

**Keith Sweat**
40 West 57th Street
New York, NY 10019
"Singer"

**D.B. Sweeney**
8942 Wilshire Blvd.
Beverly Hills, CA 90211
"Actor"

**Matthew Sweet**
315 Ponce De Leon Avenue #755
Decatur, GA 37212
"Singer"

**Inga Swenson**
10100 Santa Monica Blvd. #2500
Los Angeles, CA 90067
"Actress"

**Rick Swenson**
c/o General Delivery
Two Rivers, AK 99716
"Iditarod Champion"

**Jo Swerling, Jr.**
25745 Vista Verde Drive
Calabasas, CA 91302
"Writer, Producer"

**Staphanie Swift**
P.O. Box 9864
Canoga Park, CA 91309
"Pornstar"

**Doug Swingley**
c/o General Delivery
Simms, MT 59477
"Musher, Dog Breeder"

**Loretta Swit**
23852 Pacific Coast Highway
# PMB 416
Malibu, CA 90265
"Actress"

**Barry Switzer**
700 Timberall
Norman, OK 73072
"Football Coach"

**Tracy Brooks Swope**
8730 Sunset Blvd. #480
Los Angeles, CA 90069
"Actress"

**SWV**
6464 Sunset Blvd. #610
Hollywood, CA 90028
"R&B Group"

**Eric Sykes**
9 Orme Court
London W2 ENGLAND
"Actor, Writer, Director"

**The Sylvers**
1900 Ave. of the Stars #1600
Los Angeles, CA 90067
"Vocal Group"

**Sylvia Syms**
47 West Square
London SE11 4SP ENGLAND
"Actress"

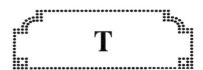

**2 Live Crew**
250 West 57th Street #821
New York, NY 10107
"Rap Group"

**Mr. T**
15208 La Maida Street
Sherman Oaks, CA 91403
"Actor"

**Cary-Hiroyuki Tagawa**
6363 Wilshire Blvd. #419
Beverly Hills, CA 90048
"Actor"

**Paul Tagliabueruss**
410 Park Avenue
New York, NY 10022
"Football [NFL] Commissioner"

**Taj Mahal**
200 West Superior #202
Chicago, IL 60610
"Musician"

**Miiko Taka**
14560 Round Valley Drive
Sherman Oaks, CA 91403
"Actress"

**Take Six**
89 Fifth Avenue #700
New York, NY 10003
"Vocal Group"

**George Takei**
419 N. Larchmont Blvd. #41
Los Angeles, CA 90004
"Actor"

**Nita Talbot**
3420 Merrimac Road
Los Angeles, CA 90049
"Actress"

**Gay Talese**
154 East Atlantic Blvd.
Ocean City, NJ 08226
"Writer"

**Maria Tallchief**
2739 Elston Avenue
Chicago, IL 60647
"Ballerina"

**Patricia Tallman**
1801 E. Tropicana #19, PMB 2161
Las Vegas, NV 89119
"Actress"

**Russ Tamblyn**
2633 Lincoln Blvd. #612
Santa Monica, CA 90405
"Actor"

**Jeffrey Tambor**
9150 Wilshire Blvd., #350
Beverly Hills, CA 90212
"Actor"

**Amy Tan**
215 South La Cienega Blvd., PH
Beverly Hills, CA 90211
"Novelist"

**Tangerine Dream**
P.O. Box 29242
Oakland, CA 94604
"Rock & Roll Group"

**Alain Tanner**
12 Chemin du Pointe-du-Jour
Geneva SWITZERLAND
"Film Director"

**Roscoe Tanner**
1109 Gnome Trail
Lookout Mountain, TN 37350
"Tennis Player"

**J. Randy Taraborelli**
c/o Simon & Schuster
1230 Avenue of the Americas
New York, NY 10020
"Author"

**Quentin Tarantino**
7966 Beverly Blvd. #300
Los Angeles, CA 90048
"Actor, Director"

**Jimmy Tarbuck**
118 Beaufort Street
London SW3 6BU ENGLAND
"Comedian"

**Fran Tarkington**
3340 Peachtree Road NE #2570
Atlanta, GA 30326
"Ex-Football Player"

**Larena Tate**
9830 Wilshire Blvd.
Beverly Hills, CA 90212
"Actress"

**Bernie Taupin**
450 N. Maple Drive #501
Beverly Hills, CA 90210
"Lyricist"

**Benedict Taylor**
4 Great Queen Street
London WC28 5DG ENGLAND
"Actor"

**Buck Taylor**
2899 Agoura Road #275
Westlake Village, CA 91361
"Actor"

**Christine Taylor**
9560 Wilshire Blvd. #516
Beverly Hills, CA 90212
"Actress"

**Cindi Taylor**
Wild On/E
5670 Wilshire Blvd.
Los Angeles, CA 90036
"Singer"

**Delores Taylor**
P.O. Box 840
Moorpark, CA 93020
"Actress"

**Elizabeth Taylor**
P.O. Box 55995
Sherman Oaks, CA 91413
"Actress"

**Holland Taylor**
2676 Hollyridge Drive
Los Angeles, CA 90068
"Actress"

**Jackie Lynn Taylor**
P.O. Box 3182
Citrus Heights, CA 95611
"Actress"

**James Taylor**
1250 - 6th Street #401
Santa Monica, CA 90401
"Singer"

**Josh Taylor**
422 S. California Avenue
Burbank, CA 91505
"Actor"

**Lawrence Taylor**
122 Canterbury Lane
Williamsburg, VA 23188
"Ex-Football Player"

**Leigh Taylor-Young**
11300 W. Olympic Blvd. #610
Los Angeles, CA 90064
"Actress"

**Lili Taylor**
151 El Camino Drive
Beverly Hills, CA 90212
"Actress"

**Meldrick Taylor**
1158 N. York Road
Warminster, PA 18974
"Boxer"

**Meshach Taylor**
6300 Wilshire Blvd. #900
Los Angeles, CA 90048
"Actor"

**Niki Taylor**
8362 Pines Blvd., #334
Hollywood, FL 33024
"Model"

**Renee Taylor**
16830 Ventura Blvd. #326
Encino, CA 91436
"Actress, Writer"

**Rip Taylor**
1133 North Clark Street
Los Angeles, CA 90069
"Actor"

**Rod Taylor**
2375 Bowmont Drive
Beverly Hills, CA 90210
"Actor"

**Roger Taylor**
Salterwwell Farm
Moreton-In -The-Marsh
Gloucestershire ENGLAND
"Drummer"

**Ludmilla Tcherina**
42 cours Albert ler
75008 Paris, FRANCE
"Ballerina"

**Lewis Teague**
2190 N. Beverly Glen Blvd.
Los Angeles, CA 90077
"Film Director"

**Tears For Fears**
2100 Colorado Avenue
Santa Monica, CA 90404
"Rock & Roll Group"

**Renata Tebaldi**
Piazzetta Guastalla 1
I-20122 Milan ITALY
"Opera Singer"

**Dr. Edward U. Teller**
Radiation Laboratory
P.O. Box 808
Livermore, CA 94550
"Physicist, Author"

**Christopher Templeton**
11333 Moorpark Street
North Hollywood, CA 91602
"Actress"

**The Temptations**
P.O. Box 1821
Ojai, CA 93024
"R & B Group

**Victoria Tennant**
4526 Wilshire Blvd.
Los Angeles, CA 90010
"Actress"

**Jon Tenney**
9560 Wilshire Blvd. #516
Beverly Hills, CA 90212
"Actor"

**Toni Tennille**
3612 Lake View Road
Carson City, NV 89703
"Singer"

**Chalee Tennison**
2100 West End Avenue #1000
Nashville, TN 37203
"Singer"

**Judy Tenuta**
13504 Contour Drive
Sherman Oaks, CA 91423
"Comedienne"

**Lee Tergeson**
252 North Larchmont Blvd. #200
Los Angeles, CA 90004
"Actor"

**Studs Terkel**
850 West Castlewood
Chicago, IL 60640
"Novelist"

**Ernie Terrell**
111336 South Parnell
Chicago, IL 60628
"Boxer"

**Danny Terrio**
1560 Broadway #1308
New York, NY 10036
"Dancer"

**Malcolm Terris**
14 England's Lane
London NW3 ENGLAND
"Actor"

**Clark Terry**
24 Westland Drive
Glen Cove, NY 11542
"Musician"

**John Tesh**
P.O. Box 6010
Sherman Oaks, CA 91413
"TV Show Host, Musician"

**Vinny Testaverde**
15 Tall Oak Court
Oyster Bay Cove, NY 11791
"Football Player"

**Lauren Tewes**
157 West 57th Street #604
New York, NY 10019
"Actress"

**Baroness Margaret Thatcher**
Chester Square Belgravia
London ENGLAND
"Former Prime Minister"

**Phyllis Thaxter**
400 South Beverly Drive #101
Beverly Hills, CA 90212
"Actress"

**Brym Thayer**
400 S. Beverly Drive #101
Beverly Hills, CA 90212
"Actress"

**Joe Theismann**
5912 Leesburg Pike
Falls Church, VA 22041
"Ex-Football Player"

**Charlize Theron**
3737 W. Magnolia Blvd. #300
Burbank, CA 91505
"Actress"

**David Thewlis**
76 Oxford Street
London W1N 0AX ENGLAND
"Actor"

**Alan Thicke**
10505 Sarah
Toluca Lake, CA 91602
"Actor, TV Show Host, Singer"

**Ursula Thiess**
1940 Bel Air Road
Los Angeles, CA 90077
"Actress"

**Tiffani-Amber Thiessen**
1122 S. Robertson Blvd. #15
Los Angeles, CA 90035
"Actress"

**Lynne Thigpen**
35 West 20th Street
New York, NY 10011
"Actress & Audiobooks Reader"

**Roy Thinnes**
1910 Madison Avenue
Memphis, TN 38104
"Actor"

**Third World**
151 El Camino Drive
Beverly Hills, CA 90212
"Raggae Band"

**Betty Thomas**
7920 Sunset Blvd.
Los Angeles, CA 90046
"Actress"

**B.J. Thomas**
P.O. Box 120003
Arlington, TX 76012
"Singer, Songwriter"

**Clarence Thomas**
1-1st Street N.E.
Washington, DC 20566
"Supreme Court Justice"

**Damien Thomas**
31 Kensington Church Street
London W8 4LL ENGLAND
"Actor"

**Dave Thomas**
429 Santa Monica Blvd. #500
Santa Monica, CA 90401
"Comedian"

**David Clayton Thomas**
31863 Sea Level Drive
Malibu, CA 90265
"Singer"

**Debi Thomas**
292 S. Michigan Avenue #810
South Bend, IN 46601
"Ice Skater"

**Ernest Thomas**
3350 Barham Blvd.
Los Angeles, CA 90068
"Actor"

**Heather Thomas**
1122 S. Robertson Blvd. #15
Los Angeles, CA 90035
"Actress, Model"

**Helen Thomas**
2501 Calvert Street N.W.
Washington, DC 20008
"News Correspondent"

**Irma Thomas**
P.O. Box 26126
New Orleans, LA 70186
"Singer"

**Isaiah Thomas**
400 Renaissance Center #300
Detroit, MI 48243
"Basketball Exec. &Ex-Player"

**Jay Thomas**
6500 Wilshire Blvd. #2200
Los Angeles, CA 90048
"Singer, Songwriter"

**Jonathan Taylor Thomas**
955 S. Carrillo Drive #300
Los Angeles, CA 90048
"Actor"

**Kristin Scott Thomas**
8500 Wilshire Blvd. #700
Beverly Hills, CA 90211
"Actress"

**Kurt Thomas**
1826 Brook Terrace Trail
Dallas, TX 75232
"Actor, Athlete"

**Marlo Thomas**
420 East 54th Street #22-F
New York, NY 10022
"Actress, Writer"

**Michael Tilson Thomas**
201 Van Ness Avenue
San Francisco, CA 94102
"Music Composer & Director"

**Philip Michael Thomas**
P.O. Box 3714
Brooklyn, NY 11202
"Actor"

**Richard Thomas**
4963 Los Feliz Blvd.
Los Angeles, CA 90027
"Actor, Director"

**Harry Thomason**
4024 Radford Ave. Bldg. 5 #104
Studio City, CA 91604
"Film Producer"

**Tim Thomerson**
2635 - 28th Street #14
Santa Monica, CA 90405
"Actor, Comedian"

**Tony Thomopoulos**
1280 Stone Canyon
Los Angeles, CA 90077
"Film Executive"

**Andrea Thompson**
c/o Court TV
600 Third Avenue #200
New York, NY 10016
"Actress"

**Bobby Thompson**
122 Sunlit Drive
Watchung, NJ 07060
"Banjoist"

**Brian Thompson**
1010 Olive Lane
La Canada, CA 91011
"Actor"

**Daley Thompson**
1 Church Row
Wandsworth Plain
London SW18 1ES ENGLAND
"Track Athlete"

**Emma Thompson**
24 Hanway Street
London W1P 9DD ENGLAND
"Actress"

**Ernest Thompson**
Rt. 1, Box 3248
Ashland, NH 03217
"Screenwriter"

**Sen. Fred Thompson (IL)**
701 Pennsylvania Avenue NW
Washington, DC 20004
"Politician"

**Hank Thompson**
5 Rushing Creek Court
Roanoke, TX 76262
"Singer, Songwriter"

**Hilarie Thompson**
13202 Weddington Street
Van Nuys, CA 91401
"Actress"

**Jack Thompson**
12754 Sarah Street
Studio City, CA 91604
"Actor"

**Lea Thompson**
c/o Starr & Co.
350 Park Avenue, 9th Floor
New York, NY 10022
"Actress"

**Linda Thompson**
751 Bridgeway #300
Sausalito, CA 94965
"Actress"

**Sada Thompson**
P.O. Box 490
Southbury, CT 06488
"Actress"

**Shawn Thompson**
5319 Biloxi Avenue
North Hollywood, CA 91601
"Actor"

**Sophie Thompson**
13 Shorts Garden
London WC2H 9AT ENGLAND
"Actress"

**The Thompson Twins**
9 Eccleston Street
London SW1W 9LXENGLAND
"Rock & Roll Trio"

**Dorrie Thomson**
3349 Cahuenga Blvd. West #2
Los Angeles, CA 90068
"Actress"

**J. Lee Thompson**
9595 Lime Orchard Road
Beverly Hills, CA 90210
"Film Director"

**Courtney Thorne-Smith**
10100 Santa Monica Blvd. #2500
Los Angeles, CA 90067
"Actress"

**Billy Bob Thornton**
955 S. Carrillo Drive #300
Los Angeles, CA 90048
"Actor"

**Ian Thorpe**
Box 3286, Belconnen DC, Act. 2817
Canberra 267 AUSTRALIA
"Swimmer & Diver"

**Jeremy Thorpe**
2 Orme Square Bayswater
London W2 4RS ENGLAND
"Political Leader"

**Linda Thorson**
145 West 45th Street #1204
New York, NY 10036
"Actress"

**Three Degrees**
2756 N. Green Valley Pkwy. #449
Las Vegas, NV 89014
"Rock & Roll Group"

**Richard Thornburgh**
2540 Massachusetts Avenue NW
#405
Washington, DC 20005
"ex-Government Official"

**Malachi Throne**
11805 Mayfield Avenue #306
Los Angeles, CA 90049
"Actor"

**Ingrid Thulin**
Kevingerstrand 7b
S-18231 Danderyd, SWEDEN
"Actress"

**Uma Thurman**
9830 Wilshire Blvd.
Beverly Hills, CA 90212
"Actress"

**Greta Thyssen**
444 East 82nd Street
New York, NY 10228
"Actress"

**Paul W. Tibbets**
5574 Knollwood Drive
Columbus, OH 43227
"Singer"

**Cheryl Tiegs**
457 Cuesta Way
Los Angeles, CA 90077
"Model"

**Maura Tierney**
9830 Wilshire Blvd.
Beverly Hills, CA 90212
"Actress"

**Tiffany**
225 West 57th Street #500
New York, NY 10019
"Singer"

**Pamela Tiffin**
15 West 67th Street
New York, NY 10023
"Actress, Model"

**Kevin Tighe**
P.O. Box 453
Sedro Woolley, WA 98284
"Actor"

**Nadja Tiller**
Kathi-Kobus-Str.24
80797 Munich GERMANY
"Actress"

**Mel Tillis**
P.O. Box 1630
Branson, MO 65615
"Singer"

**Pam Tillis**
P.O. Box 128575
Nashville, TN 37212
"Singer"

**Floyd Tillman**
4 Music Square East
Nashville, TN 37203
"Singer"

**Johnny Tillotson**
19948 Mayall Street
Chatsworth, CA 91311
"Singer"

**Jennifer Tilly**
1465 Lindacrest Drive
Beverly Hills, CA 90210
"Actress"

**Meg Tilly**
321 South Beverly Drive #M
Beverly Hills, CA 90212
"Actress"

**Grant Tinker**
531 Barnaby Road
Los Angeles, CA 90077
"TV Executive"

**Aaron Tippin**
38 Music Square East #300
Nashville, TN 37203
"Singer"

**Laurence Tisch**
Island Drive North
Rye, NY 10580
"TV Executive"

**Steve Tisch**
14454 Sunset Blvd.
Pacific Pallisades, CA 90272
"Television/Film Executive"

**Dennis Tito**
1800 Alta Mura Drive
Pacific Palisades, CA 90272
"Space Tourist"

**Y.A. Tittle**
168 Elena Avenue
Atherton, CA 94027
"Ex-Football Player"

**Christopher Titus**
10700 Ventura Blvd., 2nd Floor
Studio City, CA 91604
"Actor"

**TLC**
9830 Wilshire Blvd.
Beverly Hills, CA 90212
"R&B Trio"

**Oliver Tobias**
2D Wimpole Street
London W1G OEB ENGLAND
"Actor"

**Richard Todd**
Chinham Farm
Faringdon, Oxfordshire
ENGLAND
"Actor"

**Tony Todd**
1505 - 10th Street
Santa Monica, CA 90401
"Actor"

**Alvin Toffel**
2323 Bowmont Drive
Beverly Hills, CA 90210
"Author"

**Tokyo Rose (Iva Toguri)**
1443 Winnemac Street W.
Chicago, IL 60640
"Traitor"

**John Toland**
1 Long Ridge Road
Danbury, CT 06810
"Author"

**Billy Joe Toliver**
6938 Norris Ferry Road
Shreveport, LA 71106
"Football Player"

**Susan Tolsky**
10815 Acama Street
North Hollywood, CA 91602
"Actress"

**David Toma**
P.O. Box 854
Clark, NJ 07066
"Writer"

**Alberto Tomba**
I-40068 Castel de Britti
ITALY
"Skier"

**Marisa Tomei**
120 W. 45th Street #3600
New York, NY 10036
"Actress"

**Lily Tomlin**
P.O. Box 27700
Los Angeles, CA 90027
"Comedian, Actress, Writer"

**Angel Tompkins**
11935 Kling Street #10
Valley Village, CA 91607
"Actress"

**Tone Loc**
18653 Ventura Blvd. #340
Tarzana, CA 91356
"Singer"

**James Toney**
6305 Wellesley
West Bloomfield, MI 48322
"Boxer"

**Carrot Top**
420 Sylvan Drive
Winter Park, FL 32789
"Comedian"

**Chaim Topol**
22 Vale Court, Maidville
London W9 ENGLAND
"Actor, Director"

**Peter Tork**
P.O. Box 1821
Ojai, CA 93024
"Musician"

**Justin Torkildsen**
7800 Beverly Blvd. #3371
Los Angeles, CA 90036
"Actor"

**Rip Torn**
c/o Pure Arts
8840 Wilshire Blvd.
Beverly Hills, CA 90211
"Actor, Director"

**Joe Torre**
20 Lawrence Lane
Premium Point
Harrison, NY 10528
"Baseball Manager"

**Dean Torrence**
221 Main Street #P
Huntington Beach, CA 92648
"Singer, Songwriter"

**Gwen Torrence**
P.O. Box 361965
Decatur, GA 30036
"Track & Field"

**Dara Torres**
1750 East Boulder Street
Colorado Springs, CO 80909
"Swimmer"

**Liz Torres**
1680 North Vine Street #617
Hollywood, CA 90028
"Singer, Actress"

**Robert Torti**
8436 West Third Street #740
Los Angeles, CA 90048
"Actor"

**Nina Totenberg**
133 North Carolina Avenue SE
Washington, DC 20003
"News Correspondent"

**Toto**
34 North Palm Street #100
Ventura, CA 93001
"Rock & Roll Group"

**Audrey Totter**
7095 Hollywood Blvd. #1006
Hollywood, CA 90028
"Actress"

**Lupita Tovar**
1527 North Tigertail Road
Los Angeles, CA 90049
"Actress"

**Constance Towers**
2100 Century Park West #10263
Los Angeles, CA 90067
"Actress"

**Vecepia Towery**
9899 Santa Monica Blvd., PMB
2002
Beverly Hills, CA 90212
"Survivor Show Contestant"

**Robert Towne**
1417 San Remo Drive
Pacific Palisades, CA 90272
"Film Writer, Director"

**Colleen Townsend**
503 Seward Street NW
Washington, DC 20003
"Actress"

**Pete Townshend**
The Boathouse, Ranelagh Dr.
Twickenham TW1 1Q2 ENGLAND
"Singer"

**Robert Townsend**
2934 1/2 N. Beverly Glen Circle
Los Angeles, CA 90077
"Director, Actor, Comedian"

**Tony Trabert**
115 Knotty Pine Trail
Ponte Vedra, FL 32082
"Tennis Player"

**Michelle Trachtenberg**
P.O. Box 251735
Los Angeles, CA 90025
"Actress"

**The Tramps**
1560 Broadway #1308
New York, NY 10036
"R&B Group"

**Fred Travalana**
P.O. Box 260171
Encino, CA 91426
"Comedian, Actor, Writer"

**Daniel J. Travanti**
1077 Melody Road
Lake Forest, IL 60045
"Actor"

**Kylie Travis**
1196 Summit Drive
Beverly Hills, CA 90210
"Actress"

**Nancy Travis**
231 S. Cliffwood Avenue
Los Angeles, CA 90049
"Actress"

**Randy Travis**
P.O. Box 121137
Nashville, TN 37212
"Singer, Songwriter"

**Ellen Travolta**
5923 Wilbur Avenue
Tarzana, CA 91356
"Actress"

**John Travolta**
P.O. Box 3560
Santa Barbara, CA 93130
"Actor, Singer"

**Alex Trebek**
10202 W. Washington Blvd.
Culver City, CA 90232
"Game Show Host"

**Les Tremayne**
901 South Barrington Avenue
Los Angeles, CA 90049
"Actor"

**Anne Tremko**
10100 Santa Monica Blvd. #2500
Los Angeles, CA 90067
"Actress"

**John Trenhaile**
4 Wailands Crescent Lewes
East Sussex BNT 2QT ENGLAND
"Author"

**Adam Trese**
8912 Burton Way
Beverly Hills, CA 90211
"Actor"

**Lee Trevino**
1901 W. 47th Place #200
Westwood, KS 66205
"Golfer"

**Judd Trichter**
10264 Rochester Avenue
Los Angeles, CA 90024
"Actor"

**Trini Triggs**
3178 Allen Marthaville Road
Robeline, LA 71469
"Singer"

**Connor Trinneer**
9200 Sunset Blvd. #1130
Los Angeles, CA 90069
"Actor"

**Jean-Louis Trintignant**
20 Avenue Rapp
75007 Paris FRANCE
"Actor"

**Linda Tripp**
27285 Boyce Mill Road
Greensboro, MD 21639
"Betrayed Monica Lewinsky"

**Jean Tripplehorn**
350 Fifth Avenue #3505
New York, NY 10118
"Actress"

**Travis Tritt**
1103 - 17th Avenue South
Nashville, TN 37212
"Singer"

**Bryan Trotter**
3868 Forest Drive
Doylestown, PA 18901
"Hockey Player"

**Tom Troup**
8829 Ashcroft Avenue
Los Angeles, CA 90048
"Actor"

**Michael Trucco**
P.O. Box 99
China Springs, TX 76633
"Actor"

**Garry Trudeau**
459 Columbus Avenue #113
New York, NY 10024
"Cartoonist"

**Bianca Trump**
P.O. Box 8095
West Palm Beach, FL 33407
"Pornstar"

**Blaine Trump**
166 Avenue of the Americas
New York, NY 10013
"New York Socialite"

**Donald Trump**
721 Fifth Avenue
New York, NY 10022
"Real Estate Executive"

**Ivana Trump**
P.O. Box 8104
West Palm Beach, FL 33407
"Former wife of Donald Trump"

**Ivanka Trump**
P.O. Box 8095
West Palm Beach, FL 33407
"Daughter of Donald Trump"

**Michael Tucci**
1425 Irving Avenue
Glendale, CA 91201
"Actor"

**Stanley Tucci**
9830 Wilshire Blvd.
Beverly Hills, CA 90212
"Actor"

**Chris Tucker**
19133 Briafield Way
Tarzana, CA 91356
"Composer, Actor"

**Marshall Tucker Band**
315 S. Beverly Drive, #206
Beverly Hills, CA 90212
"Rock & Roll Group"

**Michael Tucker**
197 Oakdale Avenue
Mill Valley, CA 94941
"Actor"

**Tanya Tucker**
330 Franklin Road #135-A-257
Brentwood, TN 37027
"Singer"

**Tommy Tune**
50 East 89th Street
New York, NY 10128
"Dancer, Director"

**ex-Sen. John Tunney**
c/o Cloverleaf Group
1445 Fifth Street
Santa Monica, CA 90401
"Ex-Senator"

**Robin Tunney**
12250 Addison Street
Valley Village, CA 91607
"Actress"

**HRM King Tupou IV**
Palace Officiale
Nuku'alofa TONGA
"Royalty"

**Ann Turkel**
9877 Beverly Grove
Beverly Hills, CA 90210
"Actress"

**Christy Turlington**
9560 Wilshire Blvd. #516
Beverly Hills, CA 90212
"Actress"

**Glynn Turman**
3500 West Olive Avenue #1400
Burbank, CA 91505
"Actor"

**Dr. Debbye Turner**
P.O. Box 12450
St. Louis, MO 63132
"Beauty Contest Winner"

**Grant Turner**
P.O. Box 414
Brentwood, TN 37027
"Singer"

**Ike Turner**
905 Viewpoint Drive
San Marcos, CA 92069
"Musician"

**Janine Turner**
9830 Wilshire Blvd.
Beverly Hills, CA 90212
"Actress"

**Karri Turner**
1875 Century Park East #2250
Los Angeles, CA 90067
"Actress"

**Kathleen Turner**
163 Amsterdam Avenue #210
New York, NY 10023
"Actress"

**Admiral Stansfield Turner**
P.O. Box 2117
Springfield, VA 22152
"Military Leader"

**Ted Turner**
1050 Techwood Drive NW
Atlanta, GA 30318
"Broadcast & Sports Executive"

**Tina Turner**
Villa Ana Fleur
F-06230 Villefranche-sur-Mer
FRANCE
"Singer"

**Scott Turow**
Sears Tower #8000
Chicago, IL 60606
"Novelist"

**Aida Turturro**
9057C Nemo Street
West Hollywood, CA 90069
"Actress"

**John Turturro**
987 Terracina Street
Santa Paula, CA 93060
"Actor"

**Nicholas Turturro**
5201 Calvin Avenue
Tarzana, CA 91356
"Actor"

**Rita Tushingham**
4 Kingly Street
London W1R 5LF ENGLAND
"Actress"

**Desmond Tutu**
Box 1092, Milnerton 7441
Capetown SOUTH AFRICA
"Arch-Bishop"

**Shania Twain**
Q Prime
729 - 7th Avenue, 10th Floor
New York, NY 10019
"Singer"

**Shannon Tweed**
11300 W. Olympic Blvd. #619
Los Angeles, CA 90064
"Actress, Model"

**Twiggy**
4 St. George's House
15 Hanover Square
London W1R 9AJ ENGLAND
"Actress, Singer"

**Dwight Twilly**
P.O. Box 1821
Ojai, CA 92024
"Singer, Songwriter"

**Alexandra Tydings**
8383 Wilshire Blvd. #550
Beverly Hills, CA 90211
"Actress"

**Aisha Tyler**
c/o Endeavor
9701 Wilshire Blvd., 10th Floor
Los Angeles, CA 90036
"Comedienne"

**Bonnie Tyler**
Aspden, Coach House
Chapel Leyse, So. Holmwood
Dorking RH5 4LJ ENGLAND
"Singer, Songwriter"

**Liv Tyler**
151 El Camino Drive
Beverly Hills, CA 90212
"Actress"

**Nikki Tyler**
4F South Main Street
PMB 307
West Bridgewater, MA 02379
"Porn Star"

**Willie Tyler**
1650 Broadway #705
New York, NY 10019
"Ventriloquist"

**Hunter Tylo**
11684 Ventura Blvd. #910
Studio City, CA 91604
"Model"

**Michael Tylo**
11684 Ventura Blvd. #910
Studio City, CA 91604
"Actor"

**Susan Tyrell**
1489 Scott Avenue
Los Angeles, CA 90026
"Actress"

**Tyrese** (Gibson)
250 West 57th Street #821
New York, NY 10107
"R & B Singer"

**Cicely Tyson**
315 West 70th Street
New York, NY 10023
"Actress"

**Mike Tyson**
10100 Santa Monica Blvd. #1300
Los Angeles, CA 90067
"Boxer"

**U2**
30-32 Sir John Rogerson's Quarry
Dublin, IRELAND
"Rock & Roll Group"

**Peter Ueberroth**
184 Emerald Bay
Laguna Beach, CA 92651
"Former Baseball Executive"

**Bob Uecker**
201 S. 46th Street
Milwaukee, WI 53214
"Actor, Baseball Announcer"

**UFO**
10 Sutherland
London W9 24Q ENGLAND
"Rock & Roll Group"

**Anneliese Uhlig**
1519 Escalona Drive
Santa Cruz, CA 95060
"Actress"

**Dr. Art Ulene**
10810 Via Verona
Los Angeles, CA 90024
"TV Medical Reporter"

**Liv Ullman**
Hafrsfjordgst. 7
0273 Oslo, NORWAY
"Actress"

**Tracey Ullman**
815 E. Colorado Street #210
Glendale, CA 91205
"Actress, Singer"

**Skeet Ulrich**
8942 Wilshire Blvd.
Beverly Hills, CA 90211
"Actor"

**Blair Underwood**
2029 Century Park East #1190
Los Angeles, CA 90067
"Actor"

**Jay Underwood**
6100 Wilshire Blvd. #1170
Los Angeles, CA 90048
"Actor"

**Brian Unger**
5750 Wilshire Blvd.
Los Angeles, CA 9036
"Actor"

**Deborah Unger**
8942 Wilshire Blvd.
Beverly Hills, CA 90211
"Actress"

**Al Unser**
7625 Central N.W.
Albuquerque, NM 87105
"Race Car Driver"

**Al Unser, Jr.**
6847 Rio Grande Blvd.
Albuquerque, NM 87107
"Race Car Driver"

**Bobby Unser**
7700 Central S.W.
Albuquerque, NM 87105
"Race Car Driver"

**Bobby Unser Jr.**
P.O. Box 25047
Albuquerque, NM 87125
"Race Car Driver"

**Del Unser**
115 Spyglass Drive
Blue Bell, PA 19422
"Race Car Driver"

**John Updike**
675 Hale Street
Beverly Farm, MA 01915
"Author"

**Gene Upshaw**
1102 Pepper Tree Drive
Great Falls, VA 22066
"Football Executive"

**Keith Urban**
P.O. Box 41085
Nashville, TN 37204
"Guitarist"

**Uriah Heep**
1257 Arcade Street
St. Paul, MN 55106
"Rock & Roll Group"

**Leon Uris**
P.O. Box 1003
Shelter Island Hgts., NY 11965
"Author"

**Usher**
8942 Wilshire Blvd.
Beverly Hills, CA 90211
"Singer"

**Sir Peter Ustinov**
8 Carburton Street
London, W1P 7DT ENGLAND
"Actor"

**Garrick Utely**
8 Carburton Street
London W1P 7DT ENGLAND
"News Correspondent"

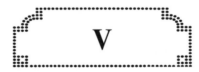

**Brenda Vaccaro**
9301 Wilshire Blvd. #300
Beverly Hills, CA 90210
"Actress"

**Jerry Vale**
1100 N. Alta Loma Rd., #1404
Los Angeles, CA 90069
"Singer"

**Nancy Valen**
13775-A Mono Way #220
Sonora, CA 95370
"Actress"

**Benita Valente**
c/o Janice Meyer
201 West 54th Street
New York, NY 10019
"Opera Singer"

**Jack Valenti**
4635 Ashby Street NW
Washington, D C 20007
"Film Director"

**Karen Valentine**
P.O. Box 1410
Washington Depot, CT 06793
"Actress"

**Scott Valentine**
8436 West Third Street #740
Los Angeles, CA 90048
"Actor"

**Valentino**
2 East 70th Street
New York, NY 10021
"Singer"

**Fernando Valenzuela**
3004 North Beachwod Drive
Los Angeles, CA 90027
"Baseball Player"

**Amber Valletta**
c/o Lee Daniels
151 West 74th Street, 8th Floor
New York, NY 10023
"Actress"

**Alida Valli**
Viale Liegi 42
00198 Rome, ITALY
"Actress"

**Frankie Valli**
9200 Sunset Blvd. #900
Los Angeles, CA 90069
"Singer"

**Richard Van Allen**
18 Octavia Street
London SW11 3DN ENGLAND
"Singer"

**Joan Van Ark**
151 El Camino Drive
Beverly Hills, CA 90212
"Actress"

**Abigail Van Buren**
P.O. Box 69440
Los Angeles, CA 90069
"Columnist"

**Courtney B. Vance**
112 South Almont Drive
Los Angeles, CA 90048
"Actor"

**Jean-Claude Van Damme**
1122 S. Robertson Blvd. #15
Los Angeles, CA 90035
"Actor"

**Lex Van den Berghe**
P.O. Box 3482
Santa Cruz, CA 95060
"TV Survivor Contestant"

**Pieter van den Hoogenband**
P.O. Box 302
6800 AH Arnhem NETHERLANDS
"Swimmer"

**James Van Der Beek**
2045 S. Barrington Avenue
Los Angeles, CA 90025
"Actor"

**Trish Van Devere**
3211 Retreat Court
Malibu, CA 90265
"Actress"

**Kiki Vandeweghe**
4 Pennsylvania Plaza
New York, NY 10019
"Ex-Basketball Player"

**Casper Van Dien**
9171 Wilshire Blvd. #406
Beverly Hills, CA 90210
"Actor"

**Titos Vandis**
1930 Century Park East #303
Los Angeles, CA 90067
"Actor"

**Mamie Van Doren**
3419 Via Lido #184
Newport Beach, CA 92663
"Actress, Singer"

**Luther Vandross**
150 East 58th Street, 19th Floor
New York, NY 10155
"Singer"

**Barry Van Dyke**
27800 Blythdale Road
Agoura, CA 91301
"Actor"

**Dick Van Dyke**
23215 Mariposa De Oro
Malibu, CA 90265
"Actor"

**Jerry Van Dyke**
P.O. Box 2130
Benton, AR 72018
"Actor"

**Leroy Van Dyke**
29000 Highway V
Smithton, MO 65350
"Singer, Songwriter"

**Amy Van Dyken**
P.O. Box 261934
Littleton, CO 80163
"Swimmer"

**Charles Van Eman**
12304 Santa Monica Blvd., #104
Los Angeles, CA 90025
"Actor"

**Vangelis**
195 Queens Gate
London W1 ENGLAND
"Composer"

**Alex Van Halen**
12024 Summit Circle
Beverly Hills, CA 90210
"Musician"

**Eddie Van Halen**
20411 Chapter Drive
Woodland Hills, CA 91364
"Guitarist, Songwriter"

**Vanilla Ice**
510 S. Coast Hwy.
Laguna Beach, CA 92651
"Rap Singer"

**Merete Van Kemp**
10000 Santa Monica Blvd. #305
Los Angeles, CA 90067
"Actress"

**Dick Van Patten**
13920 Magnolia Blvd.
Sherman Oaks, CA 91423
"Actor"

**James Van Patten**
14411 Riverside Drive #15
Sherman Oaks, CA 91423
"Actor"

**Joyce Van Patten**
2005 Sierra Place
Glendale, CA 91208
"Actress"

**Nels Van Patten**
14411 Riverside Drive #18
Sherman Oaks, CA 91423
"Actor"

**Tim Van Patten**
13920 Magnolia Blvd.
Sherman Oaks, CA 91423
"Actor"

**Vincent Van Patten**
13926 Magnolia Blvd.
Sherman Oaks, CA 91423
"Actor"

**Mario Van Peebles**
9560 Wilshire Blvd. #516
Beverly Hills, CA 90212
"Actor, Writer, Director"

**Ricky Van Sheldon**
6424 Bresslyn Road
Nashville, TN 37205
"Singer"

**Deborah Van Valkenburgh**
2025 Stanley Hills Drive
Los Angeles, CA 90046
"Actress"

**Monique Van Vooren**
165 East 66th Street
New York, NY 10021
"Actress, Singer"

**Steve Van Zandt**
9150 Wilshire Blvd. #350
Beverly Hills, CA 90212
"Singer, Guitarist"

**The Vapors**
44 Valmoral Drive
Woking, Surrey, ENGLAND
"Rock & Roll Group"

**Nia Vardalos**
9150 Wilshire Blvd. #350
Beverly Hills, CA 90212
"Actress"

**Victor Vasarely**
83 re aux Religues
F-77410 Annet-sur-Marne,
FRANCE
"Artist"

**Vince Vaughn**
9560 Wilshire Blvd. #516
Beverly Hills, CA 90212
"Actor"

**Bobby Vee (Velline)**
P.O. Box 41
Saulk Rapids, MN 56379
"Singer, Songwriter"

**Alexa Vega**
1801 Avenue of the Stars #902
Los Angeles, CA 90067
"Actress"

**Suzanne Vega**
2565 Broadway #395
New York, NY 10025
"Singer"

**Jorge Velasquez**
770 Allerton Avenue
Bronx, NY 10467
"Horse Racer"

**Eddie Velez**
5439 Ellenvale Avenue
Woodland Hills, CA 91367
"Actor"

**Reginald Vel Johnson**
8637 Allenwood Drive
Los Angeles, CA 90046
"Actor"

**Diane Venora**
1505 10th Street
Santa Monica, CA 90401
"Actor"

**John Ventimiglia**
9150 Wilshire Blvd. #350
Beverly Hills, CA 90212
"Actor"

**Vincent Ventresca**
9057-C Nemo Street
West Hollywood, CA 90069
"Actor"

**Gov. Jesse Ventura (MN)**
75 Constitution Avenue #130
St. Paul, MN 55155
"Politician"

**Ken Venturi**
P.O. Box 5118
Akron, OH 44334
"Golf Instructor"

**Elena Verdugo**
P.O. Box 2048
Chula Vista, CA 92012
"Actress"

**Ben Vereen**
9255 Sunset Blvd. #804
Los Angeles, CA, 90069
"Dancer, Actor"

**Sofia Vergara**
9405 NW 41st Street
Miami, FL 33178
"Actress, Model"

**Paul Verhoeven**
7920 Sunset Blvd.
Los Angeles, CA 90046
"Actor"

**Dick Vermeil**
51 W. 52nd Street
New York, NY 10019
"Sportcaster"

**John Vernon**
5751 Stansbury Avenue
Van Nuys, CA 91401
"Actor"

**Kate Vernon**
1505 - 10th Street
Santa Monica, CA 90401
"Actress"

**Tricia Vessey**
9150 Wilshire Blvd. #350
Beverly Hills, CA 90212
"Actress, Model"

**Yvette Vickers**
P.O. Box 292479
Phelan, CA 92329
"Actress"

**James Victor**
1944 N. Whitley Avenue #306
Los Angeles, CA 90036
"Actor"

**Gore Vidal**
Via Fusco 20
Raville SA, 84010 ITALY
"Writer"

**Peter Vidmar**
23832 Via Roble
Coto de Caza, CA 92679
"Gymnast"

**Abe Vigoda**
1900 Avenue of the Stars #1640
Los Angeles, CA 90067
"Actor"

**Richard Viguerie**
7777 Leesburg Pike
Falls Church, VA 22043
"Professional Fund Raiser"

**Bob Vila**
P.O. Box 749
Marstons Mills, MA 02648
"Home Repair TV Host"

**Bruce Vilanch**
c/o Moffitt-Lee Productions
1428 North Gower Street
Hollywood, CA 90028
"Entertainment Writer"

**Guillermo Vilas**
Pembroke One Bldg. #525
Virgina Beach, VA 34462
"Tennis Player"

**The Village People**
P.O. Box 770850
Orlando, FL 32877
"Music Group"

**Virginia Vincent**
1001 Hammond Street
Los Angeles, CA 90069
"Actress"

**Melanie Vincz**
2212 Earle Court
Redondo Beach, CA 90278
"Actress, Model"

**Jesse Vint**
10637 Burbank Blvd.
No. Hollywood, CA 91601
"Actress"

**Bobby Vinton**
9255 Sunset Blvd. #804
Los Angeles, CA 90069
"Singer"

**Frank Viola**
844 Sweetwater Island Circle
Longwood, FL 32779
"Baseball Player"

**Lasse Viren**
Suomen Urhellulirto Ry
Box 25002 00250
Helsinki 25 FINLAND
"Track Athlete"

**Sal Visculo**
6491 Ivarene Avenue
Los Angeles, CA 90068
"Actor"

**Mike Vitar**
3500 West Olive Avenue #1400
Burbank, CA 91505
"Actor"

**Monica Vitti**
Via F. 38, Siacci
I-00197 Rome, ITALY
"Actress"

**Marina Vlady**
15, rue Paul Sevel
F-75008 Paris FRANCE
"Actress"

**Karl Micheal Vogler**
Auweg 8, Seehof
D-82418 Seehausen
GERMANY
"Actor"

**Jon Voight**
9830 Wilshire Blvd.
Beverly Hills, CA 90212
"Actor"

**Sen. George Voinovich (OH)**
Dirksen Senate Office Building
#B34
Washington, DC 20510
"Politicain"

**Paul Volcker**
International Economic Dept.
Princeton University
Princeton, NJ
"Former Monetary Treasurer"

**Nedra Volz**
5606 East Fairfield Street
Mesa, AZ 86205
"Actress"

**Helene von Damm-Gurtler**
Hotel Sacher bei der Oper
1010 Vienna, AUSTRIA
"Diplomat"

**Betsy Von Fursterberg**
230 Central Park West
New York, NY 10028
"Actress"

**Diane von Furstenberg**
389 West 12th Street
New York, NY 10014
"Fashion Designer"

**Kurt Vonnegut, Jr.**
P.O. Box 27
Sagaponack, NY 11962
"Author"

**Max Von Sydow**
18 rue Troyan
F-75017 Paris FRANCE
"Actor"

**Richard von Weizsacker**
Meisenstr. 6
D-14195 Berlin GERMANY
"Ex-President of Germany"

**Lark Voorhies**
10635 Santa Monica Blvd., #130
Los Angeles, CA 90025
"Actress"

**W**

**Adam Wade**
257 Park Avenue South #900
New York, NY 10010
"Actor, Singer"

**Russell Wade**
47-287 West Eldorado Drive
Indian Wells, CA 92260
"Actor"

**Virginia Wade**
Sharstead Court
Sittingbourne
Kent, ENGLAND
"Tennis Player"

**Lanny Wadkins**
6002 Kettering Court
Dallas, TX 75248
"Golfer"

**Lyle Waggoner**
1124 Oak Mirage
Westlake Village, CA 91362
"Actor"

**Chuck Wagner**
1419 N. Hollywood Way
Burbank, CA 91505
"Actor"

**Helen Wagner**
1268 East 141st Street
Brooklyn, NY 11230
"Actress"

**Jack Wagner**
1134 Alta Loma Road #115
West Hollywood, CA 90069
"Actor, Singer"

**Jane Wagner**
P.O. Box 27700
Los Angeles, CA 90027
"Writer, Producer"

**Lindsay Wagner**
P.O. Box 5002
Sherman Oaks, CA 91403
"Actress"

**Lou Wagner**
8527 Wonderland Avenue
Los Angeles, CA 90046
"Actor"

**Natasha Gregson Wagner**
8383 Wilshire Blvd., 530
Beverly Hills, CA 90211
"Actress"

**Robert Wagner**
1465 Lindacrest Drive
Beverly Hills, CA 90210
"Actor"

**Porter Wagoner**
P.O. Box 290785
Nashville, TN 37229
"Singer, Songwriter"

**Mark Wahlberg**
P.O. Box 850304
Braintree, MA 02185
"Actor, Talk Show Host"

**Bea Wain**
9955 Durant Drive, #305
Beverly Hills, CA 90212
"Singer"

**Liam Waite**
P.O. Box 5617
Beverly Hills, CA 90210
"Actor"

**Ralph Waite**
73317 Ironwood Street
Palm Desert, CA 92260
"Actor, Director"

**Terry Waite**
The Green Harvest, Bury
St. Edmunds, Suffolk 1P29 4DH
ENGLAND
"Clergy"

**Tom Waits**
7906 Willow Glen Road
Los Angeles, CA 90046
"Singer, Songwriter"

**Grete Waitz**
Birgitte Hammers Vel 15-G
1169 Oslo NORWAY
"Track Athlete"

**Andrzej Wajda**
ul-Jezefa Hauke Bosaka 14
01-540 Warsaw POLAND
"Director"

**Gregory Walcott**
P.O. Box 622
Canoga Park, CA 91395
"Actor"

**Jeff Wald**
3000 West Olympic Blvd.
Bldg. 2 #1400
Santa Monica, CA 90404
"Talent Agent"

**Robert Walden**
1450 Arroyo View Drive
Pasadena, CA 91103
"Actor"

**Kurt Waldheim**
Walfischgasse 8
1010 Vienna, AUSTRIA
"Ex-President of Austria"

**Janet Waldo**
15735 Royal Oak Road
Encino, CA 91316
"Actress"

**Lech Walesa**
Polskistr. 53
Gdansk - (Danzig) POLAND
"Politician"

**Christopher Walken**
40 West 57th Street
New York, NY 10019
"Actor"

**Anetia Walker**
6300 Wilshire Blvd. #910
Los Angeles, CA 90048
"Actress"

**Clint Walker**
300 - 10th Avenue South
Nashville, TN 37203
"Actor"

**Fiona Walker**
13 Despard Road
London 5NP ENGLAND
"Actress"

**Jimmie Walker**
88 Roxiticus Road
Far Hills, NJ 07931
"Actor, Comedian"

**Junior Walker**
141 Dunbar Avenue
Fords, NJ 08863
"Saxophonist"

**Mort Walker**
61 Studio Court
Stamford, CT 06903
"Cartoonist"

**Nicholas Walker**
1900 Ave. of the Stars #1640
Los Angeles, CA 90067
"Actor"

**Paul Walker IV**
8606 Wyngate Street
Sunland, CA 91040
"Actor"

**Polly Walker**
4 Windmill Street
London WIP IHF ENGLAND
"Actress"

**Robert Walker Junior**
23410 Civic Center Way #C-I
Malibu, CA 90265
"Actor"

**Samaki Walker**
c/o LA Lakers
1111 S. Figueroa Street
Los Angeles, CA 90015
"Basketball Player"

**George Wallace**
141 S. El Camino Drive #205
Beverly Hills, CA 90212
"Comedian"

**Jerry Wallace**
1161 Northwest 76th Avenue
Fort Lauderdale, FL 33322
"Singer"

**Marcia Wallace**
1312 South Genesee Avenue
Los Angeles, CA 90019
"Actress"

**Mike Wallace**
555 West 57th Street
New York, NY 10019
"Broadcast Journalist"

**Eli Wallach**
200 West 57th Street #900
New York, NY 10019
"Actor"

**The Great Wallendas**
138 Frog Hollow Road
Churchville, PA 18966
"High Wire Act"

**Jon Walmsley**
13810 Magnolia Blvd.
Sherman Oaks, CA 91403
"Actor"

**Martin Walser**
Zum Hecht 36
D-88662 Uberlingen, GERMANY
"Author, Dramatist"

**Bill Walsh**
Stanford University Football
Stanford, CA 94305
"Ex-Football Coach"

**Dylan Walsh**
9560 Wilshire Blvd. #500
Beverly Hills, CA 90212
"Actor"

**John Walsh**
5151 Wisconsin Avenue
Washington , DC 20016
"Actor"

**Kate Walsh**
2060 High tower Drive
Los Angeles, CA 90068
"Actress"

**M. Emmet Walsh**
4173 Motor Avenue
Culver City, CA 90232
"Actor"

**Jessica Walter**
27 West 87th Street #2
New York, NY 10024
"Actress"

**Lee Ann Walter**
c/o Bravo
1111 Stewart Avenue
Bethpage, NY 11714
"Actress"

**Tracey Walter**
257 North Rexford Drive
Beverly Hills, CA 90210
"Actor"

**Barbara Walters**
320 West 66th Street
New York, NY 10023
"News Journalist"

**Hugh Walters**
15 Christ Church Avenue
London NW6 7QP ENGLAND
"Actor"

**Jaime Walters**
14313 Greenleaf Street
Sherman Oaks, CA 91423
"Actor"

**Julie Walters**
76 Oxford Street
London W1N 0AX ENGLAND
"Actress"

**Melora Walters**
8383 Wilshire Blvd. #550
Beverly Hills, CA 90211
"Actress"

**Susan Walters**
1505 - 10th Street
Santa Monica, CA 90401
"Actress"

**Bill Walton**
1010 Myrtle Way
San Diego, CA 92103
"Ex-Basketball Player"

**Jess Walton**
4702 Ethel Avenue
Sherman Oaks, CA 91423
"Actress"

**Darrell Waltrip**
8701 Mallard Creek Road
Schuyler, VA 22969
"Race Car Driver"

**Joseph Wambaugh**
3520 Kellogg Way
San Diego, CA 92106
"Novelist"

**Joseph A. Wapner**
2388 Century Hill
Los Angeles, CA 90067
"TV Show Judge"

**War**
276 Fifth Avenue #507
New York, NY 10001
"R & B Group"

**Patrick Warburton**
151 El Camino Drive
Beverly Hills, CA 90212
"Actor"

**Burt Ward**
c/o Boy Wonder Visual Effects
8611 Hayden Place
Culver City, CA 90232
"Actor"

**Fred Ward**
1214 Cabrillo Avenue
Venice, CA 90291
"Actor"

**Jonathan Ward**
8436 West 3rd Street #740
Los Angeles, CA 90048
"Writer, Newscorrespondent"

**Megan Ward**
P.O. Box 481210
Los Angeles, CA 90036
"Actress"

**Rachel Ward**
1505 - 10th Street
Santa Monica, CA 90401
"Actress"

**Sela Ward**
289 S. Robertson Blvd. #469
Beverly Hills, CA 90211
"Actress"

**Jack Warden**
23604 Malibu Colony Drive
Malibu, CA 90265
"Actor"

**Clyde Ware**
1252 North Laurel Avenue
Los Angeles, CA 90046
"Writer, Producer"

**Herta Ware**
P.O. Box 151
Topanga, CA 90290
"Actress"

**Steve Wariner**
P.O. Box 157
Nolensville, TN 37135
"Singer"

**Richard Waring**
1 Chester Close
Queens Ride
London SW13 OJE ENGLAND
"TV Writer"

**Todd Waring**
145 West 45th Street #1204
New York, NY 10036
"Actor"

**Billy Warlock**
9229 Sunset Blvd. #315
Los Angeles, CA 90069
"Actor"

**Julie Warner**
1505 - 10th Street
Santa Monica, CA 90401
"Actress"

**Kurt Warner**
701 Convention Place
St. Louis, MO 63101
"Football Player"

**Malcolm-Jamal Warner**
P.O. Box 69646
Los Angeles, CA 90069
"Actor"

**Diane Warren**
1896 Rising Glen Road
Los Angeles, CA 90069
"Singer"

**Jennifer Warren**
1675 Old Oak Road
Los Angeles, CA 90049
"Actress"

**Lesley Ann Warren**
9057-C Nemo Street
West Washington, DC 90069
"Actress"

**Michael Warren**
11500 West Olympic Blvd. #510
Los Angeles, CA 90064
"Actor"

**Ruth Warrick**
903 Park Avenue
New York, NY 10021
"Actress"

**Denzel Washington**
10153 1/2 Riverside Drive
PMB 130
Toluca Lake, CA 91602
"Actor"

**Isaiah Washington**
1888 Century Park East #500
Los Angeles, CA 90067
"Actor"

**Ted Wass**
11733 Valleycrest Road
Studio City, CA 91604
"Actor"

**Dale Wasserman**
1680 Valecroft Avenue
Westlake Village, CA 91361
"Playwright"

**Gedde Watanabe**
1632 Westerly Terrace
Los Angeles, CA 90026
"Actor"

**Waterboys**
3 Monmouth Road
London W2 ENGLAND
"Rock & Roll Group"

**John Waters**
c/o Atomic Books
1100 West 36th Street
Baltimore, MD 21211
"Director, Writer"

**Rep. Maxine Waters (CA)**
Rayburn House Office Building
#2344
Washington, DC 20515
"Politicain"

**Sam Waterson**
RR Box 232
West Cornwell, CT 06796
"Actor"

**Carlene Watkins**
11500 W. Olympic Blvd. #510
Los Angeles, CA 90064
"Actress"

**Jody Watley**
1560 Broadway #1308
New York, NY 10036
"Singer"

**Emily Watson**
76 Oxford Street
London W1N OAX ENGLAND
"Actress"

**Mills Watson**
10100 Santa Monica Blvd. #2490
Los Angeles, CA 90067
"Actor"

**Tom Watson**
1901 West 47th Place #200
Westwood, KS 66205
"Golfer"

**Charlie Watts**
P.O. Box 170429
San Francisco, CA 94117
"Drummer"

**James G. Watt**
P.O. Box 3705
Jackson Hole, WY 83001
"Former Secretary of Interior"

**Ruby Wax**
Ferry House
Cherie Crescent Road
Bournemouth Dorset BH2 5LQ
ENGLAND
"Television Host"

**Rep. Henry A. Waxman (CA)**
House Rayburn Bldg. #2204
Washington, DC 20515
"Politician"

**Damon Wayans**
9830 Wilshire Blvd.
Beverly Hills, CA 90212
"Actor"

**Dwayne Wayans**
16405 Mulholland Drive
Los Angeles, CA 90049
"Actor"

**Keenan Ivory Wayans**
9830 Wilshire Blvd.
Beverly Hills, CA 90212
"Actor"

**Kim Wayans**
1742 Granville Avenue #2
Los Angeles, CA 90025
"Actress"

**Marlon Wayans**
9830 Wilshire Blvd.
Beverly Hills, CA 90212
"Actor"

**Shawn Wayans**
9830 Wilshire Blvd.
Beverly Hills, CA 90212
"Comedian, Actor"

**Kristina Wayborn**
3350 Barham Blvd.
Los Angeles, CA 90068
"Actress, Model"

**Fredd Wayne**
117 Strand Street
Santa Monica, CA 90405
"Actor, Writer"

**Michael Wayne**
10424 Kling Street
North Hollywood, CA 91602
"Film Executive"

**Patrick Wayne**
10502 Whipple Street
North Hollywood, CA 91602
"Actor"

**Shawn Weatherby**
9229 Sunset Blvd. #311
Los Angeles, CA 90069
"Actress, Model"

**Carl Weathers**
10960 Wilshire Blvd. #826
Los Angeles, CA 90024
"Actor"

**Bob Weatherwax**
16133 Soledad Canyon Road
Canyon Country, CA 91351
"Animal Trainer"

**Dennis Weaver**
P.O. Box 257
Ridgeway, CO 81432
"Actor"

**Earl Weaver**
3000 SW 62nd Place
Miami, FL 33155
"Ex-Baseball Manager"

**Fritz Weaver**
161 West 75th Street
New York, NY 10023
"Actor"

**Sigourney Weaver**
P.O. Box 38
New York, NY 10150
"Actress"

**Hugo Weaving**
Box 478, King's Cross
NSW 2011 AUSTRALIA
"Actor"

**Jimmy Webb**
1173-A - 2nd Avenue #178
New York, NY 10021
"Singer, Composer"

**Lucy Webb**
1360 N. Crescent Heights #3-B
Los Angeles, CA 90046
"Actress, Comedienne"

**Andrew Lloyd Webber**
Trump Tower
725 Fifth Avenue
New York, NY 10022
"Composer"

**Steven Weber**
8942 Wilshire Blvd.
Beverly Hills, CA 90211
"Actor"

**William Webster**
4777 Dexter Street, NW
Washington, D.C. 20007
"Ex-F.B.I. Director"

**Ann Wedgeworth**
70 Riverside Drive
New York, NY 10024
"Actress"

**Caspar Weinberger**
700 New Hampshire Avenue NW
Washington, DC 20037
"Former Government Official"

**Carl Weintraub**
400 S. Beverly Drive #101
Beverly Hills, CA 90212
"Actor"

**Jerry Weintraub**
27740 Pacific Coast Hwy.
Malibu, CA 90265
"Film Producer"

**Peter Weir**
Post Office
Palm Beach 2108 AUSTRALIA
"Film Director"

**Tom Weiskepf**
7580 East Gray Road #204
Scottsdale, AZ 85260
"Golfer"

**Sam Weisman**
4448 Tujunga Avenue
No. Hollywood, CA 91602
"Actor"

**Michael Weiss**
P.O. Box 12311
Burke, VA 22009
"Olympic Men's Figure Skater"

**Michael T. Weiss**
9701 Wilshire Blvd., 10th Flr.
Beverly Hills, CA 90212
"Actor"

**Morgan Weisser**
1030 Superba Avenue
Venice, CA 90291
"Actor"

**Bruce Weitz**
18826 Erwin Street
Reseda, CA 91335
"Actor"

**Ezer Weizman**
2 Haddekill Street
Caesarea ISRAEL
"Politician"

**Raquel Welch**
9903 Santa Monica Blvd. #514
Beverly Hills, CA 90212
"Actress, Singer, Writer"

**Tahnee Welch**
P.O. Box 823
Beverly Hills, CA 90213
"Actress"

**Ex-Gov. William Weld**
120 Zaccheus Mead Lane
Greenwich, CT 06831
"Politician"

**Frank Welker**
10635 Santa Monica Blvd. #130
Los Angeles, CA 90025
"Actor, Comedian"

**Peter Weller**
853 - 7th Avenue #9A
New York, NY 10019
"Actor"

**Robb Weller**
4249 Beck Avenue
Studio City, CA 91604
"TV Show Host"

**William Wellman, Jr.**
410 North Barrington Avenue
Los Angeles, CA 90049
"Actor"

**David Wells**
1751 Pinnacle Drive #1500
McLean, VA 22102
"Baseball Player

**Dawn Wells**
11684 Ventura Blvd. #965
Studio City, CA 91604
"Actress"

**Kitty Wells**
P.O. Box 1189
Madison, TN 37116
"Singer"

**George Wendt**
9150 Wilshire Blvd. #350
Beverly Hills, CA 90212
"Actor"

**Lina Wertmuller**
via Principessa Clotilde 5
00196 Rome, ITALY
"Film Director"

**Tina Wesson**
9899 Santa Monica Blvd., PMB
2002
Beverly Hills, CA 90212
"Survivor Show Contestant"

**Adam West**
P.O. Box 3477
Ketchum, ID 83340
"Actor"

**Chandra West**
955 South Carrillo Drive #300
Los Angeles, CA 90048
"Actress"

**Jerry West**
175 Toyota Plaza
Memphis, TN 38103
"Ex-Basketball Player"

**Red West**
6676 Memphis-Arlington
Bartlett, TN 38135
"Actor, Author"

**Shelly West**
2802 Columbine Place
Nashville, TN 37204
"Singer"

**Timothy West**
46 North Side
Wandsworth Common
London SW18 ENGLAND
"Actor"

**Dr. Ruth Westheimer**
900 West 190th Street
New York, NY 10040
"Sex Theapist"

**James Westmoreland**
8019 1/2 West Norton Avenue
Los Angeles, CA 90046
"Actor"

**Gen. William Westmoreland**
1 Gadsden Way #CTG
Charleston, SC 29412
"Military Leader"

**Celia Weston**
1505 - 10th Street
Santa Monica, CA 90401
"Actress"

**David Weston**
123A Grosvenor Road
London SW1 ENGLAND
"Actor"

**Haskell Wexier**
P.O. Box 2230
Hollywood, CA 90078
"Cinematograhper"

**Frank Whaley**
9255 Sunset Blvd. #1010
West Hollywood, CA 90069
"Actor

**Joanne Whaley**
9830 Wilshire Blvd.
Beverly Hills, CA 90212
"Actress"

**Justin Whalin**
15501 Briarwood Drive
Van Nuys, CA 91403
"Actor"

**Wheezer**
10900 Wilshire Blvd. #1000
Beverly Hills, CA 90067
"Actor"

**Lisa Whelchel**
30408 Olympic Street
Castaic, CA 91384
"Actress"

**Shannon Whirry**
8827 Beverly Blvd.
Los Angeles, CA 90048
"Actress"

**Lou Whitaker**
4781 Highland place
Lakeland, FL 33813
"Ex-Baseball Player"

**Ian Whitcomb**
P.O. Box 451
Altadena, CA 91001
"Singer, Actor, Producer"

**Barry White**
151 El Camino Drive
Beverly Hills, CA 90212
"Singer, Songwriter"

**Betty White**
P.O. Box 491965
Los Angeles, CA 90049
"Actress"

**Bradley White**
8730 Sunset Blvd. #480
Los Angeles, CA 90069
"Actor"

**Bryan White**
10351 Santa Monica Blvd. #306
Los Angeles, CA 90025
"Singer"

**Jaleel White**
1122 S. Robertson Blvd. #15
Los Angeles, CA 90035
"Actor"

**Karyn White**
3300 Warner Blvd.
Burbank, CA 91505
"Singer"

**Michael White**
5420 Camelot Road
Brentwood, TN 37027
"Singer"

**Michael Jai White**
1640 South Sepulveda Blvd. #218
Los Angeles, CA 90025
"Actor"

**Peter White**
8730 Sunset Blvd. #480
Los Angeles, CA 90069
"Actor"

**Reggie White**
501 Nelson Place
Nashville, TN 37214
"Football Player"

**Sharon White**
380 Forest Retreat
Hendersonville, TN 37075
"Singer, Guitarist"

**Thelma White**
Motion Picture Country Home
23450 Calabasas
Woodland Hills, CA 91364
"Singer"

**Vanna White**
10202 W. Washington Blvd. #5300
Culver City, CA 90232
"TV Personality, Model"

**Geoffrey Whitehead**
81 Shaftesbury Avenue
London W1 ENGLAND
"Actor"

**Billie Whitelaw**
76 Oxford Street
London W1D 1BS ENGLAND
"Actress"

**The White's**
P.O. Box 2158
Hendersonville, TN 37075
"C&W Group"

**Whitesnake**
9200 Sunset Blvd. #530
Los Angeles, CA 900692
"R & R Group"

**Heather Whitestone**
2 Ocean Way #1000
Atlantic City, NJ 08401
"Former Miss America"

**Bradley Whitford**
5761 Valley Oak Drive
Los Angeles, CA 90068
"Actor"

**Barbara Whiting**
1085 Waddington Street
Birmingham, MI 48009
"Actress"

**Margaret Whiting**
41 West 58th Street #5A
New York, NY 10019
"Singer"

**Slim Whitman**
2825 Blue Brick Drive
Nashville, TN 37214
"C & W Singer"

**Stuart Whitman**
749 San Ysidro Road
Santa Barbara, CA 93108
"Actor"

**James Whitmore**
4990 Puesta Del Sol
Malibu, CA 90265
"Actor"

**James Whitmore, Jr.**
1284 La Brea Drive
Thousand Oaks, CA 91362
"Actor"

**Jane Whitney**
5 TV Place
Needham, MA 02192
"TV Talk Show Host"

**Roger Whittaker**
1730 Tree Blvd. #2
St. Augustine, FL 32086
"Singer, Songwriter"

**The Who**
250 West 57th Street #821
New York, NY 10107
"Rock & Roll Group"

**Tom Wicker**
229 West 43rd Street
New York, NY 10036
"Columnist"

**Kathleen Widdoes**
24 East 11th Street
New York, NY 10003
"Actress"

**Elie Wiesel**
745 Common Wealth Avenue
Boston, MA 02215
"Author, Journalist"

**Simon Wiesenthal**
Salvatorgasse 6
A-1010 Vienna AUSTRIA
"Jewish Leader"

**Dianne Wiest**
40 West 57th Street
New York, NY 10019
"Actress"

**Kelly Wiglesworth**
5225 San Pablo Dam Road
El Sobrante, CA 94803
"Survivor Show Contestant"

**Mats Wilander**
Vickersvagen 2
S-352 53 Vaxjo, SWEDEN
"Tennis Player"

**The Wilburn Brothers**
P.O. Box 50
Goodlettsville, TN 37072
"C&W Group"

**Larry Wilcox**
10 Appaloosa Lane
Canoga Park, CA 91307
"Actor, Director"

**Shannon Wilcox**
1753 Centinela Avenue #A
Santa Monica, CA 90404
"Actress"

**Jack Wild**
68 Old Brompton Road
London SW7 3LQ ENGLAND
"Actor"

**Kim Wilde**
1 Stevenage Road
Nebrowth, Herts. ENGLAND
"Singer, Songwriter"

**Gene Wilder**
1511 Sawtelle Blvd. #115
Los Angeles, CA 90025
"Actor, Writer, Director"

**James Wilder**
8601 Wilshire Blvd. #801
Beverly, Hills, CA 90211
"Actor"

**Ex-Gov. L. Douglas Wilder**
3215 Hawthorne Avenue
Richmond, VA 23222
"Politician"

**Yvonne Wilder**
11836 Hesby Street
North Hollywood, CA 91607
"Actress"

**Michael Wilding, Jr.**
34 Ellis Rance Road
Santa Fe, NM 87505
"Actor"

**Donna Wilkes**
16228 Maplegrove Street
La Puente, CA 91744
"Actress"

**Jamaal Wilkes**
7846 West 81st Street
Playa del Rey, CA 90291
"Ex-Basketball Player"

**June Wilkinson**
1025 N. Howard Street
Glendale, CA 91207
"Actress"

**George Will**
c/o Washington Post Writers Group
1150 -15th Street NW
Washington, DC 20071
"Columnist, Writer"

**Fred Willard**
5056 Wodley Avenue
Enccino, CA 91436
"Actor"

**Jo Ann Willette**
9460 Wilshire Blvd. #300
Beverly Hills, CA 90212
"Actress"

**Kathleen Willey**
2642 New Timer Way
Powhattan, VA 23139
"Ex-Unpaid White House Aid"

**HRH Prince William**
Highgrove House
Gloucestershire ENGLAND
"Royalty"

**Williams & Ree**
P.O. Box 163
Hendersonville, TN 37077
"Vocal Duo"

**Andy Williams**
2500 West Highway 76
Branson, MO 65616
"Singer, Actor"

**Anson Williams**
24615 Skyline View Drive
Malibu, CA 90265
"Actor"

**Mayor Anthony Willams**
1350 Pennyslvania Avenue NW
#520
Washington, DC 20004
"Politician"

**Barry Williams**
10100 Santa Monica Blvd. #2490
Los Angeles, CA 90067
"Actor"

**Brain Williams**
4001 Nebraska Avenue, NW
Washington, DC 20016
"Newscaster"

**Billy Williams**
586 Prince Edward Road
Glen Ellyn, IL 60137
"Ex-Baseball Player"

**Billy Dee Williams**
18411 Hatteras Street #204
Tarzana, CA 91356
"Actor"

**Bruce Williams**
P.O. Box 547
Elfers, FL 34680
"Radio Personality"

**Cara Willaims Dann**
146 South Peck Drive
Beverly Hills, CA 90212
"Actress"

**Clarence Williams III**
9057A Nemo Street
West Hollywood, CA 90069
"Actor"

**Darnell Williams**
8436 W. Third Street #740
Los Angeles, CA 90048
"Actor"

**Deneice Williams**
P.O. Box 3172
Beverly Hills, CA 90212
"Singer"

**Don Williams**
P.O. Box 1547
Goodlettsville, TN 37070
"Singer, Songwriter"

**Edy Williams**
1638 Blue Jay Way
Los Angeles, CA 90069
"Actress, Model"

**Esther Williams**
520 Washington Blvd., PMB 409
Marina del Rey, CA 90292
"Actress"

**Hal Williams**
P.O. Box 14405
Palm Desert, CA 92255
"Actor"

**Hank Williams, Jr.**
Hwy. 79 East
Box 850
Paris, TX 78242
"Singer, Guitarist"

**Hank Williams III**
2 Music Circle Street #212
Nashville, TN 37203
"C & W Singer"

**Jobeth Williams**
9465 Wilshire Blvd. #430
Beverly Hills, CA 90212
"Actress"

**John Williams**
13245 Riverside Drive #450
Sherman Oaks, CA 91423
"Composer, Conductor"

**Kelli Williams**
1505 - 10th Street
Santa Monica, CA 90401
"Actress"

**Kimberly Williams**
330 Bob Hope Drive #C-109
Burbank, CA 91523
"Actress"

**Mary Alice Williams**
30 Rockefeller Plaza #508
New York, NY 10020
"Broadcast Journalist"

**Mason Williams**
P.O. Box 5105
Eugene, OR 97405
"Singer, Songwriter"

**Montel Williams**
435 W. 53rd Street
New York, NY 10019
"TV Show Host"

**Olivia Williams**
76 Oxford Street
London WIN OAX ENGLAND
"Actress"

**Paul Williams**
8491 Sunset Blvd. #1150
West Hollywood, CA 90069
"Singer, Songwriter"

**Robin Williams**
1100 Wall Road
Napa, CA 94558
"Actor, Comedian, Writer"

**Ricky Williams**
7500 SW 30th Street
Davie, FL 33324
"Football Player"

**Roger Williams**
16150 Clear Valley Place
Encino, CA 91436
"Pianist"

**Serena Williams**
1360 East 9th Street #100
Cleveland, OH 44114
"Tennis Player"

**Stephanie Williams**
1269 South Orange #1
Los Angeles, CA 90019
"Actress"

**Treat Williams**
1244 - 11th Street #A
Santa Monica, CA 90401
"Actor"

**Vanessa L. Williams**
50 Old Farm Road
Chappaqua, NY 10514
"Actress"

**Vanessa Williams**
P.O. Box 858
Chappaqua, NY 10514
"Singer"

**Venus Williams**
1360 East 9th Street #100
Clevland, OH 44114
"Tennis Player"

**Fred Williamson**
10880 Wilshire Blvd. #1101
Los Angeles, CA 90024
"Actor"

**Bruce Willis**
1122 S. Robertson Blvd. #15
Los Angeles, CA 90035
"Actor, Singer"

**Brian Wilson**
200 W. Superior 3202
Chicago, IL 60610
"Musician"

328 Overlook Circle
Jackson, MS 39213
"Singer"

**Dick Wilson**
2705 Cricket Hollow Court
Henderson, NV 89014
"Actor"

**Elizabeth Wilson**
200 West 57th Street #900
New York, NY 10019
"Actress"

**Jeannie Wilson**
10358-A Riverside Drive
North Hollywood, CA 91602
"Actress"

**Jennifer Wilson**
1947 Lakeshore Drive
Branson, MO 65616
"Actress"

**Lambert Wilson**
91 rue Saint-Honore
75001 Paris FRANCE
"Actor"

**Mary Wilson**
889 S. Brentwood Blvd. #201
St. Louis, MO 63105
"Singer"

**Melanie Wilson**
12400 Ventura Blvd. #136
Studio City, CA 91604
"Actress"

**Nancy Wilson**
2820 W. Charleston #C-22
Las Vegas, NV 89102
"50's Singer"

**Nancy Wilson**
9255 Sunset Blvd. #407
Los Angeles, CA 90069
"Pop Singer"

**Peta Wilson**
12754 Sarah Street
Studio City, CA 91604
"Actress"

**Rita Wilson**
9830 Wilshire Blvd.
Beverly Hills, CA 90212
"Actress"

**Sheree J. Wilson**
7218 South Jan Mar Drive
Dallas, TX 75230
"Actress"

**Stuart Wilson**
P.O. Box 5617
Beverly Hills, CA 90210
"Actor"

**Tom Wilson**
9220 Sunset Blvd. #106
Los Angeles, CA 90069
"Cartoonist"

**Brian Wimmer**
3375 Creek Road
Salt Lake City, UT 84121
"Actor"

**The Winans**
5214 Maryland Way #300
Brentwood, TN 37027
"Gospel Singers"

**Paul Winchell**
78845 Golden Reed Drive
Palm Desert, CA 92211
"Actor"

**William Windom**
P.O. Box 1067
Woodacre, CA 94973
"Actor"

**Dave Winfield**
2325 Stratford Circle
Los Angeles, CA 90077
"Baseball Player"

**Paul Winfield**
5693 Holly Oak Drive
Los Angeles, CA 90068
"Actor"

**Oprah Winfrey**
P.O. Box 909715
Chicago, IL 60690
"TV Show Host, Actress"

**Debra Winger**
8500 Wilshire Blvd. #700
Beverly Hills, CA 90211
"Actress"

**Jason Wingreen**
4224 Teesdale Avenue
North Hollywood, CA 91604
"Actor"

**Henry Winkler**
1122 S. Robertson Blvd. #15
Los Angeles, CA 90035
"Actor, Producer"

**Michael Winner**
31 Melbury Road
London W14 8AB ENGLAND
"Writer, Producer"

**Mare Winningham**
9560 Topanga Canyon Blvd., #103
Chatsworth, CA 91311
"Actress"

**Kate Winslet**
34-43 Russell Street
London, WC2B 5HA ENGLAND
"Actress"

**Edgar Winter**
26033 Mulholland Hwy.
Calabasas, CA 91302
"Key Boardist"

**Johnny Winter**
35 Hayward Avenue
Colchester, CT 06415
"Singer"

**Judy Winter**
Merzstr. 14
D-81679 Munich GERMANY
"Singer"

**Jonathan Winters**
755 Romero Canyon Road
Santa Barbara, CA 93108
"Comedian, Actor"

**Shelley Winters**
1244-A 11th Street
Santa Monica, CA 90401
"Actress"

**Steve Winwood**
9830 Wilshire Blvd.
Beverly Hills, CA 90212
"Singer, Songwriter"

**Billy Wirth**
9255 Sunset Blvd., #1010
Los Angeles, CA 90069
"Actor"

**Norman Wisdom**
The Lhen, Andreas
Ramsay 1M7 3EH Isle of Man UK
"Actor"

**Bill Withers**
1995 Broadway, #501
New York, NY 10023
"Singer"

**Googie Withers**
1740 Pittwater Road
Bay View NSW 2104 AUSTRALIA
"Actress"

**Jimmy Witherspoon**
223 1/2 E. 48th Street
New York, NY 10017
"Singer, Musician"

**Reese Witherspoon**
9100 Wilshire Blvd., 16th Floor
Beverly Hills, CA 90212
"Actress"

**Tim Witherspoon**
161 Liberty Drive
Langhome, PA 19047
"Boxer"

**Alicia Witt**
1122 Robertson Blvd. #15
Los Angeles, CA 90035
"Actress"

**Paul Junger Witt**
1438 North Gower Street
Los Angeles, CA 90028
"TV Producer"

**Karen Witter**
247 South Beverly Drive #102
Beverly Hills, CA 90212
"Actress, Model"

**Kevin Wixted**
10100 Santa Monica Blvd.
Suite #700
Los Angeles, CA 90067
"Actor"

**Mr. Wizard (Don Herbert)**
P.O. Box 83
Canoga Park, CA 91305
"TV Personality"

**Charles Wolcott**
P.O. Box 155
Haifa, ISRAEL
"Composer

**Dick Wolf**
9560 Wilshire Blvd. #516
Beverly Hills, CA 90212
"Producer"

**Peter Wolf**
110 West 57th Street #300
New York, NY 10019
"Singer, Songwriter"

**Scott Wolf**
1122 S. Robertson Blvd. #15
Los Angeles, CA 90035
"Actor"

**Michael Wolfe**
41 Landowne Road
London W11 26Q ENGLAND
"Actor"

**Tom Wolfe**
21 East 79th Street
New York, NY 10021
"Writer"

**David L. Wolper**
8489 West Third Street
Los Angeles, CA 90048
"Film Director"

**Sherilyn Wolter**
8271 Melrose Avenue #110
Los Angeles, CA 90046
"Actress"

**Bobby Womack**
1800 Argle Avenue #408
Hollywood, CA 90046
"Singer"

**Stevie Wonder**
12702 Landale Street
Studio City, CA 91604
"Singer, Songwriter"

**B.D. Wong**
1505 - 10th Street
Santa Monica, CA 90401
"Actor"

**John Woo**
450 North Roxbury Drive #800
Beverly Hills, CA 90210
"Film Director"

**Elijah Wood**
8500 Wilshire Blvd. #700
Beverly Hills, CA 90211
"Actor"

**Lana Wood**
868 Masterson Drive
Thousand Oaks, CA 91360
"Actress"

**Bokeem Woodbine**
8942 Wilshire Blvd.
Beverly Hills, CA 90211
"Actor"

**John Wooden**
17711 Margate Street #102
Encino, CA 91316
"Ex-Basketball Coach"

**Frank Woodruff**
170 North Crescent Drive
Beverly Hills, CA 90210
"Director, Producer"

**Judy Woodruff**
P.O. Box 2626
Washington, DC 20013
"Broadcast Journalist"

**James Woods**
760 N. La Cienega Blvd.
Los Angeles, CA 90069
"Actor, Director"

**Michael Woods**
1608 Courtney Avenue
Los Angeles, CA 90046
"Actor"

**Robert S. Woods**
227 Central Park W. #5-A
New York, NY 10024
"Actor"

**Rosemary Woods**
3700 South Union Avenue
Alliance, OH 44601
"Secretary to President Nixon"

**Tiger Woods**
5909 Sea Otter Place
Carlsbad, CA 92008
"Golfer"

**Bob Woodward**
2907 "Q" Street NW
Washington, DC 20007
"News Corespondent"

**Edward Woodward**
Ravens Court, Calstock
Cornwall PL18 9ST ENGLAND
"Actor"

**Joanne Woodward**
1120 - 5th Avenue #1C
New York, NY 10128
"Actress, Director"

**Morgan Woodward**
3350 Barham Blvd.
Los Angeles, CA 90068
"Actor"

**Marjorie Woodworth**
807 North La Brea Avenue
Inglewood, CA 90301
"Actress"

**Chuck Woolery**
2756 N. Green Valley Parkway #449
Las Vegas, NV 89014
"TV Show Host"

**Sheb Wooley**
123 Walton Ferry Road #200
Hendersonville, TN 37075
"Singer"

**Tom Wopat**
P.O. Box 128031
Nashville, TN 37212
"Actor, Director"

**Joanne Worley**
P.O. Box 2054
Toluca Lake, CA 91610
"Actress"

**Mary Woronov**
4350 1/4 Beverly Blvd.
Los Angeles, CA 90004
"Actress"

**Cal Worthington**
3815 Florin Road
Sacramento, CA 95823
"Car Dealer"

**Herman Wouk**
303 Crestview
Palm Springs, CA 92264
"Writer"

**Steve Wozniak**
16400 Blackberry Hill Road
Los Gatos, CA 95030
"Computer Builder"

**Fay Wray**
721 Fifth Avenue
New York, NY 10022
"Actress"

**Clare Wren**
5757 Wilshire Blvd. #473
Los Angeles, CA 90036
"Actress"

**Cobina Wright, Jr.**
1326 Dove Meadow Road
Solvang, CA 93463
"Actress"

**Max Wright**
11500 West Olympic Blvd. #510
Los Angeles, CA 90064
"Actor"

**Steven Wright**
9200 Sunset Blvd. #900
Los Angeles, CA 90069
"Comedian"

**Teresa Wright**
948 Rowayton Wood Drive
Norwalk, CT 06854
"Actress"

**Robert Wuhl**
10590 Holman Avenue
Los Angeles, CA 90024
"Comedian, Actor, Writer"

**Kari Wuhrer**
P.O. Box 69188
Los Angeles, CA 90069
"Singer & Actress"

**Jane Wyatt**
651 Siena Way
Los Angeles, CA 90077
"Actress"

**Shannon Wyatt**
8949 Falling Creek Court
Annandale, VA 22003
"Actress"

**Andrew Wyeth**
c/o General Delivery
Chadds Ford, PA 19317
"Artist"

**Chris Wylde**
3313 1/2 Barham Blvd.
Los Angeles, CA 90068
"Comedian"

**Noah Wyle**
1122 S. Robertson Blvd. #15
Los Angeles, CA 90035
"Actor"

**Gretchen Wyler**
11754 Barranca Road
Camarillo, CA 93012
"Actress"

**Jane Wyman**
P.O. Box 25899
Los Angeles, CA 90025
"Actress"

**George Wyner**
3450 Laurie Place
Studio City, CA 91604
"Actor"

**Dana Wynter**
1317 - 5th Street #200
Santa Monica, CA 90401
"Actress"

**Steve Wynn**
P.O. Box 610
Las Vegas, NV 89101
"Casino Owner"

**Sarah Wynter**
9220 Sunset Blvd. #106
Los Angeles, CA 90069
"Actress"

**Wynonna**
325 Bridge Street
Franklin, TN 37064
"Singer"

**Amanda Wyss**
9229 Sunset Blvd., #311
Los Angeles, CA 90069
"Actress"

**Frank Yablans**
100 Bull Path
East Hampton, NY 11937
"Film Writer, Producer"

**Andrea Yaeger**
P.O. Box 10970
Aspen, CO 81612
"Tennis Player"

**General Chuck Yaeger**
P.O. Box 128
Cedar Ridge, CA 95924
"Retired Military General"

**Jeff Yagher**
15057 Sherview Place
Sherman Oaks, CA 91403
"Actor"

**Roslyn Yalow**
3242 Tibbett Avenue
Bronx, NY 10463
"Nobel Prize Winner"

**Kristi Yamaguchi**
3650 Montecito Drive
Fremont, CA 94536
"Ice Skater"

**Emily Yancey**
247 South Beverly Drive #102
Beverly Hills, CA 90212
"Actress"

**Wierd Al Yankovic**
5725 Green Oak Drive
Los Angeles, CA 90068
"Singer, Songwriter"

**Yanni**
P.O. Box 46996
Eden Prairie, MN 55344
"Musician"

**Cale Yarborough**
2723 West Palmetto Street
Florence, SC 29501
"Race Car Driver"

**Glenn Yarborough**
P.O. Box 158
Malibu, CA 90265
"Singer"

**Mollie Yard**
1000-16th Street N.W.
Washington, DC 20036
"Feminist Leader"

**Claire Yarlett**
9460 Wilshire Blvd. #300
Beverly Hills, CA 90212
"Actor"

**Celeste Yarnail**
13775-A Mono Way #220
Sonora, CA 95370
"Actress"

**Amy Yasbeck**
1205 Benedict Canyon
Beverly Hills, CA 90210
"Actress"

**Carl Yastrzemski**
8 Whittler Place #C
Boston, MA 02114
"Ex-Baseball Player"

**Petet Yates**
3340 Caroline Avenue
Culver City, CA 90230
"Film Director"

**Chuck Yeager**
P.O. Box 579
Penn Valley, CA 95946
"Ex-Military Test Pilot"

**Jeana Yeager**
2634 Hwy. 50
Campbell, TX 75422
"Avaitrix"

**Steve Yeager**
P.O. Box 34184
Granada Hills, CA 91394
"Ex-Baseball Player"

**Trisha Yearwood**
1505 - 16th Avenue South
Nashville, TN 37212
"Singer"

**Yellowjackets**
173 Brighton Avenue
Boston, MA 02134
"Jazz Group"

**Boris Yeltsin**
Uliza Twerskaya
Jamskaya 2
Moscow, Russia
"President of Russia"

**Michelle Yeoh**
9560 Wilshire Blvd. #516
Beverly Hills, CA 90212
"Actress"

**David Yip**
15 Golden Square #315
London W1R 3AG ENGLAND
"Actor"

**Dwight Yoakam**
1908 Wedgewood Avenue
Nashville, TN 37212
"Singer, Guitarist"

**Philip Yordan**
4895 Mt. Elbrus Drive
San Diego, CA 92117
"Screenwriter"

**Francine York**
14333 Addison Street #315
Sherman Oaks, CA 91423
"Actress"

**Kathleen York**
409 Noth Camden Drive #202
Beverly Hills, CA 90210
"Singer, Songwriter, Actress"

**Michael York**
9100 Cordell Drive
Los Angeles, CA 90069
"Actor"

**Susannah York**
13 Shorts Garden
London WC2H 9AT ENGLAND
"Actress"

**Bud Yorkin**
250 North Delfern Drive
Los Angeles, CA 90077
"Writer, Producer"

**Tina Yothers**
280 S. Beverly Drive #400
Beverly Hills, CA 90212
"Actress"

**Andrew Young**
1088 Veltrie Circle S.W.
Atlanta, GA 30311
"Ex-Mayor of Atlanta"

**Burt Young**
43 Navy Street #300
Venice, CA 90291
"Actor, Screenwriter"

**Chris T. Young**
5959 Triumph Street
Commerce, CA 90040
"Actor"

**Earl Young**
4344 Livingston Avenue
Dallas, TX 75206
"Drummer"

**Jesse Colin Young**
P.O. Box 31
Lancaster, NH 03584
"Singer, Songwriter"

**Keone Young**
14724 Ventura Blvd. #505
Sherman Oaks, CA 91403
"Actor"

**Neil Young**
1460 - 4th Street #210
Santa Monica, CA 90401
"Singer, Songwriter"

**Raymond Young**
Hampton Cottage
7 Church Street
Littlehampton BN1Y 5 EL EN-
GLAND
"Actor"

**Richard Young**
1275 Westwood Blvd.
Los Angeles, CA 90024
"Actor"

**Sean Young**
727 - 12th Street
Santa Monica, CA 90402
"Actress"

**Steve Young**
261 E. Broadway
Salt Lake City, UT 84111
"Football Player"

**Jack Youngblood**
4377 Steed Terrance
Winter Park, FL 32792
"Ex-Football Player"

**Malika Yuba**
230 Park Avenue #550
New York, NY 10069
"Actor"

**Harris Yulin**
40 West 86th Street #5-C
New York, NY 10024
"Actor"

**Rick Yune**
1411 Fifth Street #405
Santa Monica, CA 90401
"Actor"

**Chow Yung-Fat**
2/F 192 Prince Edward Road
West Kowloon Hong Kong CHINA
"Actor"

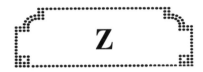

**Grace Zabriskie**
1800 S. Robertson Blvd. #426
Los Angeles, CA 90035
"Actress"

**John Zaccaro**
22 Deepdene Road
Forest Hills, NY 11375
"Businessman"

**Pia Zadora**
1143 Summit Drive
Beverly Hills, CA 90210
"Actress, Singer"

**Saul Zaentz**
2600 10th Street
Berkeley, CA 94710
"Film & Record Producer"

**Paula Zahn**
820 First Street NE
Washington, DC 20002
"News Anchor & Reporter"

**Steve Zahn**
1964 Westwood Blvd. #400
Los Angeles, CA 90025
"Actor"

**Roxanne Zal**
8265 Sunset Blvd. #101
Los Angeles, CA 90046
"Actress"

**Billy Zane**
450 N. Rossmore Avenue #1001
Los Angeles, CA 90004
"Actor"

**Lisa Zane**
209 S. Orange Drive
Los Angeles, CA 90036
"Actress"

**Richard Zanuck**
9465 Wilshire Blvd. #930
Beverly Hills, CA 90212
"Film Producer"

**Carmen Zapata**
6107 Ethel Avenue
Van Nuys, CA 91405
"Actress"

**Ahmet Zappa**
P.O. Box 5265
North Hollywood, CA 91616
"Singer"

**Dweezil Zappa**
P.O. Box 5265
North Hollywood, CA 91616
"Singer"

**Moon Zappa**
P.O. Box 5265
North Hollywood, CA 91616
"Singer"

**Renee Zellweger**
9830 Wilshire Blvd.
Beverly Hills, CA 90212
"Actress"

**Jacklyn Zeman**
12186 Laurel Terrace
Studio City, CA 91604
"Actress"

**Robert Zemackis**
1880 Century Park East #900
Los Angeles, CA 90067
"Writer, Director"

**Anthony Zerbe**
1175 High Road
Santa Barbara, CA 93150
"Actor"

**Cathrine Zeta-Jones**
151 Central Park West
New York, NY 10023
"Actress"

**Ian Ziering**
2700 Jalmia Drive
West Hollywood, CA 90046
"Actress"

**Efrem Zimbalist, Jr.**
1448 Holsted Drive
Solvang, CA 93463
"Actor"

**Stephanie Zimbalist**
3500 West Olive Avenue #1400
Burbank, CA 91505
"Actress"

**Don Zimmer**
2 Avon Circle #2
Rye Brook, NY 10573
"Ex-Baseball Player"

**Adrian Zmed**
8721 Sunset Blvd. #205
West Hollywood, CA 90069
"Actor"

**Kim Zmeskal**
3635 Woodridge Blvd.
Fairfield, OH 95014
"USA Olympic Gymnastist"

**"Fuzzy" Zoeller**
12701 Covered Bridge Road
Sellersburg, IN 47172
"Golfer"

**Ethan Zohn**
320 East 22nd Street
New York, NY 10010
"Survivor Show Contestan"

**Louis Zorich**
684 Broadway #7-E
New York, NY 10012
"Actor"

**Jerry Zucker**
9830 Wilshire Blvd.
Beverly Hills, CA 90212
"Film Director, Producer"

**Pinchas Zuckerman**
711 West End Avenue #5K-N
New York, NY 10025
"Violinist"

**Daphne Zuniga**
P.O. Box 1249
White River Junction, VT 05001
"Actress"

**Edward Zwick**
1 Latimer Road
Santa Monica, CA 90402
"Television Writer, Director"

**ZZ Top**
P.O. Box 163690
Austin, TX 78716
"Singer"

## Other Places to write Celebrities: Movie Studios, TV Networks and Record Companies

### Major Movie Studios:

Columbia Pictures
(Sony Pictures Entertainment, Inc.)
10202 West Washington Blvd.
Culver City, CA 90232

Fox, Inc.
10201 West Pico Blvd.
Los Angeles, CA 90035

Home Box Office, Inc.
2049 Century Park East, Suite 4100
Los Angeles, CA 90067

MGM-Pathe Communications Co.
10000 West Washington Blvd.
Culver City, CA 90232

Orion Pictures Corporation
1888 Century Park East
Los Angeles, CA 90067

Paramount Communication, Inc.
New York (Home Office)
15 Columbus Circle
New York, NY 10023

Paramount Communication, Inc.
West Coast Office:
5555 Melrose Avenue
Los Angeles, CA 90038

Touchstone Pictures
500 South Buena Vista Street
Burbank, CA 91521

Twentieth Century Fox
P.O. Box 900
Beverly Hills, CA 90213

Universal Pictures
100 Universal City Plaza
Universal City, CA 91608

Warner Bros., Inc.
4000 Warner Blvd.
Burbank, CA 91522

### Major Television Network:

ABC
77 West 66th Street
New York, NY 10023

ABC
West Coast Studio:
2040 Avenue of the Stars
Century City, CA 90067

CBS
51 West 52nd Street
New York, NY 10019

CNN
One CNN Center
P.O. Box 105366
Atlanta, GA 30348

Fox Broadcasting Company
10201 West Pico Blvd.
Los Angeles, CA 90035

NBC
New York (Home Office)
30 Rockefeller Plaza
New York, NY 10112

NBC
West Coast Studio:
3000 Alameda Avenue
Burbank, CA 91523

CNBC
2200 Fletcher Avenue
Ft. Lee, NJ 07024

ESPN
935 Middle Street
Bristol, CT 06010

PBS
1320 Braddock Place
Alexandria, VA 22314

United Paramount Network
P.O. Box 251735
Los Angeles, CA 91522

WB Television Network
400 Warner Blvd., Bldg. 34R
Burbank, CA 91522

Black Entertainment Network
1232 31st Street N.W.
Washington, DC 20007

Comedy Central
1775 Broadway
New York, NY 10019

Court TV
600 Third Avenue, 2nd Flr.
New York, NY 10016

C-SPAN
400 N. Capitol Street NW#650
Washington, DC 20001

The Discovery Channel
7700 Wisconsin Avenue
Bethesda, MD 20814

The Disney Channel
3800 West Alameda Avenue
Burbank, CA 91505

E! Entertainment Television
5670 Wilshire Blvd.
Los Angeles, CA 90036

Encore or Starz!
5445 DTC Parkway, Suite 600
Englewood, CO 80111

The Family Channel
2877 Guardian Lane
P.O. Box 2050
Virgina Beach, VA 23450

Fox News Channel
1211 Avenue of the Americas
New York, NY 10036

The Golf Channel
7580 Commerce Center Drive
Orlando, FL 32819

Home Shopping Network
1529 U.S. Route 19 So.
Clearwater, FL 33546

The Movie Channel
1633 Broadway
New York, NY 10019

MTV, Nickelodeon or VH1
1515 Broadway
New York, NY 10036

The Nashville Network
2806 Opryland Drive
Nashville, TN 37214

QVC
1365 Enterprise Drive
West Chester, PA 19380

Show Time
1633 Broadway
New York, NY 10019

The Travel Channel
2690 Cumberland Parkway, #500
Atlanta, GA 30339

TV Food Network
1177 Avenue of the America
New York, NY 10036

The Weather Channel
2600 Cumberland Parkland
Atlanta, GA 30339

## Major Record Companies:

CBS Records, Inc.
51 West 52nd Street
New York, NY 10019

EMI
810 Seventh Avenue
8th Floor
New York, NY 10019

Emeral Records
830 Glastonbury Road
Suite 614
Nashville, TN 37217

Erika Records, Inc.
9827 Oak Street
Bellflower, CA 90706

MCA Records
70 Universal City Plaza
Universal City, CA 91608

Motown Record Company
6255 Sunset Blvd.
17th Floor
Los Angeles, CA 90028

PolyGram Records, Inc.
825 Eighth Avenue
New York, NY 10019

PolyGram Records: Nashville
901 - 18th Avenue South
Nashville, TN 37212

RCA Records, Inc.
P.O. Box 126
405 Tarrytown Road
Suite 335
Elmsford, NY 10523

SBK Records
1290 Avenue of the Americas
New York, NY 10104

Warner Music International
75 Rockefeller Plaza
New York, NY 10019

## Other Places to Write Sports Celebrities: Baseball, Basketball and Football Teams

**Major League Baseball**
The Office of the Commissioner of
Baseball
245 Park Avenue, 31st floor
New York, NY 10167
Commissioner:
Allan H. (Bud) Selig

**American League Teams:**
Anaheim Angels
2000 Gene Autry Way
Anaheim, CA 93806

Baltimore Orioles
333 West Camden Street
Baltimore, MD 21201

Boston Red Sox
4 Yawkey Way
Boston MA 02215

Chicago White Sox
333 West 35th Street
Chicago, IL 60016

Cleveland Indians
Jacobs Field
2401 Ontario Street
Cleveland, OH, 44115

Detroit Tigers
Comerica Park
2100 Woodward Ave.
Detroit, MI 48201

Kansas City Royals
1 Royal Way
Kansas City, MO 64141

Minnesota Twins
34 Kirby Puckett Place
Minneapolis, MN 55415

New York Yankees
161st St. & River Avenue
Bronx, NY 10451

Oakland Athletics
Network Associates Coliseum
7000 Coliseum Way
Oakland, CA. 94621

Seattle Mariners
SAFECO Field
1250 1st Ave. S.
Seattle, WA 98134

Tampa Bay Delvis Rays
Tropicana Field
One Tropicana Drive
St. Petersburg, FL 33705

Texas Rangers
1000 Ballpark Way #400
Arlington, TX 76011

Toronto Blue Jays
1 Blue Jays Way, Suite 3200
SkyDome
Toronto, Ontario M5V 1J1

**AMERICAN LEAUGE**

Arizona Diamondbacks
401 East Jefferson Street
Phoenix, AZ 85001

Atlanta Braves
755 Hank Aaron Drive
Atlanta, GA 30315

Chicago Cubs
1060 West Addison
Chicago, IL 60613

Cincinnati Reds
100 Main Street
Cincinnati, OH 45202

Florida Marlins
Pro Player Stadium
2267 Dan Marino Blvd.
Miami, FL 33028

Houston Astros
501 Crawford Street
Houston, TX 77002

Los Angeles Dodgers
1000 Elysian Park Avenue
Los Angeles, CA 90012

Milwaukee Brewers
One Brewers Way
Milwaukee, WI 53214

Montreal Expos
4549 Ave. Pierre deCoubertin
Montreal Quebec CANADA
H1V3N7

New York Mets
Shea Stadium
123-01 Roosevelt Avenue
Flushing, NY 11368-1699

Philadelphia Phillies
Veterans Stadium
3501 South Broad Street
Philadelphia PA 19148

Pittsburgh Pirates
PNC Park at North Shore:
115 Federal Street
Pittsburgh, PA 15212

San Diego Padres
8880 Rio San Diego Drive #400
San Diego, CA 92112

San Francisco Giants
Pacific Bell Park
24 Willie Mays Plaza
San Francisco, CA 94107

St. Louis Cardinals
250 Stadium Plaza
St. Louis, MO 63102

**National Basketball Association:**

Olympic Tower
645 Fifth Avenue
New York, NY 10022
Commissioner:
David Stern

Atlanta Hawks
One CNN Center, #405
South Tower, Suite 405
Atlanta, GA 30303

Boston Celtics
151 Merrimac Street, 5th Floor
Boston, MA 02114

Charlotte Hornets
100 Hive Drive
Charlotte, NC 28217

Chicago Bulls
980 North Michigan Avenue
Suite #1600
Chicago, IL 60611

Cleveland Cavaliers
Gateway Arena
1 Center Court
Cleveland, OH 44115

Dallas Mavericks
The Pavilion
2909 Taylor Street,
Dallas, TX 75226

Denver Nuggets
1000 Chopper Circle
Denver, CO 80204

Detroit Pistons
The Palace
3777 Lapeer Road
Auburn Hills, MI 48057

Golden State Warriors
Oakland Coliseum Arena
7000 Coliseum Way
Oakland, CA 94621

Houston Rockets
2 Greenway Plaza, Suite 400
Houston, TX 7704

Indiana Pacers
300 East Market Street
Indianapolis, IN 46204

Los Angeles Clippers
3939 South Figueroa
Los Angeles, CA 90037

Los Angeles Lakers
Staple Center
1111 S. Figueroa Street
Los Angeles, CA 90015

Memphis Grizzlies
175 Toyota Plaza, Suite 150
Memphis, TN 38103

Miami Heat
AmericanAirlines Arena
701 Areana Blvd.
Miami, FL 33136

Milwaukee Bucks
The Bradley Center
1001 North Fourth Street
Milwaukee, WI 53203

Minnesota Timberwolves
600 First Avenue North
Minneapolis, MN 55403

New Jersey Nets
405 Murray Hill Parkway
East Rutherford, NJ 07073

New Orleans Hornets
1501 Girod Street
New Orleans, LA 70113

New York Knickerbockers
Madison Square Garden
Two Pennsylvania Plaza
New York, NY 10121

Orlando Magic
Orlando Arena
One Magic Place
Orlando, FL 32801

Philadelphia 76ers
3601 S. Broad Street
Philadelphia, PA 19148

Phoenix Suns
201 East Jefferson
Phoenix, AZ 85001

Portland Trail Blazers
One Center Court
Suite 200
Portland, OR 97227

Sacramento Kings
One Sports Parkway
Sacramento, CA 95834

San Antonio Spurs
SBC Center
One SBC Center
San Antonio, Texas 78219

Seattle Supersonics
351 Elliott Ave. W., Suite 500
Seattle, WA 98119

Toronto Raptors
150 York Street, Suite 1100
Toronto, Ontario
M5H 3S5  CANADA

Utah Jazz
301 West South Temple
Salt Lake City, UT 84101

Washington Wizards
MCI Center
601 "F" Street NW
Washington, DC 20004

**National Football League**:
410 Park Avenue
New York, NY 10022
Commissioner:
Paul Tagliabue

**American Football Conference:**
Baltimore Ravens
1101 Russell Street
Baltimore, MD 21230

Buffalo Bills
One Bills Drive
Orchard Park, NY 14127

Cincinnati Bengals
Paul Brown Stadium
Cinncinnati, OH 45202

Denver Broncos
1900 West Eliot
Denver, CO 80204

Indianapolis Colts
100 South Capitol Avenue
Indianapolis, IN 46225

Jacksonville Jaguars
1 Stadium Place
Jacksonville, FL 32202

Kansas City Chiefs
One Arrowhead Drive
Kansas City, MO 64129

Miami Dolphins
Joe Robbie Stadium
2269 N.W. 199th Street
Miami, FL 33056

New England Patriots
60 Washington Street
Foxboro, MA 02035

New York Jets
Giants Stadium
East Rutherford, NJ 07073

Oakland Raiders
3911 South Figueroa Street
Los Angeles, CA 90037

Pittsburgh Steelers
100 Art Rooney Avenue
Pittsburgh, PA 15212

San Diego Chargers
9449 Friars Road
San Diego, CA 92120

Seattle Seahawks
201 South King Street
Seattle, WA 98033

Tennessee Oilers
Liberty Stadium
335 South Hollywood
Memphis, TN 38104

**National Football Conference:**
Arizona Cardinals
Sun Devil Stadium
Tempe, AZ 85287

Atlanta Falcons
4400 Falcon Parkway
Flowery Brach, GA 30542

Carolina Panters
227 West Trade Street #1600
Charlotte, NC 28202

Chicago Bears
Soldier Field
Chicago, IL 60605

Dallas Cowboys
1 Cowboys Parkway
Irving, TX 75063

Detroit Lions
1200 Featherstone Road
Pontiac, MI 48057

Green Bay Packers
1265 Lombardi Avenue
Green Bay, WI 54303

St. Louis Rams
4245 North King Hwy
St. Louis, MO 63115

Minnesota Vikings
500 - 11th Avenue South
Minneapolis, MN 55415

New Orleans Saints
1500 Poydras Street
New Orleans, LA 70112

New York Giants
Giants Stadium
East Rutherford, NJ 07073

Philadelphia Eagles
Veterans Stadium
Broad Street & Pattison Avenue
Philadelphia, PA 19148

Phoenix Cardinals
Sun Devil Stadium
Fifth Street
Tempe, AZ 85287

San Francisco 49ers
3Com Park
San Francisco, CA 94124

Tampa Bay Buccaneers
Tampa Stadium
North Dale Mabry
Tampa, FL 33607

Washington Redskins
FedEX Field
Washington, DC 20003

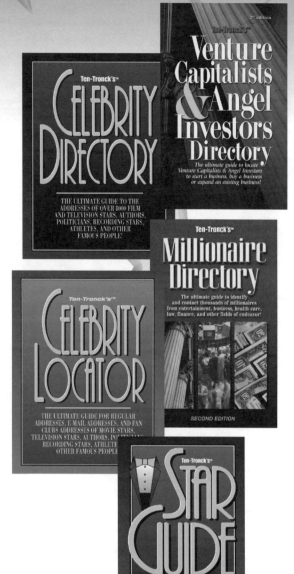